A History
of the British
Gas Industry

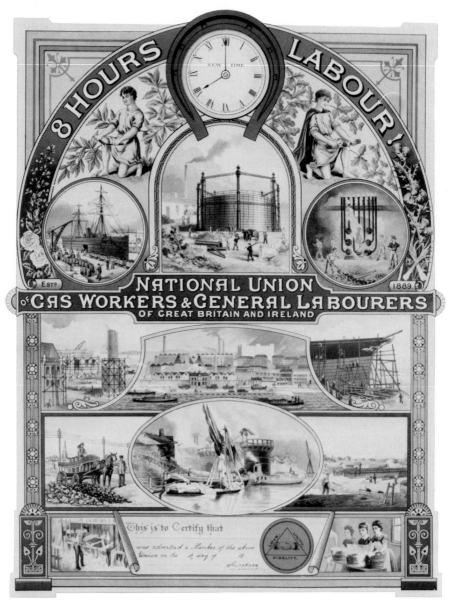

Certificate of the National Union of Gas Workers and General Labourers. In the ornate Victorian tradition it depicts many aspects of gas manufacture. The clock at the top denotes the achievement of the 8-hour day.

A History
of the British
Gas Industry

Trevor I. Williams

OXFORD UNIVERSITY PRESS
1981

Oxford University Press, Walton Street, Oxford OX2 6DP
London Glasgow New York Toronto
Delhi Bombay Calcutta Madras Karachi
Kuala Lumpur Singapore Hong Kong Tokyo
Nairobi Dar es Salaam Cape Town
Melbourne Auckland
and associate companies in
Beirut Berlin Ibadan Mexico City

Published in the United States by
Oxford University Press, New York

British Library Cataloguing in Publication Data
Williams, Trevor I.
A history of the British gas industry.
1. Gas industry – Great Britain – History
I. Title
338.4'7'6650941   TP732.G7
ISBN 0–19–858157–2

Set by Western Printing Services Ltd
Printed in Great Britain
at the University Press, Oxford
by Eric Buckley
Printer to the University

Foreword

by Sir Denis Rooke
Chairman of British Gas

I welcome this history as a concise summary for the general reader of the trends and events which have influenced the gas industry over 150 years. It highlights the strengths of the industry, particularly in recovering from the period in the 1950s when gas seemed under threat of going out of business altogether. It describes the way in which, even before the discovery of natural gas, management and staff of the Gas Council and Area Boards rebuilt the industry without subsidy and set it on the road to success.

Dr Williams takes the creation of the British Gas Corporation in January 1973 as a convenient point at which to draw his history to a close. Coincidentally, the period since that date has been one of unprecedented change and disruption in the world energy economy. That same year saw the Arab cartel increase oil prices while cutting supplies, stimulating a great deal of heart searching—and perhaps at that time, unnecessary alarm—over the availability of oil in the West.

The disruption to oil supplies following the Iranian revolution in 1979 created a substantially increased demand for gas, some of which the industry plans to be able to satisfy by bringing forward investment in capital projects for transmission and storage capacity, and in the development of Morecambe Gas Field. These projects are part of a planned capital expenditure over the early years of the 1980s amounting to some £4,000 million at out-turn prices. The Corporation's healthy financial position should provide the basis for this expenditure to be found from internal sources, even allowing for the imposition by government of a levy on gas sales.

The management of major engineering projects has become a fact of life over the last two decades but the gas industry has always been one which depended not only on the skill and dedication of its engineers and scientists, but on their ability to lead and direct the industry. The roles of gas 'engineer' and 'manager' have been inseparable from the earliest gas works to the latest natural gas terminal. Engineers in British Gas, whether home-grown or recruited from other disciplines, have always developed the wider skills of management. Many of the innovations in British industrial management were pioneered by gas engineer/managers. I am pleased to say that these opportunities remain as alive today, as at any time in the past.

The technology directed to maintaining the integrity of our gas supply system is of the highest possible standard. Britain's gas engineering technology and its managerial skills are respected throughout the world, and are themselves marketable commodities.

In my many contacts with other of the world's gas industries it is clear that, not only do they respect our expertise, but also they envy the integrated nature of our industry. Particularly, the benefits of our integration—to conservation, safety, and the long-term planning of energy resources—are clearer to those nations with relatively fragmented industries, than they may be to those who have promulgated the 'dis-integration' of our own.

British Gas, and the Gas Council and Area Boards before it, has a notable profit-making tradition. The Corporation has made a loss only when forced to do so by the constraints of Government price control policy. As the Cinderella industry, however, which borrowed heavily in the 50s and 60s to rebuild its business from the bottom up—one of the Corporation's high points came in the 1976/7 financial year when it became self-financing. This was the product of two decades of investment. The Corporation repaid all its National Loan Fund debt through early repayments and in 1979/80 began to deposit temporary surpluses with the NLF, attracting interest, and remaining available to the industry at a later date.

The Corporation's policies and prices, both in the tariff and non-tariff markets, have been the subject of considerable attention. Domestic prices, for so long the subject of price restraint policies of successive Governments, were to be singled out by the Conservative government in 1980 to rise by 10 per cent more than inflation over each of the 3 years 1980/1, 81/2, and 82/3.

As for industrial prices, there has been much controversy about British energy consumers being at a disadvantage compared with their Continental competitors. A Task Force of the National Economic Development Council reported in March 1981 that 95 per cent of industrial users suffered no such disadvantage but that the remainder, who account for the bulk of energy consumed, were paying more by the end of the previous year—largely because of the strength of the pound. The Chancellor in his budget announced that concessions were to be made to such users. For gas customers they amounted to savings of around £73 million in total—continuing a process of help to industrial gas users that has been going on for many years.

In 1973/4 came the five-fold increase in oil prices and the first energy crisis. The gas industry decided that it would not seek immediately to match the price of oil in renewing industrial contracts. So increases for its customers always lagged behind those of oil users. More recently in the wake of the Iranian revolution and further massive oil price rises, the Corporation decided again that it should temper increases to its existing customers, so that the majority of them have been having their contracts renewed first at around 75 per cent of the market price of the competing fuel and then, as oil prices increased further and gas prices remained where they were, 70 per cent of the market price. If the Corporation had forced up their prices to the full market level it would have earned a further £200 million.

As I write this foreword, a report from the Monopolies and Mergers Commission on the appliance retailing activities of the Corporation is under consideration by the government, being one of a number of uncertainties to which the Corporation has been subject during the 1980/1 financial year. There remains the threat to the Corporation's oil and exploration interests about which there has been so much speculation following proposals in the last election.

This is not a history solely of what has become the nationalised gas supply industry, however, and as it makes clear the strengths of gas in the British energy scene are derived in no small part from the long-standing co-operation which exists between gas supplier and the gas producer; between marketeers and appliance manufacturers; between our planners and those contractors who have consistently worked with us to achieve targets on multi-million pound developments without which the riches of the North Sea would have remained below the sea bed. I would like to take this opportunity to acknowledge publicly this long and fruitful collaboration which I am sure will continue. As Trevor Williams's history demonstrates, the gas industry has constantly to be looking to the future, and its financial strength in the early 1980s will be matched by the increasing scale of challenges to be encountered.

Increased emphasis on conserving fuel, and on the development of still more efficient ways of using gas will continue to be a preoccupation in the gas industry as it has been since the 1950s when gas had to promote fuel-efficiency to survive. Further expansion of premium markets for gas are planned in the coming decades, together with continued emphasis on ensuring that gas is used—as far as is practicable—only for appropriate purposes. Challenges will come with the acquisition of new supplies of oil-associated gas from the North Sea. Finally, exploring for new supplies of natural gas, and preparing for a return in the distant future to gas manufacturing—based on modern gasification processes for substitute natural gas in which British Gas is a world leader—all these will constitute the tasks for coming decades. Decades for which, as this book ably demonstrates, this industry has been preparing over more than a century.

6 April 1981

Preface

IN the introduction to his *English Social History* in 1944 G. M. Trevelyan
wrote that 'without social history, economic history is barren and political
history is unintelligible'. Today, it is widely recognised that two other
factors, the scientific and the technological, must also be taken into account
in any general history and particularly in any study of the history of western
civilisation over the last three centuries. Significant though they are, these
newer factors are still not always given sufficient weight. For this, a number
of reasons can be adduced, but two seem paramount. Firstly, historians are
still recruited largely from the arts departments of universities and thus
normally have little or no exposure to science or engineering; inevitably they
find these subjects difficult to understand and to relate to their own.
Secondly, the number of serious students of the history of science and
technology is still relatively small and they have tended to follow narrow
specialist studies—often with a sociological rather than a technological
emphasis— that are not easily incorporated into any broad conspectus.

For many years I have been interested in the history of science and
technology, both as a discipline in its own right and as a complement to
political, economic, and social history. With this background the British gas
industry has a particular appeal, for there are few industries which so clearly
illustrate the consequences of the interplay of all these factors. In particular,
it provides a valuable object lesson in the powerful, and sometimes dominant, role of technology. The industry came into existence only because of
the development of a relatively crude technology for the large-scale manufacture of combustible gas by carbonising coal in retorts. Over the course of
more than a century this technology was refined and extended to various
complex high-pressure processes for the total gasification of coal. Then,
largely in response to the diminishing supply and rising cost of good coking
coal after the last war, the industry developed new processes based on the
use of oil as a raw material. At about the same time, liquefied natural gas
began to be imported from the Sahara, to supplement supplies of manufactured gas. This phase was short-lived, however, for the discovery of a vast
underground field of natural gas at Slochteren in Holland in 1959, and the
subsequent discovery of related gasfields below the North Sea, brought the
British industry into yet another area of technology. Quite suddenly, what
many had come to regard as an old-fashioned industry blossomed out into
the realm of high technology. On the one hand, gas had to be located and
extracted under conditions never before attempted in any part of the world.
On the other, a national high-pressure distribution network had to be
established and every appliance in Britain had to be converted not only to

burn the new kind of gas but to burn it with minimal interruption of supply. The necessary conversion programme was a triumph of management as much as of technology. Over and above this, there were complex economic factors demanding, among other things, formulation of a policy to control rate of extraction and of a new marketing strategy; social factors arising from the fact that the industry served some 14 million individual customers at all levels in society; and political factors stemming from the close, but by no means clearly defined, relationship of a nationalised industry to the government of the day. This political factor was not wholly novel, for throughout its history the gas industry has been subject to political constraints.

The gas industry in Britain effectively dates from the formation of the Gas Light and Coke Company in 1812 and until nationalisation in 1948 it was in the hands of a multiplicity of private and municipal undertakings. The present nationalised industry is thus relatively young but its short history spans many of the major developments, including a sevenfold expansion in capacity; the transition from coal to oil as a raw material; the importation of liquefied natural gas; and the exploitation of the North Sea fields, culminating in a total reliance on indigenous natural gas.

So far as the long pre-nationalisation period is concerned there can be no official history, for the undertakings concerned no longer exist to bless it. Nor is this an official history of the later period, for although this book was commissioned by the British Gas Corporation it has not been formally endorsed by them. The Corporation provided me with valuable facilities—most particularly the use of their well-stocked headquarters library—and made available a wealth of published information and internal reports, including material inherited from the old private and municipal companies. Nevertheless, they left me free to utilise this material as I thought best and to put my own interpretation on it.

To discern the main factors that have influenced the history of the gas industry in Britain is relatively easy; it is much more difficult to describe their interplay, over a period of more than a century and a half, and to present this in a reasonably logical and readable manner. At one extreme, one could follow through each thread successively from beginning to end, and then attempt an overall synthesis: at the other, one could attempt a continuous chronology of the industry as a whole, keeping all the main factors under constant review. As a compromise I have divided this history into three main sections covering respectively the period of evolution of coal carbonisation up to the Second World War; nationalisation and the switch from coal to oil as a raw material for manufactured gas; and the advent of North Sea gas. While these periods correspond to changes in the basic technology, they are also significant in political, economic, and social terms. Within these three periods I have tried to concentrate on various major themes over periods long enough to record some substantial progress, at the same time cross-referencing as far as practicable to other aspects.

Where to start this history presented no great problem. Where to end it was a different matter, for in the nature of things vigorous and continuously evolving industries are not given to providing natural breaks in their programmes. For want of anything better, I have chosen 1973, the year in which the present British Gas Corporation was established, as the *terminus ad quem*: this formally marked the translation—already happening in practice—from the regional to the central organisation which was implicit in dependence on a single source of gas supply outside all the existing Regions. I make no apologies, however, for running beyond this date on occasions when to have observed it strictly would have left a particular theme hanging in the air.

Compromise has also been necessary in respect of the level of treatment. This book is aimed at the general reader with an interest in current affairs and the history of events that have led up to them. I have, therefore, tried to keep technicalities to a minimum consistent with establishing the basic facts and arguments. For the benefit of more specialised readers, who would prefer a longer and deeper study, references to particular points in the argument are numbered sequentially in each chapter and listed at the end of it. Additionally, each chapter is followed by a bibliography designed to provide further background reading. In general, both references and bibliography include only material that should be fairly readily accessible through academic or public libraries, though I have quoted also some key documents compiled within the industry.

A corporate body can express itself only through its members and it is a pleasure to acknowledge the help and advice I have received from members of the British Gas Corporation and its predecessor the Gas Council, established in 1948. It was natural that at the beginning of my task I should seek the counsel of Sir Henry Jones, who was Chairman of the Gas Council during the formative years 1960–71. Before nationalisation he had been a director of several gas companies and his family has been connected with the industry since 1835, a period spanning almost the whole of that covered by this history. He was kind enough to read the first draft of the book, and in its final form this has benefited greatly from the comments he made. Among others within the industry who have given time to discuss and consider the work are Sir Denis Rooke, present Chairman of the Corporation, and his immediate predecessor Sir Arthur Hetherington; Mr James Buckley, former Member for Marketing; Sir Ernest Woodroofe; Mr B. G. H. Clegg, Chairman of Northern Region; Mr Ernest Harman, formerly Chairman of South Western Region; Mr J. B. Horne, Assistant Distribution Engineer, Southern Region; Mr K. E. Abbs, formerly Industrial Relations Manager, Gas Council; Dr L. A. Moignard, then Assistant Director of the Midlands Research Station; Dr F. A. Burden of Watson House; Mr P. W. Graham of London Research Station; Mr A. T. Wyatt, Head of Industrial Relations Planning, British Gas Corporation; and Mr Charles Ellis, former Chief Press Officer. The book was initiated by Mr A. J. Vinegrad, the Corporation's Public Relations Adviser, and I greatly appreciated suggestions he made concerning the general scope of the work and his advice on sources of information within the industry, including a number of important reports and publications by Sir Kenneth Hutchison, formerly Deputy Chairman of the Gas Council.

I also received much helpful advice from outside the industry. In this connection I must mention Mr R. Kelf-Cohen, a former Under-Secretary in the Ministry of Fuel and Power, to whose books I have frequently referred; Mrs Joanna Spencer, a former Under-Secretary in the Ministry of Power; and Mr Angus Beckett, formerly Under-Secretary in charge of the Gas Division of the Ministry of Fuel and Power. I am indebted, too, to Lady Macleod of Borve, first Chairman of the National Gas Consumers' Council; Mr A. J. Adam, former Chairman of the Society of British Gas Industries Technical Committee and former Technical Director of Main Gas Appliances Limited; and Mr Geoffrey Battison, editor-in-chief of Gas World Publications.

The preparation of a book of this kind demands much library research. In this connection I am particularly indebted to Miss I. Keller, Librarian of the Corporation's headquarters library in London, and Miss Barbara Evans, Librarian of the Institution of Gas Engineers, both of whom showed much patience in tracking down necessary material. Last, but by no means least, my thanks are due to Mr David Butler, Information Manager of the Corporation, who for the duration of the project has been my point of liaison with it, arranging meetings with past and present members of the nationalised industry and visits to a number of its establishments, and generally making my path easy.

While the comments and advice of people so knowledgeable about the gas industry was of very great value to me, I would not like to put any of them into the position of seeming to endorse what I say here, whether it be on matters of fact or of opinion. Of necessity, it must always be the author who weighs the pros and cons of an argument and is ultimately responsible for any errors of fact or interpretation into which he may fall.

On a personal note, I would like to conclude by remarking that some forty years ago I had a brief and wholly undistinguished experience of the gas industry as student/assistant in the laboratory of the Bristol Gas Company at Canon's Marsh. This was very near the end of the life of the traditional coal carbonisation process and I recall very clearly the dirt and smoke and heat generated when the incandescent contents of the retorts were discharged. This was dramatic and exciting for the onlooker but not much of a way of life. The contrast with the modern industry, as exemplified by an on-shore terminal such as Bacton, is very striking. The industry has changed more since the end of the last war than throughout the whole of its previous history.

Oxford.   TREVOR I. WILLIAMS.
October 1979.

Contents

List of Figures   xv

List of Plates   xvi

List of Maps   xvii

PART I: THE BEGINNINGS

1. The Prehistory of the Gas Industry   3
2. The First Commercial Projects   6

PART II: DEVELOPMENT OF THE INDUSTRY UP TO THE FIRST WORLD WAR

3. Manufacture and Distribution   15
4. The Early Structure of the Industry   26
5. Appliances   31
6. Development of Government Control   40
7. Management and Workers   45
8. The First World War   51

PART III: THE INTER-WAR YEARS

9. Technical Changes   57
10. Changes in the Structure of the Industry   68

PART IV: THE SECOND WORLD WAR AND MOVES TOWARDS NATIONALISATION

11. The Gas Industry and the Second World War   81
12. Plans for Post-War Reorganisation   89

PART V: NATIONALISATION AND ITS AFTERMATH: THE MODERN INDUSTRY

13. The Post-War Nationalisation Programme   103
14. Introduction of New Manufacturing Processes   121
15. Natural Gas   139
16. North Sea Exploration and Development   156
17. Conversion   180
18. Marketing North Sea Gas   205

19. A New Structure for a New Industry   224
20. Relations with Government   243
21. Industrial Relations   262
22. The Industry and its Customers   270
23. Gas and the Energy Pattern   283

  Index   299

List of Figures

All illustrations not otherwise attributed come from the archives of the British Gas Corporation.

     Page

1. Gas works constructed by Clegg for Rudolf Ackermann's Repository of Fine Arts in the Strand (1812).   16
   Source: *King's Treatise* 1878, Vol. 1, Fig. 3, p. 25.

2. Scrubbers at Nine Elms, *c.* 1870.   17

3. Condenser and washer-scrubber at Tunbridge Wells, *c.* 1870.   17

4. Station meter from the Bromley Works (1876).   20
   Source: *King's Treatise* 1878, Vol. 2, Fig. 20, p. 39.

5. The laying of gas mains, *c.* 1880.   21

6. Compressed air drawing machine in a horizontal retort gas works (1894).   23
   Source: West's Gas Improvement Company Catalogue 1894.

7. Best and Holden's mechanical stoker, *c.* 1870.   23
   Source: *King's Treatise* 1878, Vol. 1, Fig. 273, p. 266.

8. Street lighting at rate-payers' expense.   28
   Source: Institution of Gas Engineers Archives.

9. Advertisement for portable gas, 1837.   29

10. The adaptation of the Argand oil burner for gas.   32

11. Ornate gas lamp from the Grand Vestibule of the new Paris Opera House, completed 1874.   33
    Source: *King's Treatise* 1882, Vol. 3, Fig. 56, p. 42.

12. Street lamp on the Thames Embankment.   34
    Source: *King's Treatise* 1882, Vol. 3, Fig. 101, p. 59.

13. Ornate gas fire, *c.* 1875.   35
    Source: *King's Treatise* 1882, Vol. 3, Fig. 229, p. 242.

14. Domestic hot plate, *c.* 1875.   36
    Source: *King's Treatise* 1882, Vol. 3, Fig. 206, p. 231.

15. Imperial gas stove, *c.* 1875.   37
    Source: *King's Treatise* 1882, Vol. 3, Fig. 244, p. 245.

16. Early example of small engine by Tyson of Philadelphia.   38
    Source: *King's Treatise* 1882, Vol. 3, Fig. 258, p. 250.

17. Otto internal combustion engine, *c.* 1880.   39
    Source: *King's Treatise* 1882, Vol. 3, Fig. 169, p. 201.

18. Mr Therm.   134

List of Plates

All illustrations not otherwise attributed come from the archives of the British Gas Corporation.

Certificate of the National Union of Gas Workers and General Labourers.
Frontispiece

Between pages 142 and 143

1. Diorama of William Murdock's gas-lit house in Redruth.
   Source: Science Museum. Crown Copyright.
2. The banqueting hall of the Brighton Pavilion.
3. Gas cooking in the Reform Club, London, in the 1840s.
4. The pre-payment (coin-in-the-slot) meter.
   Source: Science Museum. Crown Copyright.
5. B. W. Maughan's famous water heater—the 'geyser'.
   Source: Science Museum. Crown Copyright.
6. The Gas Light and Coke Company's huge plant at Beckton.
   Source: *King's Treatise*, 1878, Vol. 1, Frontispiece.
7. Beckton Gas Works, showing the interior of No. 9 retort house.
8. Improved cooker (*c.* 1875).
   Source: *King's Treatise*, 1882, Vol. 3, Fig. 191, p. 225.
9. Black Beauty cooker, 1887.
   Source: Science Museum. Crown Copyright.
10. Radiation New World cooking stove of 1923.
    Source: Science Museum. Crown Copyright.
11. The Main Mayflower frameless cooker of the 1970s.
12. Women at work in gas manufacture during the First World War.
13. Lurgi plant completed at Westfield in 1960.
14. Original sketch for the Woodall-Duckham patent vertical retort (1903).
    Source: Babcock Woodall-Duckham Limited, Crawley.
15. The East Greenwich jetty of the South Metropolitan Gas Company in 1924.
    Source: *Century of Gas in South London*. South Metropolitan Gas Company 1924, p. 16.
16. The laboratory of the South Metropolitan Gas Company as it appeared in 1924.
    Source: *A Century of Gas in South London*, p. 8.

Between pages 206 and 207

17. Carbonisation plant at Muirkirk (1977).
18. The Catalytic Rich Gas plant at the Bromley-by-Bow works.
19. St Just, Cornwall (1946).
20. Gas showroom in Frome in 1946.
21. Canvey Island Terminal, Essex.

22. The *Methane Pioneer*.
23. Geophysical exploration of the sea bed.
24. Underwater pipeline being laid.
25. The drilling rig *Mr Louie*.
26. Aerial view of the Bacton Terminal.
    Source: Shell.
27. Flare-off of town gas at Westminster.
28. Advanced field welding.
29. A store for conversion kits.
30. Polyethylene pipe being laid.
31. The manufacture of electric lamp bulbs.
32. Steel ingot heated in gas-fired furnace.

List of Maps

Growth of the national gas high pressure transmission system 1966–1978/9
                                                        pages 226–7

PART I

THE BEGINNINGS

1

The Prehistory of the Gas Industry

IT is commonly supposed that the order of events in the gas industry was the introduction of coal-gas, which remained supreme for about 150 years, and its subsequent supersession by natural gas, mainly during the present century. While this statement is broadly true, it needs some qualification, for in fact natural hydrocarbon gas was used as a fuel long before manufactured coal-gas was ever thought of. Joseph Needham [1] states that the Chinese used natural gas to evaporate salt in Szechuan at least as early as the second century A D, and possibly as much as five centuries earlier: the gas was conducted to the pans through bamboo tubes. As is well known, emanations of natural gas occur widely and are commonly associated with deposits of coal and petroleum; primitive peoples must certainly have made some limited use of these. The perpetual fire of the temple of Vesta, the Roman hearth-goddess, may well have been maintained by natural gas. Marco Polo visited Baku in 1272 and described the burning of natural gas at the fire-temple there. In 1618 the French philosopher Jean Tardin studied a 'burning fountain' near Grenoble, and concluded that its flames were like those of coal or oil [2]. Half a century later, in Britain, Thomas Shirley described to the Royal Society [3], an escape of inflammable gas from a famous burning spring associated with a coal-pit near Wigan. This gas, fire-damp, was already all too familiar to coal-miners. In 1730, James Lowther, a Whitehaven mine owner, brought fire-damp up from the coal seams through a pipe and burned it continuously at the surface. He also collected it in bladders, and demonstrated its burning power to the Royal Society [4]. Carlisle Spedding, agent for Lord Lonsdale's mines, proposed that such gas should be distributed throughout Whitehaven in underground pipes and used to light the streets. This offer was refused by the magistrates, but Spedding did light his own office.

The discovery of coal-gas cannot properly be attributed to any one person, but by the beginning of the eighteenth century it was well known that an inflammable gas could be generated by heating coal in a closed vessel. This was a long way, however, from turning the discovery to practical account, even on a modest scale. Perhaps the first person clearly to elucidate the basic principles was John Clayton. His experiments were conducted about 1684, but not made known until more than half a century later [5, 6]. From his account, Clayton's interest had clearly been aroused by Shirley's description of the burning spring near Wigan; he dug deeper than Shirley and found 'Shelly' (shaley) coal only half a yard down. He then describes how:

I got some coal and distilled it in a Retort in an open Fire. At first there came over only *Phlegm*, afterwards a black *Oil*, and then, likewise, a *Spirit* arose which I could nowise condense. . . . I observed that the Spirit which issued out caught Fire at the Flame of the Candle, and continued burning with Violence as it issued out, in a Stream, which I blew out, and lighted again, alternately, for several times; after which I fixed a Bladder, squeezed and void of Air, to the pipe of the Receiver. I have frequently taken one of these Bladders, and pinching a Hole therein with a Pin, and compressing gently the Bladder near the Flame of a Candle, it at once took Fire it would then continue flaming till all the Spirit was compressed out of the Bladder.

This description is quoted verbatim because it epitomises the manufacture and storage of gas as practised in the gas industry in the nineteenth century and well into the twentieth. It thus gives some justification for the claim that Clayton was the father of the gas industry. Richard Watson, professor of both chemistry and divinity at the University of Cambridge, and later bishop of Llandaff, conducted more sophisticated experiments and described them in his *Chemical Essays* (2nd edn. 1782). He noted that 96 ounces of 'Newcastle pit coal' yielded 28 ounces of gas. He also suggested that gas from coke-ovens—introduced after Abraham Darby, in 1709, discovered a means of smelting iron-ore with coke instead of charcoal—might be put to practical use. As we shall see later, coke-oven gas was to become an important supplement to ordinary coal-gas, but not until the twentieth century.

While these observations served to demonstrate the possibilities of coal-gas, they led to no practical developments. Meanwhile, in Belgium, Jan Minckelers [7], a professor at the University of Louvain, became interested in coal-gas for quite a different reason. In 1783, the Montgolfier brothers had made their first ascent in a hot-air balloon and there was intense interest in this exciting aerial development. It was realised that a gas lighter than air, such as hydrogen (discovered in 1766 by Henry Cavendish) was a useful alternative to hot air, and Minckelers examined the possibilities of coal-gas for this purpose. On 1 October 1784, he filled an old gun barrel with powdered coal and heated it strongly to produce gas. This was used to fill a small unmanned balloon, which made a flight of 25 km. More to the immediate point, Minckelers in the same year used the gas to illuminate his lecture room at Louvain.

The literature of the latter part of the eighteenth century provides plenty of examples of similar limited applications of coal-gas for lighting [8]. J. G. Pickel, professor of pharmacology at Wurzburg, lighted his laboratory in 1785; W. A. Lampadius used it to light the Dresden castle of the Elector of Saxony in 1799. But none of these amounted to anything approaching an industrial enterprise. This had to await the advent of men of broader vision, in particular Philippe Lebon in France and William Murdock and Frederick Winsor in Britain.

REFERENCES

[1] NEEDHAM, Joseph. *Science and Civilisation in China*, Vol. IV, pt. 1, p. 66, Cambridge University Press, Cambridge (1962).
[2] Idem. *Clerks and Craftsmen in China and the West*, Cambridge University Press, Cambridge (1970).
  TARDIN, J. *Historie naturelle de la fontaine qui brusle près de Grenoble*, Tournon (1618).
[3] SHIRLEY, T. *Philosophical Transactions of the Royal Society* (1667), pp. 482–4.
[4] *Philosophical Transactions of the Royal Society* (1733), pp. 109–13.
[5] Ibid. (1739/40), pp. 59–61.
[6] LAYTON, WALTER T. *The Discoverer of Gas Lighting: Notes on the Life and Work of the Rev. John Clayton, DD, 1657–1725*, London (1926).
[7] ADRY, E. *Un Siècle d'éclairage 1824–1924*, pp. 41–4, Antwerp (1925).
[8] ELTON, Arthur. Gas for Light and Heat, in: *A History of Technology* (ed. Charles Singer, E. J. Holmyard, A. R. Hall, and Trevor I. Williams), Vol. IV, p. 261, Clarendon Press, Oxford (1958).

BIBLIOGRAPHY

NEWBIGGING, Thomas and FEWTRELL, W. T. (ed.). *King's Treatise on the Science and Practice of the Manufacture and Distribution of Coal Gas*, King, London (1878).
CHANDLER, Dean. *Outline of History of Lighting by Gas*, South Metropolitan Gas Co., London (1936).
SINGER, Charles, HOLMYARD, E. J., HALL, A. R. and WILLIAMS, Trevor, I. *A History of Technology*, Vol. IV, Ch. 9, Clarendon Press, Oxford (1958).
MATTHEWS, W. *An Historical Sketch of the Origin, Progress and Present State of Gas-Lighting*, London (1827).
CHANDLER, Dean and LACEY, A. Douglas. *The Rise of the Gas Industry in Britain*, British Gas Council, London (1949).
DE MOULLPIED, A. T. Coal Gas as an Illuminant, *Discovery*, **8**, 183 (1927).

2

The First Commercial Projects

B Y the end of the eighteenth century it was clear from practical demonstrations that an inflammable gas, burning with a luminous flame, could be generated by strongly heating coal in a closed vessel. Translating this into a viable commercial enterprise was, however, to prove a long and arduous task, and one in which scientists were not prominent.

For the start of this new phase we must turn to France, where Philippe Lebon, who had been brought up among the charcoal burners of the Joinville area, began, apparently about 1791, to study the generation of gas by heating wood. He moved to Paris in 1798 and in the following year took out a patent (extended in 1801) 'for new methods of employing combustible materials more effectively, either for heating or lighting or to obtain various products' [1]. To publicise his invention, Lebon—then an engineer attached to the *Service des Ponts et Chaussées*—staged a public exhibition in 1801 in the Hotel Seignelay in what is now the rue Saint-Dominique. Wood-generated gas was burned in two '*thermolampes*', one to heat and light the house, the other to illumine the garden. The exhibition attracted much attention.

Among those who saw it was Gregory Watt, second son of James Watt, perhaps the greatest of British engineers, who contrived to be in Paris even though France and England were still technically at war. Gregory was impressed and sent a report home to his father's company, Boulton and Watt, who were then firmly established in the manufacture of steam engines. An important part of Boulton and Watt's business lay in Cornwall, where the steam engine was proving invaluable for pumping water from tin mines, permitting the working of previously inaccessible levels. Their chief engine-erector there was a Scottish engineer William Murdock (originally Murdoch), who had been experimenting on lines similar to those of Lebon in France. As early as 1792 he had used coal-gas to light the room of a house in Cross Street, Redruth. (See Plate 1.) The resources of Boulton and Watt's famous Soho Foundry in Birmingham were very appropriate for the manufacture of apparatus necessary for further trials, and in 1798 Murdock went there to continue his experiments. Gregory Watt's report from Paris provided a further stimulus, and a public demonstration was organised in Britain to mark the Peace of Amiens in 1802. The front of the Soho works was illuminated by two gas flares, and William Matthews [2] records: 'The illumination of Soho Works on this occasion was one of extraordinary splendour . . . Birmingham poured forth its numerous population to gaze at, and to admire this wonderful display of the combined effects of science and art' [3]. In the following two years a further sum of about £5000 was spent on development, and a permanent gas-lighting system was installed in the foundry. Murdock was provided with a young assistant, Samuel Clegg, of whom we shall hear more later.

By this time, Boulton and Watt felt sufficient confidence in their apparatus to canvass for orders, and their first installation was in the cotton-mill of Phillips and Lee, at Salford near Manchester, one of the largest in the country. Fifty lamps were supplied with gas from six cast-iron retorts, each charged with about 15 cwt of coal. Surplus gas was stored in iron holders sealed by water. By 1807 the installation had been extended to cover the entire factory, Lee's own house, and a private road; 271 Argand burners (p. 32) and 633 cockspurs in all [4]. The importance of Murdock's work was recognised by the Royal Society in 1808 by the award of their Rumford Gold Medal, appropriately inscribed *Ex Fumo Dare Lucem* (To give light out of smoke). No attempt was made to patent his process, and this later proved a serious error.

Meanwhile, Clegg had left the firm in 1805 and set up as a gas engineer on his own account. His first major installation was in Henry Lodge's cotton mill near Halifax; he claimed that his contract for this pre-dated Murdock's for Phillips and Lee by a fortnight.

THE GAS LIGHT AND COKE COMPANY

There, for the moment, we must leave developments in Britain and return to France. In Paris, Lebon had failed to gain local support, but he did attract the attention of a colourful German entrepreneur, Frederick Albert Winzer. He tried unsuccessfully to buy one of Lebon's *thermolampes*, but contrived to make one for himself. Having failed to sell this in any European country, he aimed to try his luck in Britain in 1803. Here circumstances were more propitious. First, the new race of factory owners was anxious to find a safer and more effective form of lighting. Secondly, the war had caused a sharp rise in the price of conventional illuminants based on tallow and whale-oil. Finally, in 1804 Lebon was murdered in the *Champs Elysées* in Paris; this virtually stopped all further initiative there and elsewhere in Europe. Against this, Winsor—as he now called himself—had the disadvantage of being conspicuously foreign in speech and manner and an obsessional belief in the virtues of gas-lighting that blinded him to the very considerable practical and economic difficulties. From a pretentious headquarters in Pall Mall he launched a vigorous publicity campaign. Like Lebon and Murdock before him, he staged spectacular public demonstrations, first on the walls of Carlton House Terrace, and later in Pall Mall (June 1807). It would appear, however, that the possibilities of street lighting by gas in London were first demonstrated, earlier in 1807, at the Golden Lane Brew-

ery. Before these practical demonstrations, Winsor campaigned by pamphlets and lectures. There seemed no limit to the benefits he claimed for gas;
on the one hand, it would alleviate pulmonary diseases, and on the other it
would relieve the plight of the unhappy chimney boys, for whose protection
a society had been formed in 1803. Better still, it offered the prospect of
enormous profits. In 1807, he proposed the abolition of the use of raw coal;
only coke and gas should be allowed. A £50 share in his proposed National
Heat and Light Company would give an annual return of £6000 and an
eventual capital appreciation of £120 000. Even though this was recognised
as embodying much extravagant nonsense, it nevertheless began to be felt
that there might be money to be made out of Winsor's proposals. This was
encouraged by the fact that he had enlisted the services of Samuel Clegg to
improve his apparatus. Looking back, it is clear that he saw clearly in his
fertile mind a principle that his rivals had failed to recognise: that the future
of gas lay not in local generation but in central generation and distribution to
consumers through a system of mains and pipes.

As public opinion began to swing in Winsor's favour, so opposition to
such a revolutionary new system began to develop: Winsor certainly had
much to contend with. Sir Walter Scott ridiculed a madman 'proposing to
light London with—what do you think? Why, with smoke!' and two distinguished scientists added their quota. W. H. Wollaston thought 'they might as
well try to light London with a slice from the Moon'; the great Sir Humphry
Davy wondered whether the dome of St Paul's might serve as a gasholder. It
was argued—the more effectively because this was the time of the
Napoleonic Wars—that the replacement of oil by gas would be disastrous
for national defence; the whaling fleet was a valuable—allegedly, essential—source of recruits for the Royal Navy. The demonstrated brilliance
of gas-lighting had not blinded observers to its smell nor to the risk of
explosion.

The first overt move towards exploiting Winsor's schemes was made in
1807, when a group of influential backers met at the Crown and Anchor
tavern in the Strand. It appears that from the start the lead was taken by
James Ludovic Grant, who was in due course to become the first Governor
of the Gas Light and Coke Company. Winsor's business acumen was
doubted, and he was firmly steered into the role of publicist and technical
adviser.

There then began a long battle to obtain the necessary authority to
proceed. At that time, and indeed up to 1856, any company in England
which raised capital by selling shares, was in law no more than a partnership:
if it became insolvent all its members were liable to have their private
property seized to meet the debts. Only a Royal Charter or a Private Act of
Parliament could give exemption. The magnitude of the operations proposed by the grandiosely named New Patriotic Imperial and National Light
and Heat Company were clearly such that the necessary capital could not be

raised if individual subscribers were to be held liable beyond the limit of their subscription. An initial approach made to the Chancellor of the Exchequer was unsuccessful. He referred the matter to the Privy Council, who were of the opinion that only the King would give a decision. But George III wanted no part in such a controversial proposal, and the matter was referred to the Law Officers of the Crown; they advised that the only possible means of procedure was by Act of Parliament [6].

The first attempt to obtain this was made in 1809, and was presented on behalf of the more modestly named Gas Light and Coke Company. The case was argued at great length before a Parliamentry Committee of Inquiry [7]. It was vigorously opposed by Murdock and his supporters, on three principal grounds. First, it ignored Murdock's claim to be the pioneer of gas lighting in Britain. Secondly, the size of the enterprise would create a virtual monopoly and drive other firms, even those as big as Boulton and Watt, out of business. Thirdly, the limitation of liability was a dangerous principle. As Herbert Heaton has remarked [8], in a different context: 'The close connection between stocks, speculation, and original sin had once more been demonstrated.' Supporting evidence—including that of Frederick Accum, a professional chemist who had once been assistant to Humphry Davy—did not convince the Committee, and the application failed. Despite the outcome, Murdock was incensed by 'the very unfair and illiberal manner' in which he was mentioned, and made a public reply [9]. However, a further application, seeking to raise only £200 000 capital rather than £1 million, was successful in 1810, though not without stringent conditions. Application for a Charter could not be made until £100 000 had been raised, and the whole £200 000 had to be raised within three years. Street lighting had to be provided at a charge no higher than that for oil. On the other hand, the company had achieved the all-important right to dig up the streets to lay its mains, and no limitation was set on the price that might be charged to private consumers. Territorially, its powers extended over the Cities of London and Westminster, and the Borough of Southwark; in those days this was effectively the whole of London. In 1812, the necessary financial conditions having been fulfilled, the Charter was duly granted and the Gas Light and Coke Company—often called the Chartered Company—came formally into existence. The first meeting of the Court of Directors was held on 24 June 1812, in temporary offices at 27 Norfolk Street, just off the Strand. Thus was born the modern gas industry in Britain. Although mills, colleges, and other large institutions continued to have individual installations, the future lay with general public supply from centrally located gas works.

Even though experiences in London showed that gas lighting was not the road to a quick fortune predicted by Winsor, the convincing demonstrations of the practicability of gas lighting led to gasworks being established throughout the country. In 1819 it was reported that gas lighting had been installed in Edinburgh, Glasgow, Liverpool, Bristol, Bath, Cheltenham,

Birmingham, Leeds, Manchester, Exeter, Chester, Macclesfield, Preston, and Kidderminster, among others [10]. Respectability was conferred on the new industry by Royal patronage: in 1821 The Prince Regent introduced gas for lighting the Music Room and Banqueting Hall of his Pavilion at Brighton. (See Plate 2.) By 1829, some 200 companies had been formed; the first municipal undertaking was formed in Manchester in 1817.

REFERENCES

[1] NEWBIGGING, Thomas and FEWTRELL, W. T. (ed.). *King's Treatise on the Science and Practice of the Manufacture and Distribution of Coal Gas*, pp. 10–11, King, London (1878).

[2] MATTHEWS, William. *An Historical Sketch of the Origin and Progress of Gas-Lighting*, p. 6, London (1827).

[3] CLEGG, S. Jr. *A Practical Treatise on the Manufacture and Distribution of Coal-Gas*, London (1841).

[4] MURDOCK, W. An Account of the Application of the Gas from Coal for Economical Purposes, *Philosophical Transaction of the Royal Society*, Pt. 1, pp. 124–32 (1808).

[5] HANNA, W. *Memoirs of the Life and Writings of Thomas Chalmers, DD LI D*, Vol. 1, p. 115, London (1849).

[6] *Report of James Ludovic Grant Esq.*, Chairman, and the other acting Trustees of the Fund for assisting Mr Winsor in his experiments: to the subscribers to that Fund at a Meeting convened by Public Advertisements at the Crown and Anchor Tavern in the Strand, on the 26th May 1808, London (1808).

[7] Minutes of Evidence taken before Select Committee re Bill to incorporate certain Persons for procuring Coke, Oil, Tar, Pitch, Ammoniacal Liquor, Essential Oil, and Inflammable Air from Coal, and for other purposes (1809), (220), III, 315.

[8] HEATON, Herbert. *Economic History of Europe*, p. 572, Harper, New York (1936).

[9] MURDOCK, William. A letter to a Member of Parliament from Mr William Murdock in Vindication of his Character and Claims in Reply to a Recent Publication by the Committee for Conducting through Parliament a Bill for Incorporating a Gas-light and Coke Company, London (1809).

[10] ACCUM, F. C. *Description of the Process of Manufacturing Coal Gas for the Lighting of Streets, Houses and Public Buildings*, p. 3, London (1819).

BIBLIOGRAPHY

ACCUM, F. C. *Description of the Process of Manufacturing Coal Gas for the Lighting of Streets, Houses, and Public Buildings*, London (1819).

CHANDLER, Dean and LACEY, A. Douglas. *The Rise of the Gas Industry in Britain*, British Gas Council, London (1949).

CHANDLER, Dean. *Outline of History of Lighting by Gas*, South Metropolitan Gas Co., London (1936).

CLEGG, S., Jr. *A Practical Treatise on the Manufacture and Distribution of Coal-Gas*, London (1841).

DOWNIE, R. Angus. William Murdock, *Blackwoods Magazine*, **245**, 266–74 (1939).

EVERARD, Stirling. *The History of the Gas Light and Coke Company 1812–1949*, Benn, London (1949).

EDINBURGH REVIEW, January, 1809. Review of three recent papers advancing the respective claims of Murdock and Winsor; viz:

(1) MURDOCK, William. 'An Account of the Application of the Gas From Coal for Economical Purposes', *Philosophical Transactions of the Royal Society*, pt. 1, pp. 124–32 (1808).

(2) Considerations on the Nature and Objects of the intended Light and Heat Company, London (1808).

(3) WINSOR, F. A. 'To be Sanctioned by an Act of Parliament: A National Light and Heat Company', London (1807).

MATTHEWS, William. *An Historical Sketch of the Origin and Progress of Gas-Lighting*, London (1827) (2nd edn. 1832).

MURDOCK, Alexander. *Light without Wick: a Century of Gas-Lighting*, Maclehose, Glasgow (1892).

SMILES, S. *Lives of Boulton and Watt*, London (1865).

The Gas Light and Coke Company 1812–1912, London (n.d.) (c. 1912).

PART II

DEVELOPMENT OF THE INDUSTRY
UP TO THE FIRST WORLD WAR

3

Manufacture and Distribution

THE Gas Light and Coke Company obtained its charter early in 1812 and by the end of 1815 nearly thirty miles of gas-main had been laid in London. The foundation of the British gas industry had thus been established, but it had to overcome many difficulties, both technical and commercial, before it could regard itself as firmly established.

MANUFACTURE AND PURIFICATION OF GAS

Crude coal-gas is a material of variable composition, which depends on—among other factors—the source of the coal and the conditions of carbonisation, especially the temperature of the retorts. The main constituents—representing perhaps 85 per cent of the total—are methane and hydrogen, together with some carbon monoxide, say 5 per cent. In addition, however, there are small quantities of a very great number of impurities. Some, such as nitrogen and carbon dioxide, are harmless, insofar as they merely dilute the gas. Others, however, are objectionable, because of their smell, or because, like carbon monoxide, they are poisonous: such are ammonia, sulphuretted hydrogen, and cyanogen. At an early stage in the development of the industry it was realised that some purification of the gas before distribution to the consumer was necessary. However, an odourless gas was never the target; the smell of gas was the best warning of leakage.

Pioneer work in gas purification was carried out by Edward Heard, who had been an assistant to Winsor; in 1806 he obtained a patent [1] for the purification of gas with dry lime. In the same year, however, Samuel Clegg introduced the method of wet liming, which soon became almost universal [2]. A bucketful of lime suspended in 50 gallons of water would purify about 20 000 cubic feet of gas [3]. A compact triple purifier based on this principle was shortly devised by John Malam [4].

In 1817 Reuben Phillips, of Exeter, patented a process for purifying gas with slaked lime just damp enough to make its particles cohere [5]. Phillips' method was much improved by Malam [6], but not widely adopted in urban areas of Britain until the 1860s; by 1890 it was in use in most large towns. But Phillips reaped no benefit, for which the gas companies were roundly condemned by W. R. Bowditch [7].

The relatively early adoption of dry-liming by provincial works was partly due to the fact that, after exposure to air, the spent lime found a ready local market for agricultural use. By contrast, the offensive wet liming residue ('blue billy') was difficult to dispose of and the subject of much public complaint. One way or another, gasworks based on coal were never popular neighbours.

From about 1850 iron oxide began to be used for gas purification. The history of its introduction is complicated by protracted arguments and litigation over patent rights [8, 9] but the facts are clear enough. The noxious sulphur compounds in raw gas, notably sulphuretted hydrogen, will combine with iron oxide to form iron sulphide: on exposure to air the latter is slowly converted back to iron oxide [10]. The conversion is not complete, because some of the sulphide is converted to elemental sulphur, but nevertheless the oxide could in practice be used several times over. The importance of the process is indicated by the fact that F. C. Hills, eventually the

Fig. 1. Gas works constructed by Clegg for Rudolf Ackermann's Repository of Fine Arts in the Strand (1812).

Fig. 2. Scrubbers at Nine Elms, *c*. 1870. Such purifiers were a conspicuous feature of coal-carbonisation gas works.

Fig. 3. Condenser and washer-scrubbers at Tunbridge Wells, *c*. 1870.

most successful of the protagonists, made over £100 000 from his patents
even before their duration was extended by the courts.

By the first decade of this century, general practice was first to wash the
cooled gas thoroughly in scrubbers to remove ammonia; the resulting crude
concentrated ammoniacal liquor was a valuable by-product. It was then
further treated in purifiers containing slaked lime or iron oxide [11].

Gaseous impurities were not the only ones the coal-gas manufacturer had
to contend with; another product of carbonisation is coal tar. In the early
days of the industry this was a nuisance—since it could not easily be
dumped—and manufacturers got rid of it as best they could by burning it to
heat the retorts. About 1820 a tar-distillery was set up near Edinburgh; one
of its products was the naphtha used by Charles Macintosh to prepare the
famous waterproof rubberised fabric he patented in 1823. A much bigger
outlet developed from about 1840, when increasing quantities of heavy oil
(creosote) distilled from coal-tar were required for preserving the timber
sleepers of the rapidly expanding railway system. Then, in 1856, W. H.
Perkin prepared mauve, the first of the synthetic dyestuffs. This heralded
the rise of a great new organic chemicals industry based on dyes but soon
extending to drugs, explosives, photographic chemicals, and a host of other
new products. For all these, the main source of the necessary raw materials—benzene, anthracene, etc.—proved to be coal-tar. At the end of the
century, this embarrassing by-product was fetching £1 a ton [12]; total
production in 1900 was 650 000 tons [13]. However, the gas industry did not
participate to any great extent in these new developments, as the general
practice was to sell the crude tar to independent tar-distillers.

Originally, retorts were of cast-iron, set vertically, but about the middle of
the century it became apparent that higher operating temperatures were
advantageous. This led to the general introduction of fire-clay retorts with
self-sealing lids, the latter the invention of Robert Morton (1869). This
greatly eased the work of the stokers. For greater ease of discharge these
were set at an angle and then, almost universally, horizontally: several
retorts, each holding 2 to 3 cwts of coal, were heated in one furnace. Later,
history reversed itself. Towards the end of the century, inclined retorts
(popularly known by the stokers as 'Ally Slopers') again found favour,
especially in smaller works, where power stoking was not economic.

Coke—the residue left in the retort after gas and tar have been expelled—
was one of the designated products of the original Chartered Company.
Cleggs, however, showed little interest in by-products, regarding his task as
the production of gas. Coke was sold direct to consumers or to merchants;
this was assisted by the growing interest in smokeless fuels as a means of
combating the smoke nuisance in London and other large cities. The busi-

ness was lucrative: in 1880, when production of coke was a little over 10 million tons, it was estimated that sales should show a return of 40–70 per cent on the cost of coal.

METERING, STORAGE, AND DISTRIBUTION

As in any other industry, careful cost control was of great importance to the gas industry. Implicit in this was the ability to measure the amount of gas made. Precise instruments were introduced at an early date: the crucial importance of these may be judged from the following description [14]:

. . . by this instrument, all the gas made is recorded hourly and daily; it serves as a check on the quantity and quality of the coals carbonized; it shows whether the operations in the retort-houses are being successfully conducted or otherwise; and, as far as regards the production and sale of gas, it affords convincing means of ascertaining the operations of the company.

As befitted its key position the big station meter was often of the ornate design beloved of the Victorians.

The most conspicuous feature of the traditional gas works was the gasholder, necessary to ensure continuity of supply. Basically, it was very simple: an inverted iron bell rose and fell in a circular tank containing water to provide a seal. By the beginning of the First World War there was great variety of design: in particular simple holders, consisting of only one section or lift, had been widely supplemented by compound types. There had been an enormous increase in size. A gasholder with a capacity of 750 000 cubic feet was then regarded as small; a giant six-lift holder at East Greenwich was 300 feet in diameter and rose to a height of 180 feet. Its capacity was 12 million cubic feet.

Gasholders were from the beginning a matter of great public concern. Despite evidence to the contrary, they were long regarded as serious explosion hazards if the least leak occurred. As early as 1814, however, Clegg had convincingly demonstrated the falsity of this to a committee of the Royal Society, headed by the President, Sir Joseph Banks. Seizing a pick, he drove a hole through the wall of a gasholder and applied a light to the escaping gas, which merely burned fiercely as a long jet [15].

Although gas mains in the USA were made of wood as late as the 1870s, cast-iron mains were used in Britain from the outset. Individual consumers were supplied through narrow-bore tubing: this was known as 'barrel' because in fact much of it consisted of old musket barrels, in plentiful supply after the war with France.

This use of short lengths entailed a multiplicity of joints and corresponding risk of leakage, which was both expensive and potentially dangerous. A measure of the loss was provided in 1875/6, when 21 companies in the West of Scotland notified a loss of gas due to leakage ranging from 10 to 20 per

Fig. 4. Station meter from the Bromley Works (1876). Such meters were of ornate design, as befitted their position in the Works.

cent [16]. As loss was in proportion to the pressure of the gas, it was in the interests of the companies to keep this as low as possible.

From an early stage, therefore, much attention was paid to pressure-controlling devices, or governors. Most were based on a single diaphragm actuated by gas pressure. In 1879 James Stott introduced a much more sophisticated and sensitive governor involving a mercury seal [17].

COAL SUPPLIES

For two reasons the supply of coal was a constant worry to the gas manufacturers. Firstly, not all coal is suitable for gas-making and the number of pits able to supply a suitable quality was limited. Secondly, the industry, like most single-product industries, could find itself at the mercy of its suppliers. The experience and policy of the Chartered Company [18]—designed to secure uninterrupted supplies, come what may—was fairly typical of the large concerns, though the multiplicity of small ones had of necessity to lead a hand-to-mouth existence. Initial experience with London coal merchants was unsatisfactory.

Fig. 5. The laying of gas mains was a major and disruptive undertaking (*c*. 1880).

In 1826, the Chartered Company became buyers on the London Coal Exchange in their own right and chartered collier brigs to transport their purchases direct to their own works. In 1846 coal was being shipped to them on the Thames at the rate of 60 000 tons per annum. The Chartered Company then proceeded to purchase their own ships and, in 1839, acquired control of a colliery. For a time, a policy of vertical integration was adopted. Steam vessels were engaged on long-term charter about the middle of the century and this initiated a policy of making long-term contracts with individual colliery owners large enough (upwards of 100 000 tons a year) to make it worth their while to build steam colliers—far more reliable than sail—solely for this business. The giant Imperial Gas Light and Coke Company pursued a similar policy. (See Plate 15.)

The importance of coal contracts was forcibly illustrated in the 1870s, when prices were rising. J. O. Phillips, secretary of the Chartered Company, repeatedly sought the authority of his Court (board of directors) to place three-year contracts, but this was refused. In June 1872, 80 000 tons were offered at 18*s*. 6*d*. per ton but only 14*s*. 6*d*. was offered, and this was not accepted. In the event, Phillips had to be instructed to buy 250 000 tons at the best price he could. The result was a rise in the price of gas from 4s. 6d. to 5s. per thousand cubic feet between 1873 and 1874.

MECHANICAL HANDLING

Even in an age when manual labour was cheap and plentiful, and the working day long, it was impossible to handle coal and the resulting by-products on this scale without a great deal of mechanical aid. The heavy engineering industry was quick to seize the new opportunies, partly by the extension of existing businesses and partly by the creation of new specialist firms. The necessary equipment included machinery for unloading coal trucks by tipping them bodily; moving belts for conveying coal from the storage areas to the retort houses; mechanical stokers: wagons for removing quenched coke; coal-breaking machines; gas scrubbers and purifiers; gasholders; cast-iron mains; pumps, valves, and meters; and internal railway systems. As the business became more sophisticated, a wide range of specialised laboratory equipment was necessary to carry out such tests and analyses as were necessary for efficient production and, increasingly, were required by law.

It is impossible here even to list the principal firms and their products, but many of the oldest were still active in the 1930s and appear in the 150 pages of advertising that appeared in the Jubilee edition of *Gas World* [19]. The centenary issue of *Gas Journal* (1949) included advertisements from 22 'centenarian' firms who had traded with the gas industry for 100 years and upwards [20], as well as many other useful contributions to the history of the industry 1849–1949. From a very early date the gas industry extended deep into other sectors of industry in respect of both manufacture and sale. Not until 1905, however, did those concerned with supplying the material, plant, and necessities for manufacture, distribution, and consumption of gas form their own organisation, the Society of British Gas Industries.

REFERENCES

[1] NEWBIGGING, Thomas and FEWTRELL, W. T. (ed.). *King's Treatise on the Science and Practice of the Manufacture and Distribution of Coal Gas*, Vol. 1, p. 387, King, London (1878).
[2] British Patent 3968 (1815).
[3] RICHARDS, W. *A Practical Treatise on the Manufacture and Distribution of Coal Gas*, pp. 146–7, London (1877).
[4] PECKSTON, T. S. *The Theory and Practice of Gas-Lighting, etc.*, pp. 211–12, London (1819).
[5] British Patent 4142 (1817).
[6] British Patent 1823 (1817).
[7] BOWDITCH, W. R. *The Analysis, Technical Valuation, Purification, and Use of Coal Gas*, pp. 15–16, London (1867).

Fig. 6. Compressed air drawing machine in a horizontal retort gas works (1894).

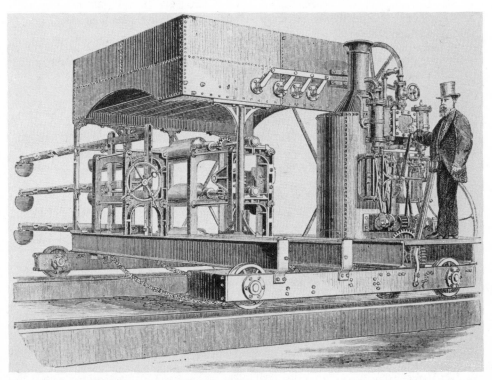

Fig. 7. Best and Holden's mechanical stoker, *c.* 1870.

[8] In: The Exchequer of Pleas, Hills versus the London Gaslight Company. Report of the Trial . . . before the Hon. Mr. Baron Bramwell . . . August, 1858. London (1858).
[9] NEWBIGGING, Thomas and FEWTRELL, W. T. (ed.). Op. cit., pp. 396-8.
[10] Ibid., p. 397.
[11] WEBBER, W. H. Y. *Town Gas and its Uses*, pp. 54-56, Constable, London (1907).
[12] LUNGE, G. *Coal-tar and Ammonia*, 5th edn., pp. 16-36, Gurney and Jackson, London (1916).
[13] BEILBY, G. T. *Journal of the Society of Chemical Industry*, 647 (1899).
[14] NEWBIGGING, Thomas and FEWTRELL, W. T. (ed.). Op. cit., Vol. II, p. 28.
[15] EVERARD, Stirling. *History of the Gas Light and Coke Company, 1812-1949*, p. 60, Benn, London (1949).
[16] Gas Managers' Association: Annual Report of the West of Scotland (1875/6).
[17] STOTT, James. *Iron Trades Journal*, December (1879).
[18] EVERARD, Stirling. op. cit., pp. 57, 76, 194, 221-2, 245.
[19] *Gas World*, No. 2595, 28 April (1934), pp. i-cxxiii; Supplements 1-35.
[20] *Gas Journal Centenary Volume*, pp. 153-9, King, London (1949).

BIBLIOGRAPHY

ANDERSON, G. *Improvements in Apparatus employed in the Manufacture of Gas*, London (1880).

CHANDLER, Dean and LACEY, A. Douglas. *Rise of the Gas Industry in Britain*, British Gas Council, London (1949).

CLEGG, S. Jr. Practical Treatise on the Manufacture and Distribution of Coal-gas: London 1841, *Gas World (Jubilee edition)*, No. 2595, 28 April (1934).

COLYER, F. *Gas Works: their Arrangement, Construction, Plant and Machinery*, London (1884).

COOPER, G. S. *By-product Coking*, 2nd edn., London (1923).

EVERARD, Stirling. *History of the Gas Light and Coke Company, 1812-1944*, Benn, London (1949).

Gas Journal Centenary Volume, King, London (1949).

HERRING, W. H. *Construction of Gas Works*, London (1892).

HOLE, Walter. *The Distribution of Gas*, 4th edn., Benn, London (1921).

HUGHE, S. *Gas Works: their Construction and Arrangement; and the Manufacture and Distribution of Coal Gas*, (revised by H. O'Conner), London (1904).

LUNGE, George. *Coal-tar and Ammonia*, 5th edn., Gurney and Jackson, London (1916).

MEADE, Alwyne. *Modern Gasworks Practice*, Benn, London (1913).

MOTT, R. A. (ed.). *History of Coke Making and of Coke Oven Managers Association*, London (1936).

NEWBIGGING, Thomas. *Handbook for Gas Engineers and Managers*, 8th edn., King, London (1913).

NEWBIGGING, Thomas and FEWTRELL, W. T. (ed.). *King's Treatise on the Science and Practice of the Manufacture and Distribution of Coal Gas*, King, London (1878).

TOMLINSON, Charles (ed.). *Cyclopaedia of Useful Arts*, Vol. I, pp. 736-53, Virtue, London (1866).

ROYLE, Harold, M. *Chemistry of Gas Manufacture*, Crosby Lockwood and Son, London (1907).
THORPE, T. E. *A Dictionary of Applied Chemistry*, Vol. 2, pp. 177–213, Longmans Green, London (1891).
WEBBER, W. H. Y. *Town Gas and its Uses*, Constable, London (1907).
WYATT, V. *Transport of Material for Gas Works*, London (1881).

4

The Early Structure of the Industry

To a considerable extent, the structure of the gas industry during the first century of its existence was determined by the nature of its product. Indeed, technological factors have been a powerful influence up to the present day. The pioneers, as we have seen, were of the opinion that gas manufacture was essentially a very localised activity. Later, Winsor made the more ambitious proposal of manufacturing gas at a central works and distributing it to individual consumers. But even Winsor at his most extravagant made no proposals for anything like a national or even regional system of manufacture and distribution. The technology of the day precluded distribution over any considerable distance. This limitation made it inevitable that, once the potential of gas had been recognised, there should develop a multiplicity of unconnected concerns meeting local demand. Those supplying the great conurbations of the manufacturing areas were comparable with the big London companies; others were almost one-man concerns.

GROWTH OF THE GAS INDUSTRY

No reliable statistics are available for the growth of the industry for rather more than the first half-century of its existence. Not until 1882 did the Board of Trade require gas undertaking, both private and municipal, to make systematic annual returns, but even these are of limited value. The accompanying table shows the overall growth of this industry from 1882 to 1912 in terms of the number of undertakings; gas sold; average size of undertaking; and capital invested.

The figures in the table speak for themselves. During this thirty year period the amount of gas sold increased threefold, and the number of undertakings roughly doubled, from 481 to 826. It would be impracticable, as well as tedious, to attempt to list them all and we must restrict ourselves to brief mention of some of them. Not surprisingly, the centre of development was London [2], not only because of its dense population, but because it was the home of the original Chartered Company. Before the middle of the century a dozen other companies were in operation in London. Before long, it was apparent that there were too many, and soon after mid-century a long, and not always amiable, process of amalgamation began, with the Gas Light and Coke Company emerging as the leader. In 1867, the Company realised that its cramped works near the centre of London were impracticable and it acquired a very large site at East Ham. It was six miles from their nearest

GROWTH OF UK GAS UNDERTAKING 1882–1912 [1]

	Authorised Companies				Authorised Local Authority Undertakings			
Year	Number of undertakings	Gas sold (million cu ft)	Gas sold per undertaking (million cu ft)	Capital invested[1] (£000)	Number of undertakings	Gas sold (million cu ft)	Gas sold per undertaking (million cu ft)	Amount borrowed[2] (£000)
1882	352	45 485	129	32 935	148	21 129	143	17 326
1887	384	56 241	146	37 397	168	27 418	163	20 081
1892	429	66 767	156	42 416	185	36 068	195	22 735
1897	436	77 773	178	51 260	212	44 447	210	27 376
1902	454	91 956	203	77 128	256	55 776	218	35 738
1907	495	108 239	219	87 798	276	64 650	234	40 712
1912	520	126 002	242	93 730	306	72 921	238	43 682

[1] Total share and stock; premium capital paid up; loan capital raised.
[2] Loans and annuities.

point of supply, but it was cheap—because it was really marshland—and, most important, it had river frontage at which coal could be discharged direct from sea-going vessels.

The move proved very timely, for in 1868 Parliament expressed concern about the supply of gas in the City of London, and it was suggested that if no improvement could be effected, the Corporation should take over the supply companies. The threat of expropriation encouraged the Gas Light and Coke Company, the Great Central Company, and the City of London Company to amalgamate in 1870, in which year the great Beckton Works were opened. They were so named in honour of Simon Adams Beck, who had been appointed Governor of the Gas Light and Coke Company in 1860. (See Plate 6.)

The Imperial Company, established in 1820, sought to rival Beckton with a big new works at Bromley-by-Bow but this proved unsatisfactory both from the point of view of design and because the facilities for unloading coal were inadequate. In 1876, the Imperial, too, was prepared to amalgamate, joining three others that had already been absorbed—the Equitable (1842), the Western (1845), and the Victoria Docks (1858). By the outbreak of the First World War twelve London companies in all had been absorbed [3].

In the provinces, too, progress was rapid and by 1830 about two hundred undertakings had been established. Among the first were Bristol, Exeter, Liverpool, and Glasgow (1816/17) [4]. The history of gas in Manchester is of particular interest. There the Police and Improvement Commissioners installed in 1817 a very small plant to light a lamp over the police station door. Encouraged by its success, they proceeded in 1824 to promote a Parliamentary Bill to allow them to make gas to light the streets and provide a supply for the public. This was approved, and thus Manchester was the first city to establish the important principle that public bodies might use public money to engage in the manufacture of gas for the public benefit. In 1843, the

GAS ! GAS ! GAS !

Ratepayers of New Brompton.

Will you suffer the Inspectors of Lighting to burden you with an alarming taxation any longer ?
Are they to be allowed to Light up Hilly Field, Lay Field, and the outskirts of the Graveyard,
without consulting you ?   Shall the Lines, Black Lion Field, and the outskirts of the Casemate
Barracks be Lighted up ?   Will you allow the Colony to be brought to desolation at the whim
of the Gillingham Inspectors ?   Then attend a

MEETING
at   the   'NAPIER   ARMS'
ON WEDNESDAY EVENING, THE 15TH. INST.

and express your indignation at the steps about to be taken in lighting up the Fields of the Vicar
of Gillingham at your expence.

Chair to be taken at SEVEN O,CLOCK, precisely.

N.B.—The Clerk and Inspectors are respect-
fully invited to attend.

Fig. 8. Street lighting at rate-payers' expense was not universally acclaimed, as this notice
indicates (1865).

responsibility for gas manufacture was transferred from the Commissioners
to Manchester Corporation [5]. Thus was born the first of the municipal
undertakings in Britain: by 1882 there were 148 of them.

OVERSEAS DEVELOPMENTS

Up to this point we have considered the organisation of the British gas
industry in Britain, but it must be recorded that from its earliest days the
industry was actively engaged abroad. The Imperial Continental Gas Association [6] was founded in 1824; the 'Imperial' refers not to the British but to
the Austro–Hungarian Empire. By 1850 it was operating sixteen undertakings in five countries. At the end of the century the Association had assets of
£7½ million and was supplying over 7000 million cubic feet of gas per annum
to ten major European towns and cities, and twenty-nine smaller ones in
France and Austria.

BOTTLED GAS

As early as 1792 Murdock compressed coal gas for future use and in 1819
D. Gordon and E. Heard patented a process for compressing oil gas into

1850 - 1857

LONDON
Portable Gas Works

30, GREAT SUTTON STREET, CLERKENWELL.

The advantages of Portable Gas are its great illuminating power; that being made from Oil, and free from Sulphuretted Hydrogen, it cannot injure Metalic Goods, Pictures, elegant Bindings of Books, or Gilded Furniture of any description. That it gives out when burning, only about half the heat of Coal Gas. That no sparks or greasy matter can fall from the Lamps.'

Those Gentlemen who have the managing of Parish Churches, Chapels, Schools, &c. within twelve miles of London, are particularly recommended to try Portable Gas, and those who have heretofore used Street or Coal Gas, can have the Portable Gas attached to the old pipes at a very trifling expence.

Churches and Chapels Fitted up and Lighted by the Year.

From the safety, cleanliness and economy of Oil Gas, it is found peculiarly adapted for NOBLEMEN and GENTLEMEN's DWELLING HOUSES, and generally for Domestic purposes; for all Manufactories, Warehouses, Counting Houses, Taverns, Billiard Rooms, Shops, and as a moveable light in large Wine Cellars.

For all the various purposes for which, Oil, Tallow and Wax Lights are now used, the Gas is constantly used, and also for many of the largest and most elegant Public Places, Churches, Chapels, and Societies in London and its Neighbourhood.

Among the many Thousand Portable Gas Lamps constantly in use in London, no Accident has ever occurred!

Each new Customer must pay in advance for a given quantity of Gas, not less than 600 feet, to be delivered from time to time, as may be required in such Lamps as shall be selected, at the rate of 7s. per 100 feet.

As the Customer only pays for the Gas he consumes, it is in his power to economise by using more or less Gas, as business may require.

The Customer will be liable for damage done to the Lamps by mis-usage or negligence while in his possession and for the safe return of them to the Works within 20 days after the receipt of the last delivery of Gas or pay 2s. 6d. per week for the detention of each Lamp, cylender or sphere,

Public and Private Dinner Parties, Balls and Assembly Rooms lighted up for the Night only, at a very moderate expense per Night, each Light,

All Orders addressed to Mr. GEORGE HAZELDINE, Portable Gas Works, Great Sutton Street, Clerkenwell, will be attended to.

CYLENDERS	FEET of GAS	CYLENDERS	FEET of GAS
6 inches by 21	10	12 inches by 24	38
6 30	13	12 36	61
6 36	16	12 48	84
6 48	22	12 54	95
9 21	10		
9 48	48	**SPHERES.**	
9 63	64	12 in. in diameter.	15

Gas Supplied for Illuminations, Tea Gardens, &c. &c.

Fig. 9. Advertisement for portable gas, 1837. This company was short-lived, but the use of bottled gas was resumed in the 1870s, especially for railway carriages.

cylinders for sale to customers. This led to the shortlived Portable Gas Company (1825), whose most important contribution, perhaps, was to provide Michael Faraday with hydrocarbon residues from which he first obtained benzene, one of the most important of all organic chemicals. For some fifty years compressed oil gas fell into abeyance, but its use was revived in 1871 as a source of light for railway carriages in Germany. In 1876 it was adopted by the Metropolitan Railway in London, and shortly afterwards by the London and North-Western Railway. The principal suppliers were the Pintsch Company and Messrs Pope and Son. For a time, compressed oil gas—usually at 6–10 atmospheres pressure—was widely used on railways, for light buoys at sea (the hollow body of the buoy serving as the gas reservoir), and in other situations where mains supply was precluded [7].

REFERENCES

[1] Board of Trade returns 1882–1912, summarised in CHANTLER, P., *The British Gas Industry: An Economic Study*, Manchester University Press, Manchester (1938).
[2] South Metropolitan Gas Company. *A Century of Gas in South London 1824–1924*, London (1924).
  STEWART, E. G. 'Historical Index of Gasworks Past and Present Now Served by the North Thames Gas Board 1806–1957', North Thames Gas Board, (n.d.) (c. 1957).
[3] 'The Gas Light and Coke Company 1812–1912', (n.d.) (c. 1912).
[4] Corporation of the City of Glasgow (Gas Department) 'The Gas Supply of Glasgow' (1935).
[5] JESSELL, R. G. 'One Hundred and Forty Years of Gas in Manchester', City of Manchester Gas Department (1949).
[6] Imperial Continental Gas Association 1824–1974, London (1974).
[7] COPCUTT, T. *Cottage Gas Works, etc., and Portable Gas* (1860).
  THORPE, T. E. (ed.). *A Dictionary of Applied Chemistry*, Vol. III, pp. 213–16, London (1891).

5

Appliances

FROM its earliest days the gas industry saw its task as primarily the manufacture and storage of gas and its distribution to the premises of the individual consumer. This, however, was only part of the system. A wide range of equipment had to be manufactured for gas works, including both heavy plant and all the minor equipment necessary for the efficient running of a works. At the consumer end, appliances were needed for gas lighting and, later, for cookers and space heaters. Industrial and commercial consumers needed more massive equipment, such as furnaces. In general, the manufacture of this auxiliary equipment was not undertaken by the gas manufacturers themselves, and the needs were met by independent concerns. In many instances, especially in the case of heavy gas-works equipment, manufacture of auxiliary equipment was undertaken by existing firms of engineers and iron founders who were quick to seize the opportunities presented by the new and rapidly growing gas industry. In other cases—especially in the manufacture of domestic appliances, where there was almost endless opportunity for variations of style for fashion-conscious Victorians—new firms arose to supply the millions of homes that eventually constituted the domestic market.

GAS LIGHTING

We may begin our account of consumer appliances with those used for lighting, since for roughly the first half-century of the industry's existence this constituted by far the largest market for gas. The earliest devices were very primitive, little more than a burning jet enclosed, in exposed positions, in a glass globe to protect it from draughts. The design was empirical, for there was no understanding of the principles that govern the luminosity of flames: efficiency was correspondingly low. As late as 1882 it was cynically said that 'so great is the general ignorance in gas matters that a large portion of the public actually prefer bad burners to good ones, because the former need less attention' [1].

It came to be recognised that the luminosity of the gas—which gas suppliers had a legal obligation to maintain at a specified standard—depended on two opposing processes. On the one hand, there should be plenty of solid carbon (soot) within the flame, because it was the raising of this to incandescence that provided the light. At the same time a hot flame was necessary, as the hotter the particles the more brightly they glowed [2]. Two types of simple burner were in use in the nineteenth century. The most common was the fish tail or union jet, in the top of which two holes were inclined at an angle to each other; the gas streams coalesced to give a flat flame. In the batswing or slot burner the dome-shaped top had a slit cut through it. The fish tail gave a more 'rigid' flame and there was therefore less need to protect it from draughts. A large variety of such burners was on the market, many of them specially designed to suit the quality of the local gas. The most important development, however, was the adaptation of the Argand oil burner to gas [3]. This had a circular wick, to which a forced draught was directed against the flame by a glass chimney. One of the best known versions for gas was 'Sugg's London Argand', the original of which was adopted as the Parliamentary standard burner in 1868; later models gave greatly improved performance [4]. It was rivalled only by the Silber burners, which were really no more than an imitation. Later burners embodied the regenerative principles, in which the flame pre-heats the air supply, giving a brighter and whiter flame because of its higher temperature.

By the 1860s, very large and powerful gas lamps were being produced for special purposes, such as use in lighthouses. One of the first was that installed by Trinity House in 1865 in the Howth Bailey lighthouse, near Dublin. For domestic purposes, and in public buildings, however, additional light was usually generated simply by multiplying the number of burners, as in a chandelier. The great gas lamp in the foyer of the new Opera

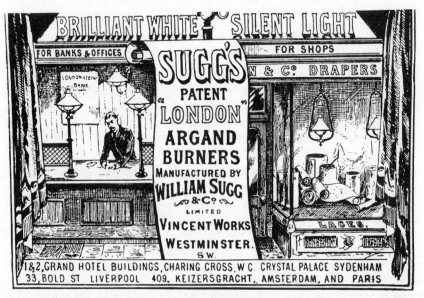

Fig. 10. The adaptation of the Argand oil burner for gas was an important innovation. It was adopted as a statutory standard for luminosity in 1868.

House in Paris (1875) weighed over six tons and had 556 burners; it cost
£1200. As a reminder of the scale of gas lighting in its heyday, it may be
remarked that this building as a whole contained 25 kilometres of piping,
supplying no less than 9200 lights controlled by 714 taps; they consumed 21
million cubic feet of gas a year [5].

But by far the most important development was the invention of the
incandescent gas mantle by the Austrian chemist Auer von Welsbach in
1885. He observed that an intense white light was emitted when gauze
impregnated with oxides of the so-called rare-earth metals (thorium,
cerium, etc.) were strongly heated, as by the burner invented by R. W.

Fig. 11. Ornate gas lamp from
the Grand Vestibule of the
new Paris Opera House,
completed 1874.

Bunsen in the 1850s. In this, as in the Argand burner, air was drawn into the
flame as it burned. For the Welsbach mantle the luminosity of the gas itself
was irrelevant; the essential was to make the flame as hot as possible to make
the mantle glow strongly. The highest temperature required complete combustion of the gas, giving an almost non-luminous flame. This invention gave
a new lease of life to gas as an illuminant, just as competition from electricity
began to be serious. By the turn of the century the gas mantle was in general
use [6]. For very powerful lights—as in factories and large buildings—
high-pressure versions were introduced. Although electric light was ultimately to triumph, gas-lighting, thanks to Welsbach, held its own until the
First World War.

Gas lighting may fairly be said to have wrought something of a social
revolution. Around 1776 James Watt and Matthew Boulton, pioneers of gas
lighting, had joined with other natural philosophers in Birmingham to form
the Lunar Society. This was so-called because it met around the time of the
full moon, so that members might the more easily and safely find their way

Fig. 12. Street lighting remained an important market until the 1930s and elaborate lamps were installed in important public places. This example is from the Thames Embankment.

home through ill-lit streets. By the middle of the nineteenth century all this was changed; city streets were brightly lit, making them safer and more conducive to social life at night. Theatres, concert halls, railway stations, and other public places too, knew a new brilliance. The ordinary home was as brightly lit as those of the rich of a generation earlier, and more conveniently, too, when pilot lights were introduced to give an instant flame. Above all, the new light encouraged reading during the dark leisure hours just as new methods of printing and paper-making were providing a flow of cheap literature of all kinds. These amenities were enjoyed even in quite

small towns, though for the truly rural community candles and lamps remained the only form of lighting until electricity began to penetrate the
remoter areas.

GAS FOR HEATING

Although Winsor's original patent envisaged the use of gas both for cooking
and for heating rooms, it could be said as late as 1882 that the question of
cooking and heating by gas, although probably destined to be one of great
importance to gas manufacturers in the future, had not had much influence
in the past [7]. From 1850 an increasing number of patents was filed, but with
little practical result. This is not altogether surprising; calorie for calorie gas
was then roughly six times as expensive as coal and even if the maximum
allowance were made for its greater efficiency in use it was still at least twice
as expensive. Presciently, the authority we have already cited [8] stated in
1882: 'when the day comes, which one may believe is not far distant, when
gas authorities will see their way to selling gas for heating purposes at a
reduced rate, it will stand shoulder to shoulder with coal on the question of
cost, and have all the other advantages to the good'.

Simple gas cookers were made at the Aetna Iron Works near Liverpool in
1824, and in 1841 the famous chef Alexis Soyer introduced gas cooking in
the Reform Club in London (Plate 3). J. Wright and Co., and Leoni and Co.,
marketed small cooking and heating appliances in the 1860s, but the first
effective breakthrough can be attributed to Magnus Ohren of the Crystal

Fig. 13. Ornate gas fire.
Refractory materials in the
grate were made
incandescent by gas flames
directed on them from the
sea monsters in front (c.
1875).

Palace District Gas Company, which in 1869 began to offer cooking and
heating stoves for hire; less successfully, this had been done by T. A. Hadley
of Devonport in 1849. Ten years later they had 600 appliances on hire,
representing a capital investment of £2160, written off at 10 per cent per
annum. In evidence to a House of Commons Committee in 1879, Ohren
testified: 'new firms are embarked in this business and all sorts of gas
apparatus are now made by the thousand' [9]. In 1879, a major exhibition of
gas apparatus was staged at Leeds. This included a wide variety of boiling
rings by T. Fletcher of Warrington. By this time the now familiar domestic
gas-cooker with oven below and boiling rings above was firmly established.
Persistent fears that gas might taint food and injure health were refuted in
the pages of *The Lancet*, and the London Hospital adopted gas cooking for
patients and staff.

Gas heaters evolved along two main lines. On the one hand there were the
so-called 'cheerful' stoves, which sought—often at the expense of efficiency
—to attract the devotees of coal-fires by generating a comfortable warm
glow. Simulated burning logs, later used in electric fires, were quite the
vogue in the 1880s. The other line of evolution was the 'gas-fire', which
concerned itself strictly with generating heat at the lowest cost. Typical of
this type was the ornate 'Imperial', essentially a convector heater. The hot
gas from the burners circulated round a central iron cone into the base of
which cold air was drawn from the room or, sometimes, from outside the
house. A steady current of warm air was discharged at the top.

The earliest heating appliances relied on a multiplicity of burners similar
to those used for lights, but by the end of the century Bunsen-type burners
were widely used, being more compact and less liable to form soot. They
were sometimes built into existing grates and covered with a honey-combed
heat-resisting ceramic which was raised to red heat.

A standard work of 1907 listed as commonplace a whole range of other gas
appliances. They included the 'geyser', invented in 1868 by B. W. Maughan
(see Plate 5) and extended before the end of the century to provide hot water

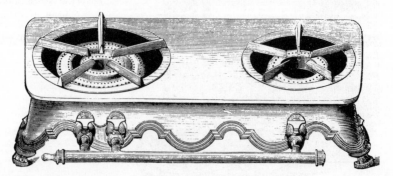

Fig. 14. Domestic hot plate, *c.* 1875.

Fig. 15. Imperial gas stove, in which hot flue gases warm an incoming current of cold air and distribute it by convection (*c.* 1875).

all over the house from a central heater; as well as boilers; blowpipes; heaters for irons in laundries; heaters for soldering irons; glue pots; and crucible heaters [10]. Gas was being used also for welding, brazing, case-hardening, shrinking iron tyres on to wheels; and melting printing-type metal.

GAS ENGINES

Finally, we must briefly mention the gas-engine, first of the successful internal combustion engines [11]. This stems from the work of the French engineer, Etienne Lenoir and, while mechanically satisfactory, it was very uneconomic compared with steam. In 1862 another Frenchman, Alphonse

Beau de Rochas, enunciated the 'factors' governing the efficiency of such engines, based on a four-stroke cycle, and showed the importance of compressing the fuel before ignition; such engines were first manufactured on a large scale by the German firm of Otto and Langen in 1878, and within a few years some 35 000 of them had been sold throughout the world. Other types had limited commercial success, but from about 1885 the Otto engine ruled supreme. Large numbers were built in Britain, under licence, by Crossley Brothers of Manchester.

The gas-engine provided industry with a power unit small enough to be used to drive individual machines, or small groups of machines, saving energy lost through belting and pulleys when large steam-engines were

Fig. 16. Early example of small engine by Tyson of Philadelphia. This differed from the internal-combustion Otto engines in that it was a steam engine in which steam was generated in a gas-fired flash boiler.

used. Rather unexpectedly, perhaps, they were for a time also used to generate electricity locally to light factories, large shops, banks, and so on. The basic reason was economic; such establishments required electricity only at certain peak periods, at which the electric supply companies charged their highest price [12]. That it was thought worthwhile to convert gas to electricity for lighting, instead of using it direct, was a further indication that the future of the industry lay with power and not light. The more far-sighted undertakings realised this: by 1878 more than a dozen important gas companies had applied for authority to supply electricity for lighting.

REFERENCES

[1] NEWBIGGING, T. and FEWTRELL, W. T. (ed.). *King's Treatise on the Science and Practice of the Manufacture and Distribution of Coal Gas*, Vol. III, p. 104, London (1882).

[2] THORPE, T. E (ed.). *A Dictionary of Applied Chemistry*, Vol. II, p. 210, London (1891).
[3] SCHRØDER, M. *The Argand Burner*, Odense (1968).
[4] TOMLINSON, C. (ed.). *Cyclopaedia of Useful Arts and Manufactures*, Vol. I, p. 749, London (1866).
[5] NEWBIGGING, T. and FEWTRELL, W. T. op. cit., pp. 37–43.
[6] WEBBER, W. H. Y. *Town Gas and its Uses*, pp. 101–21, London (1907).
[7] NEWBIGGING, T. and FEWTRELL, W. T. op. cit., pp. 215–55.
[8] Ibid., p. 225.
[9] Ibid., p. 221.
[10] WEBBER, W. H. Y. op. cit., pp. 171–94.
[11] SINGER, Charles, HOLMYARD, E. J., HALL, A. R., and WILLIAMS, Trevor, I. *A History of Technology*, Vol. V, pp. 157–60, Clarendon Press, Oxford (1958).
[12] WEBBER, W. H. Y. op. cit., pp. 241–9.

BIBLIOGRAPHY

CROMPTON, R. E. B. *Artificial Lighting in Relation to Health*, London (1884).
DE BEER, E. S. *Early History of London Street-Lighting*, London (1942).
DIBBIN, W. J. *Public Lighting by Gas and Electricity*, London (1902).
DREDGE, J. *Gas Lighting by Incandescence*, London (1887).
FLETCHER, T. *Coal Gas, as a Labour-saving Agent in the Mechanical Trades*, London (1888).
JOHNSTON, W. *Gas Lighting and the Best Mode of Applying it to Buildings*, London (1867).
SUGG, W. T. *Modern Street Lighting*, 2nd edn, London (1887).
SUGG, W. T. *Domestic Uses of Coal Gas as Applied to Lighting, Cooking, Heating and Ventilation*, London (1884).

Fig. 17. Otto internal combustion engine fuelled by gas, built by Crossley Brothers *c*. 1880.

6

Development of Government Control

CERTAIN services are of such general social importance that they have long been subject to some degree of public control. Among such public utilities, as they are commonly called, are those providing water, transport, communication, and electricity. With these must be included the supply of gas, and we have already seen that from the very beginning the London Gas Light and Coke Company had to operate within the terms of a charter granted by Parliament in 1812.

Generally speaking, the public utilities cannot operate without special privileges and to secure these certain obligations are incurred. Thus the distribution of gas, water, and electricity involves the laying of mains in public thoroughfares, and to do this special authority is needed. Clearly, chaos would result if such authority were given to several undertakings. At the same time, to give it to a single undertaking, without safeguards, would put the supplier in a monopoly position which might be exploited to the detriment of the consumer.

PRICES AND DIVIDENDS

In Britain, public control, generally exercised through local authorities, was maintained in two ways. Firstly, by imposing limits on prices and dividends; secondly, by encouraging a measure of competition. In both London and the provinces it was for a time customary to allow different supply areas to overlap or to allow a second undertaking to be established within the area of an existing supply company.

At the turn of the century, the manufacture and supply of gas was, as we noted in an earlier chapter, very largely in the hands of statutory private companies or municipal undertakings. There were, however, some hundreds of private companies which contrived to exist on the basis of local negotiation without acquiring statutory powers. They thus did not incur any corresponding legal obligations, though sometimes they had to propitiate local authorities by supplying gas for street lighting at an unremunerative rate [1]. In the main, however, they were very small undertakings operating in remote areas. In the 1930s they contributed no more than three per cent to the total quantity of gas manufactured in Britain, so that their national significance was minimal. Nevertheless, in the absence of an alternative supplier, their importance was great in their own districts and they were the subject of much local complaint.

In practice, the principle of encouraging a limited degree of competition proved less effective than it appeared in theory. In 1847, a commission set up to investigate the existing system of supplying gas concluded that 'the existence in the same town of two rival gas companies does not appear to us at all calculated to benefit the consumers. . . . Competition between companies is never long-lived. Either one of the competitors is ruined, and the survivor makes the consumer pay for the cost of the contest, or the two coalesce, and levy rates to pay a dividend upon the capital' [2].

The main provision of the Gasworks Clauses Act of 1847 was to restrict company dividends to ten per cent, a figure which appears to have been somewhat arbitrarily chosen. This requirement was modified by two qualifying provisions, and subsequently appeared over-generous. In the first place, companies were empowered to pay a higher dividend to cover any deficiency in previous years. Secondly, it was permissible for them to accumulate a fund up to one-tenth of the company's normal capital in order to provide for exceptional claims on it. The overall result was that for any reasonably managed company the ten per cent dividend was virtually cast-iron.

Naturally, the price at which gas stock changed hands was determined not only by the company's record and prospects but on the prevailing rate of interest on comparably secure investments. If the prevailing rate was ten per cent, the stock would change hands at par, but in fact it often commanded a premium. Since existing shareholders could normally take up new issues at par value, this gave them an opportunity to make a capital gain by selling any stock so acquired.

To discourage the distribution of profits out of proportion to the capital raised, a system of selling new stock by public auction was introduced. This seems first to have been introduced in Liverpool as early as 1834 and it became increasingly general until made mandatory in 1877. The auction procedure presented some practical difficulties, but it was continued until 1934, when the Gas Undertakings Act included among its provisions a requirement that the issue price of new stock should be determined by the Board of Trade.

Dividend control in itself to some extent regulated the price at which gas was sold. It became usual, from the 1840s, for clauses limiting the price of gas to ordinary consumers to be inserted in Gas Acts. This was not, however, an innovation in one particular respect: from the very outset, companies had been obliged to supply gas for street lighting on particularly favourable terms. Initially, they had to illuminate the streets both better and more cheaply than was possible by oil, the main rival to gas. Later, the position was made a little easier by requiring only that no private consumer should be provided with gas at a lower price than it was sold for street lighting. Statutory price control was not wholly satisfactory for either the supplier or the consumer, because of the lack of machinery for regular review. An expanding company, utilising new and better techniques of manufacture and the advantages of scale, might well be able to sell gas profitably at a price below that imposed upon it. On the other hand, rising costs of raw materials, need for replacement of obsolete plant, reduction in demand through population shifts or industrial recession, and so on might well mean that a maximum price fixed some years previously was no longer realistic.

Profit control can be a two-edged weapon. While it protects the public from the worst abuses it can so diminish business enterprise and efficiency that the standard of service declines. Open competition may provide the necessary incentive but, as the Surveying Officers reported in 1847, it was not wholly satisfactory for the gas industry. From shortly after the middle of the last century, the policy of encouraging direct competition was discontinued in London. The Metropolis Gas Act of 1860 introduced the concept of 'districting'; existing companies were allotted specific areas of operation and overlapping, except in special circumstances, was eliminated. The various Acts governing the conduct of the London companies were incorporated into a single set of regulations, and all were subject to the same maximum price limit. The provision for making up deficiencies in dividends under the ten per cent limit was restricted to six years. The companies prospered but consumers complained that they received little benefit.

THE SLIDING SCALE

This led to the introduction of the contentious 'sliding scale' system. Briefly, this involved two inversely related proposals: dividends might exceed ten per cent if the price of gas was reduced or, conversely, they could be reduced if the price was increased. This was not a completely new idea, for it had been incorporated in the Acts governing some provincial undertakings: for example, the Great Grimsby Act of 1867. Twelve years earlier the Sheffield Gas Company had devised the ingenious scheme of relating its directors' fees to the price of gas sold; a means of inspiring internal efficiency and external confidence. At first, the London companies were sceptical. When the Commercial Gas Company adopted the proposals in 1875, as part of a revision of its Parliamentary Charter, its associates uncharitably declared that 'if the Commercial Company could work miracles, or chose to commit suicide, they were quite willing to let them do so'. Nevertheless, before long others followed suit, generally when they had occasion to resort to Parliament for permission to change their constitution in other respects, such as by absorbing other companies. By the end of the century about half the companies, supplying two-thirds of the total output, were converted to the sliding scale.

That gas prices generally fell during the last quarter of the nineteenth century is undeniable. It is difficult, however, to distinguish the effect of the sliding scale from that of other factors. Prices generally were dropping; the efficiency of gas manufacture and distribution was improved; and, above all, the growing threat of electricity as a source of light was having far-reaching repercussions, and in itself was providing a powerful incentive to lowering prices.

Nevertheless, the consensus of opinion at the time was that the sliding scale provided a satisfactory compromise between the conflicting interests of consumers and suppliers. In 1906, a visiting delegation from Massachusetts recorded that it had gained 'the cordial support of the overwhelming majority of all classes and conditions' [3]. A writer on the public regulation of gas companies expressed the view in 1915 that it was the final solution of the gas price problem [4].

MUNICIPAL UNDERTAKINGS

Municipal undertakings, having no shareholders, were in a different position from the commercial companies. The question arose of what should be done with any surplus earned. In the early days of the industry, such surpluses were commonly paid over to the corporations concerned, and often provided them with a substantial revenue. It was argued that as the works were undoubtedly the property of the municipality, any profits arising should be used for the benefit of ratepayers. Not all customers, however, were ratepayers and even those who were were not necessarily ratepayers of the municipality concerned, for the boundaries of the gas undertakings were not always coincident with municipal boundaries. Such customers protested that they were being overcharged. By the First World War it was fairly general practice for municipal undertakings to operate, over a period, on a break-even basis. Nevertheless, as late as 1913/14, Manchester Corporation was still averaging around £50 000 p.a. from the profits of its gas-works.

The conflicting interests of private and municipal companies were the subject of legislation in the last quarter of the nineteenth century. Under the Borough Funds Act of 1872 they were forbidden to supply private customers in areas served by a statutory company. However, the Public Health Act three years later (1875) gave them authority to establish their own works if there was no statutory company, or to negotiate the purchase of an existing one.

OTHER STATUTORY OBLIGATIONS

Hitherto we have considered constraints imposed through statutory regulation of dividends and prices, but these were by no means the only restrictions imposed on gas manufacturers. For example, there was the obligation to supply. For the first forty years of the industry's existence, companies had to supply only those whom they chose, subject only to an obligation to supply gas for street lighting. But from the time of the Sheffield Gas Act of 1855 they were generally required to supply all consumers on demand, subject only to certain provisions about the customer bearing the cost of his own internal installation and of connecting this to the main supply if he was more than a specified distance from it. The obligation to supply was made general by the Gasworks Clauses Act of 1871.

Any sort of price regulation implies some control of the quality of the goods or services sold, and gas was no exception. For roughly the first century of the industry's existence, the gas supplied had to be of an agreed illuminating standard. The invention of the Welsbach incandescent gas mantle in 1885 made the luminosity of the flame itself irrelevant, and in any event the growing demand for gas as a fuel made its calorific value much more significant. Shortly before the First World War, a group of London companies succeeded in an application for calorific power to be substituted in their case for illuminating power as a measure of quality. This trend was accelerated by the war itself, as the need for increased extraction of by-products for war purposes diminished the luminosity of the gas. The Gas Act of 1916 (Standard of Calorific Power) allowed any undertaking to switch from the illuminating power to the thermal standard. The Gas Regulation Act of 1920 obliged all statutory undertakings to declare the calorific value of their gas.

REFERENCES

[1] NEWBIGGING, T. and FEWTRELL, W. T. (ed.). *King's Treatise on the Science and Practice of the Manufacture and Distribution of Coal Gas*, Vol. III, p. 63, King, London (1882).
[2] Report of the Surveying Officers on the Existing System of Lighting Towns with Gas (1847). W. A. Robson (ed.). *A Century of Municipal Progress* (1935).
[3] Special Committee to Consider the London Sliding Scale of Prices and Dividends as Applied to Gas Companies, Minority Report, p. 58, Commonwealth of Massachusetts (1906).
[4] MATTHEWS, N. *The Public Regulation of Gas Companies in Great Britain and Ireland*, 2nd edn, p. 140 (1915).

7

Management and Workers

ACCORDING to George Lunge [1] the quantity of coal distilled for the manufacture of gas in Britain at the end of the century (1898) was just over 13 million tons, more than for the whole of the rest of Europe. As the industry attained national status, staff who worked in, and for, it naturally began to seek recognised professional status and some form of association for the discussion of topics of special interest.

Of Samuel Clegg, appointed engineer to the Chartered Company in 1813, E. F. Armstrong said in the 1930s 'perhaps there is not another individual to whose zeal and ability the art of gas making is so much indebted for the variety as well as extensive utility of his inventions and improvements'. Such sweeping claims are always arguable, but it cannot be disputed that it was to Clegg and the zealous and able engineers and scientists who followed him that the industry owed its rapid growth and technological progress. It is surprising, therefore, that not until 1849 were any moves made to form a society of gas engineers, but these led to no immediate results. A Scottish Association of Gas Managers was founded in 1861, but not until two years later were any further overt moves made south of the Border. In December 1863, at a meeting in Manchester, a British Association of Gas Managers was formally inaugurated. In 1881 it changed its name to the Gas Institute. This, however, was short-lived, due to what is generally called the 'Bray affair', one of those fierce and destructive internal disputes to which learned and professional bodies are prone. The President, Secretary, and most of the Council resigned and, in 1890, set up a new body, the Institution of Gas Engineers. Despite opposition from the original Institute, still existing in a modified form as the Incorporated Gas Institute, this was incorporated in October 1890. Its purpose was 'to promote the advancement of the gas industry in all or any of its branches'. For more than ten years this uneasy situation continued, but with the Incorporated Gas Institute steadily recovering from its near demise. Ultimately, as might be expected, moves towards reconciliation and amalgamation were made, and in 1902 this was achieved. The first general meeting of the new body, the Incorporated Institution of Gas Engineers, was held in 1903. Those who want the facts of the dispute and its resolution at greater length are referred elsewhere [2].

EDUCATION AND TRAINING

From its beginning in 1881 the Gas Institute expressed an active interest in education. It did not, however, wish to set itself up as a qualifying body, like the newly founded (1877) Royal Institute of Chemistry [3], but rather to exert its influence indirectly. As President of the Institute in 1887, William Foulis declared his advocacy of 'the establishment of paid lecturers in the more important technical colleges throughout the country'.

The Institute certainly had reason to concern itself with education. Since the zenith of British industrial achievement, marked by the Great Exhibition of 1851, Britain had lost ground to foreign competitors, largely because these had fully realised the value of technical education while Britain had not [4]. In 1873, the President of the Association, Corbet Woodall, stated forcibly: 'The British Government takes less interest in the adequate education of its citizens than do the Governments of the continent.' [5]. In 1899, another President, F. D. Marshall, was still expressing the same concern, but more colourfully: '. . . from his birth, the continental engineer, is nurtured on cube roots, is swaddled in integral calculus and by the time he leaves his *alma mater* at the age of (say) 23, he is shedding algebraic formulae at every step. . . .' [6].

In the nineteenth century little was done. In 1903, an initiative was taken by the Institution of Civil Engineers, inviting eight sister institutions to take part in joint discussions 'to consider and report as to the best methods of training for all classes of engineers'. These led, in 1906, to effective cooperation between the Institution and the City and Guilds Institute, on the formulation of syllabuses for students of gas manufacture.

None of these courses were degree courses, however, and the universities were very slow to respond to the special needs of the gas industry. Naturally, a university training in engineering or science provided gas engineers with a good grasp of basic principles, but not until 1906 were their special needs recognised. In that year the University of Leeds established a Fuel Department. In 1908, on the death of G. T. Livesey, a former President, the Institution launched an appeal—which raised over £10 000—to establish the Livesey Professorship of Coal Gas and Fuel Industries at Leeds.

RESEARCH

As early as 1882, the President, G. W. Stevenson, categorically stated that 'technical research . . . is undoubtedly one of the chief functions of the Institute'. But clearly the industry was not with him, for over the next twenty years, less than £100 per annum was subscribed for this purpose [7].

With the formation of the new and united Institution of Gas Engineers in 1903, the problem was tackled more seriously. A renewed appeal for funds met with a slightly more generous response, though far short of the sixpence per million cubic feet of gas made that was hoped for. This made it possible to finance some modest research at Leeds.

Apart from books, lectures, and conferences—local, national, and international—the common medium for the communication of new scientific and technological knowledge is the periodical journal. The Institution commenced publication of its *Transactions* in 1903; this was a continuation of the *Transactions* of the former Institution and Institute. Additionally, the industry was served by various specialist journals, of which the oldest were the *Gas Journal* (1849) (originally the *Journal of Gas Lighting*), and the *Gas World* (1884).

STAFF AND WORKERS

While the gas engineers were thus striving to improve processes and methods of operation, to encourage research, and to widen their own knowledge and skill, the office staff and workers were doing their best gradually to improve their pay and working conditions. In considering these, it must be remembered that we are dealing with a highly fragmented industry consisting of a few large concerns in London and the big provincial cities, and a host of small ones.

Generally speaking the attitude of employers was the benevolent paternalism commonly encountered in Victorian industry. The well-behaved employee was treated with considerable generosity in the event of misfortune, but often harshly if he forgot his place. Thus in the early days, if an employee of the Chartered Company fell ill he might expect to receive up to four weeks' wages; in the case of an accident he could expect to receive medical expenses and be paid until fit to return. Later (1830), the *ex gratia* method of payment was abolished and a formal contributory Workmen's Benefit Scheme introduced; at the same time, a company doctor was appointed. The South Metropolitan was among other companies which inaugurated similar schemes at about the same time (1842). In 1842 a staff Superannuation Scheme was launched by the Chartered Company [8]. By the standards of the day, the staff had little cause for complaint, and it is not surprising that the Chartered Company was able to demand sureties in respect of its officers.

Again by the standards of the day, gas works employees had reason to be satisfied, especially in respect of security of employment. Having said this, it must be added that the standards of the day were poor, and those of the gas industry not among the best. The work was heavy and the hours long. It was said that '. . . a more fatiguing, dirty, uncongenial occupation scarce exists in the whole round of manual labour, nor one that so soon makes old men out of young ones'. There was originally no Sunday work, except for absolute essentials, and this was made possible by the simple expedient of forbidding customers to use gas on that day, but a seven-day week soon became general. This was usually divided into twelve-hour shifts. This was not as arduous as it sounds, for there were spells of inactivity between each 'draw' of the retorts, during which the men could read, play cards, or otherwise enjoy themselves [9]. Nevertheless, it was a long spell on duty, much of it in surroundings that were intensely hot and very dirty.

MOVES TOWARDS UNION RECOGNITION

Inevitably, there was, as in industry generally, a move towards achieving shorter hours and better pay. The repeal of the Combinations Acts in 1824 gave trade unions limited powers which—save for an Act of 1859 allowing peaceful picketing—remained largely unchanged until 1871, when the Trade Union Act gave them much fuller legal recognition, though for a few years the right of peaceful picketing was removed. The Trade Disputes Act of 1906 restored this right, conferred immunity from suits for damages, and improved the trade unions' legal status. But it must be remembered that whatever their rights might be, their powers were far more limited than they are today. Their organisation was less efficient, their resources more limited, and their membership—no more than about 5 per cent of the working population at the end of the century—relatively much smaller than is the case today.

It was in their attitude to labour disputes that the London companies found one of their few points of common ground though, paradoxically, it was often their own cut-throat competition that created such disputes. In March 1834, for example, a number of men came out on strike at the Horseferry Road works and were discharged; the strike was broken with the aid of men supplied by the Imperial and Phoenix Companies [10].

In 1859 there was again trouble at the Westminster works. The London Gas Stokers' Protection Society called a strike—which lasted four months—in protest against the seven-day week and twelve-hour shift, with one rest day a month, which was still standard practice. Again, the strike was broken by the dismissal of the strikers, the recruitment of fresh labour, and some assistance from rival companies. This kind of rough treatment has been condemned by Stirling Everard, official chronicler of the Chartered Company, who remarks that 'today [1949] it is not possible to look back on this particular episode with any feeling of gratification' [11].

Certainly such action did nothing to quell the agitation for better conditions, but the London companies remained intransigent. In 1872 the working week at Liverpool was reduced to $55\frac{1}{2}$ hours, with Saturday afternoon working to be avoided as far as possible. In the provinces, eight-hour shifts were by then fairly common, as compared with the twelve-hour shifts still worked in London.

By present standards, the companies handled their labour relations badly, but they did have real difficulties arising from increasing operating costs. These again proved a stumbling block in 1889, when the men renewed their demand for an eight-hour day and extra payment for Sundays. This time, negotiations were entered into with the National Union of Gas Stokers, led by the formidable Will Thorne, and major concessions were made. The important principle of the eight-hour day was conceded, and a new scale of wages agreed [12]. This episode marked the turn of the tide: however reluctantly, the unions had been recognised.

CO-PARTNERSHIP

The South Metropolitan took a different line from the Chartered Company in response to troubles in 1889 [13]. In 1876, both had accepted the principles of the sliding-scale (p. 42) whereby the price of gas could be linked with dividend paid. When this facility was introduced George Livesey, Chairman of South Metropolitan, tried to persuade his board to give the workmen a share in the profits but to this they would not agree. In the difficult circumstances of 1889, the decision was reversed and the workmen were offered a percentage increase in their wages for every penny reduction in the price of gas. This peace-offering the Gas Workers' Union denounced, and the stokers refused it. However, the mechanics and artisans took a different view, and asked if they could be given what the stokers had refused. Livesey agreed: all who wished might join the scheme, others could stay out. The repairing and distributing men joined in large numbers, and also three stokers. Thorne then made a fatal error: his union gave notice that unless the scheme was withdrawn, and the three stokers were dismissed, his men would strike. Livesey stuck to his guns, and the stokers came out. Other men took their place, however, and the supply of gas was maintained [13]. However, it was a different story in 1912, when Liverpool tried the same tactics. There, co-partnership had been introduced in the previous year: six men who had refused to sign co-partnership agreements were dismissed, and others came out on strike. The board had to climb down, re-instate the men, and withdraw the offending requirement [14].

Despite this uneasy start, the co-partnership scheme was a major innovation in industrial relations. Apart from giving a substantial pay bonus— almost 10 per cent in the best year—it fostered better relations between management and workers. The latter had a direct interest in the success of the company and many invested their shares in it: in 1913 the value of employees' holdings in the South Metropolitan amounted to £350 000.

The principle of co-partnership was taken up with some enthusiasm by the larger gas companies, but only to a limited extent by other industrial concerns. At nationalisation in 1949, about 58 gas undertakings had profit-sharing schemes, paying out £400 000 annually to 52 000 employees.

REFERENCES

[1] LUNGE, George. *Coal-tar and Ammonia*, 5th edn, p. 28, Gurney and Jackson, London (1916).

[2] BRAUNHOLTZ, Walter T. K. *The Institution of Gas Engineers: The First Hundred Years 1863–1963*, pp. 31–70, Institution of Gas Engineers, London (1963).

[3] RUSSELL, Colin, A., COLEY, Noel G., and ROBERTS, Gerrylynn K. *Chemists by Profession: The Origins and Rise of the Royal Institute of Chemistry*, Open University Press (1977).

[4] ASHBY, E. 'Education for an Age of Technology', in: SINGER, Charles, HOLMYARD, E. J., HALL, A. R. and WILLIAMS, Trevor I. (ed.). *A History of Technology*, Vol. V, pp. 776–98, Clarendon Press, Oxford (1958).

[5] BRAUNHOLTZ, Walter, T. K. op. cit., p. 62.

[6] Ibid., p. 203.

[7] Ibid., p. 174.

[8] EVERARD, Stirling. *History of the Gas Light and Coke Company, 1812–1949*, pp. 116–27, Benn, London (1949).

[9] Ibid., p. 244.

[10] Ibid., p. 123.

[11] Ibid., p. 201.

[12] Ibid., p. 280.

[13] South Metropolitan Gas Company. *A Century of Gas in South London*, pp. 11–14, London (1924).

[14] HARRIS, Stanley A. *The Development of Gas Supply on North Merseyside*, pp. 109–10, North Western Gas Board, Liverpool (1956).

BIBLIOGRAPHY

BRAUNHOLTZ, Walter T. K. The Institution of Gas Engineers: the First Hundred Years 1863–1963. Institution of Gas Engineers, London (1963).

CROSS, A. C. National and District Gas Organisations, *Gas Journal, Centenary Volume 1949*, p. 126, King, London (1949).

CARPENTER, C. C. *Industrial Co-partnership*, London (1914).

South Metropolitan Gas Company. *A Century of Gas in South London*, London (1924).

CLEGG, H., FOX, A. and THOMPSON, A. F. *A History of British Trade Unions since 1889*, Vol. I, 1889–1900, Clarendon Press, Oxford (1964).

EVERARD, Stirling. *History of the Gas Light and Coke Company 1812–1949*. Benn, London (1949).

HARRIS, Stanley A. *The Development of Gas Supply on North Merseyside*. North Western Gas Board, Liverpool (1956).

MINISTRY OF LABOUR. *Co-partnership in the United Kingdom*, HMSO, London (1920).

RADICE, G. and RADICE, L. *Will Thorne: Constructive Militant*, Allen and Unwin, London (1974).

WEBB, S. and WEBB, B. *History of Trade Unionism*, London (1902).

8

The First World War

FOR the gas industry, as for British industry generally, the First World War was a period of major upheaval. By the spring of 1915 it was clear that the conflict was to be prolonged. Britain's industry had fundamental defects that had to be made good. In particular, although she had been the pioneer of the synthetic dyestuffs industry the initiative had been allowed to pass to Germany [1]. Only one-fifth of the dyes needed were home produced, and those mostly of simple kinds. Further, the prospect of a long war called for a vast expansion of the explosives industry and this in turn demanded greatly increased quantities of certain basic raw materials. Of these, three were of exceptional importance. First, gunpowder had been superseded by high explosives based on organic materials, notably toluene (for TNT), and phenol (for picric acid), together with natural products such as cellulose (for guncotton), and glycerine (for dynamite). The conversion of these raw materials into explosives demanded the use of equivalent large quantities of nitric and sulphuric acid, which were also essential for the manufacture of dyes and a range of other organic chemicals. As a measure of the problem it may be noted that British production of TNT at the outbreak of war was only 20 tons weekly; during the course of hostilities no less than 238 000 tons of TNT were required. By 1917, annual production of picric acid was 32 000 tons. The nitric acid was largely derived from nitrates which, under wartime conditions, were also urgently needed as an agricultural fertiliser to increase home food production.

It became apparent that the resources of the nation could be marshalled to meet the vital needs of the armed services, and ensure that the civilian population suffered no undue hardship, only by massive government intervention in the organisation of British industry. In 1915, the Ministry of Munitions was set up by Lloyd George: this rapidly assumed virtual command of the chemical and engineering industries and of production for wartime needs generally. By the end of the war, it had a staff of 65 000 and controlled some three million workers.

This had consequences which extended far beyond the duration of the war, as W. J. Reader has pointed out:

Nobody had ever seen anything like the Ministry of Munitions before, and it is difficult to exaggerate its effect upon the later development of British industry, especially in its relations with the State. . . In the numerous dealings between government and the management of industry, in the twenties and thirties, some common experience of wartime methods could generally be taken for granted among those concerned at the highest level, especially in engineering and chemicals. As a consequence the general conception of government intervention in business affairs seemed neither so strange nor so offensive as before 1914 [2].

This comment is certainly as true of the gas industry as of the engineering and chemical industries with both of which, of course, it was closely allied.

However, as Reader also points out [3], the consequences in relation to organised labour were less fortunate. The alliance of government and industrial management could not afford to ignore the unions, and union officials could scarcely refuse to assist the organised national war effort. But to the shop-floor workers this looked like a sell-out, and they increasingly looked to their shop stewards to safeguard their interests rather than to their national officers. Those within co-partnership schemes had a further ground for discontent. The general rise in prices forced up the price of gas and the bonus gradually diminished and in many cases disappeared altogether.

The war had another far-reaching consequence. Women, whose opportunity for employment had hitherto been limited largely to domestic work— or office work, with the comparatively recently introduced typewriter— found themselves in jobs that were hitherto an entirely male preserve. They worked on the land, in the transport services, in the factories, and indeed virtually everywhere where there was a shortage of men. In the gas industry they took over many jobs, including stoking. (See Plate 12.)

By comparison with the Second World War, the physical destruction in Britain as a result of direct enemy action was negligible. Coastal shipping was constantly harassed, threatening the supply of coal, but the biggest single disaster in the gas industry occurred on 19 January 1917. On that day the disastrous Silvertown munitions explosion took place and as a result the huge No. 2 gasholder across the river at East Greenwich collapsed, struck by the shock wave; 8 million cubic feet of gas went up in one tremendous flame [4]. The main problems were chronic shortage of labour and essential supplies, and rising costs. As far as rising costs were concerned, the experience of the Chartered Company was probably fairly typical. Between 1914 and 1918, coal had risen by 82 per cent and labour by 89 per cent. Freightage had risen by a staggering 664 per cent [5]. Against this, there had been no corresponding rise in revenue, because of government price controls. In 1918 the Statutory Undertakings (Temporary Increase of Charges) Act became operative, permitting an adequate increase, but the Gas Regulations Act of 1920 re-imposed price control.

Some of the essential supplies needed by wartime Britain have been enumerated earlier in this chapter and to these the gas industry made important contributions. Coal-tar was the major source of phenol and toluene required for explosives. The industry provided ammonia, necessary for the manufacture of nitric acid and nitrogenous fertilisers, and the gas purification process provided sulphur-rich material for the manufacture of strong sulphuric acid. It provided benzole as a supplementary motor fuel and as source of explosives and dyes. When the Germans introduced gas warfare in April 1916, it provided charcoal for respirators. The British army was wholly unprepared for this form of attack, but the small Box Respirator was being issued by September of that year. This called for large quantities of absorptive charcoal, made by carbonising wood, but there were few retorts available that could be adapted for this purpose. Three gas works had suitable spare capacity, namely Greenwich (South Metropolitan), Margate, and Southend. The first was the biggest supplier, eventually carbonising 300 tons of birch wood per week to yield 20 tons of active charcoal; towards the end of the war fruit stones and nutshells were used to provide harder charcoal [6].

These supplies, augmented by imports and eked out by severely restricting non-essential uses, served to establish a satisfactory war industry in Britain by 1916/17. At the end of the war, the gas industry had to face a world that was technologically, economically, politically, and socially different from that of 1914. It did so with run-down plant and a degree of fragmentation that made unified action difficult. But against this the closely allied chemical industry had been much strengthened and Germany was prostrate. Much was achieved before the storm burst again twenty years later.

REFERENCES

[1] HABER, L. F., *The Chemical Industry 1900–1930*, pp. 184–217, Clarendon Press, Oxford (1971).
[2] READER, W. J., *Imperial Chemical Industries: A History*, Vol. I. pp. 249–57, Oxford University Press, London (1970).
[3] Ibid., p. 251.
[4] South Metropolitan Gas Company, *A Century of Gas in South London*, p. 16, London (1924).
[5] *Select Committee on Gas Undertakings (Statutory Prices) Report*, pp. 37–50 (1918).
[6] HABER, L. F. Private Communication.

PART III

THE INTER-WAR YEARS

9

Technical Changes

As has already been shown, the gas industry began with primitive apparatus, producing a crude product. With increasing knowledge and experience, and in response to public demand, economic pressure, and government requirements, both apparatus and product were steadily improved. Some of these changes we have already briefly noted, but they will now be considered in greater detail.

PROPERTIES OF GAS

From the consumer's point of view the source and composition of the gas supplied are immaterial, provided certain basic requirements are met. First, it must be of uniform quality, whether this is defined in terms of illuminating power—the most important characteristic during the industry's first hundred years—or calorific value, as during the greater part of this century. Quality must also include such factors as freedom from smell when burning, tendency to form soot, and so on. The gas must be burnable in standard appliances without repeated adjustment. Equally, of course, it is necessary for the user to have a constant supply day and night, and to be protected against price variations other than those dictated by the current economic situation. These requirements do not determine the chemical composition of the gas, but do demand certain physical properties. Of these, the most important are the calorific value, the specific gravity, and the burning velocity. These we will consider here in the context of gas made from coal, but also note that they were of great importance when the decision was taken to change from coal gas to natural gas in the 1960s. It was largely the physical differences in the two sorts of gas that then demanded the conversion of virtually every appliance in Britain and the manufacture of new ones to different designs.

The calorific value of the gas is the amount of heat released when it is fully burned. In Britain, it is measured in British Thermal Units (Btu) per cubic feet of gas. One unit is the amount of heat required to raise the temperature of one pound of water through one degree Fahrenheit. 100 000 Btu make one therm; very approximately, one therm is the amount of heat required to bring 70 gallons of cold water to the boil. Under the 1920 Gas Regulation Act, gas companies were not required to provide gas of a fixed thermal value, but were free to choose and declare the calorific value of their product. Once this was done, little variation was possible, as there was also an obligation to adjust consumers' appliances in accordance with the quality of gas supplied. Generally speaking, town gas had a calorific value of about 500 Btu per cubic foot. As we shall see later, one problem in the introduction of natural gas was that its calorific value is about twice this.

The specific gravity of the gas is its weight per unit volume: the lighter the gas, the more will pass through the orifice of a burner in a given time. Coal gas from the retort has a specific gravity of about 0.40 (Sp. gr. air = 1). The heat given by a particular burner, at a given pressure of gas, is directly proportional to the calorific value and inversely proportional to the square root of the specific gravity. The calorific value of the gas divided by the square root of the specific gravity is known as the Wobbe Number of the gas. Its derivation is not important, but it is a useful way of expressing the heat delivered by a given burner at a given pressure. Thus hydrogen and carbon monoxide have almost equal calorific values but their Wobbe Numbers are 1218 and 323 respectively. Manufactured town gas normally had a Wobbe Number of about 730.

The third property of gas important in relation to its normal use is its burning velocity. This is a measure of the speed at which a flame is propagated through it. It is usually expressed as the flame speed factor (S), measured on an arbitrary scale which assigns to hydrogen an S value of 100. The proper adjustment of this is of the utmost importance. If the S value is too high, the flame will travel back against the flow of gas and burn inside the burner at the injection orifice; that is, it 'strikes back'. On the other hand, if it is too low the speed of the gas will cause the flame to lift off the burner, and the least draught will blow it out. To put things in perspective, it may be noted that normal coal gas has an S value of about 40, compared with 14 for methane, the principal constituent of natural gas.

MAINTAINING SUPPLY

One of the problems of gas manufacture is that of maintaining a uniform supply in the face of a fluctuating demand. Initially, when gas was used almost only for lighting, the main problem was that the demand was very largely for the dark hours of the evening and early morning, and naturally there was a great difference between summer and winter. However, it was common to take advantage of the slack summer months to take some plant out of commission for repair or replacement. Population movements accentuated the difficulty, but being relatively slow were more easily compensated for. The development of gas as a source of heat, both domestic and industrial, with a heavy daytime requirement, helped increasingly to even out the demand. And, of course, the gasholders served as a reservoir on which to draw at times of heaviest demand. Even so, the gas manager was often hard pressed to maintain the supply. The South Metropolitan records [1] an anxious Christmas in 1917. The great No. 2 gasholder was still out of action after the Silvertown explosion and three successive days of black fog and hard frost gave an unprecedented demand of 401 million cubic feet for the week—47 million above the pre-war period. For forty-eight hours the pressure was reduced, but the supply was maintained.

Partly for these reasons, and partly in the interests of general efficiency, the industry looked for means of boosting the supply, particularly by means that could be put into operation at short notice. An obvious method, of course, was for an undertaking with a deficit to purchase gas in bulk from one with a surplus. Apart from the fact that in the absence of a national gas grid this was feasible only between neighbouring undertakings, and climatic factors would affect all roughly equally, the practice was illegal until a Special Order was made under the Gas Regulation Act 1920. Although 31 statutory undertakings immediately availed themselves of this facility, the number was still only 52 in 1935. In 1938, only 0.4 per cent of all gas sold in Britain was acquired in this way [2]. One undoubted obstacle was the difference in the nature of the gas—especially its calorific value—made by different undertakings. This made it difficult to provide a blend satisfactory to the appliances of all consumers.

In theory, coke-oven gas appeared an attractive source of additional supply, but in practice there were considerable difficulties. From the early eighteenth century coke had been used for smelting iron, and this was prepared by carbonising coal in coke-ovens—commonly with a charge of around 20 tons—using essentially the same process as that in the gas industry. The type of coal used, however, was different, as the smelting process required a very strong coke that would not crumble under the great weight imposed on it at the bottom of a blast-furnace. The nature of the gas produced, however, was virtually the same as that produced in gas works, and there were no major practical difficulties in blending the two to provide a gas that conformed with statutory requirements. But in some respects these very requirements were an obstacle: coke ovens operate in step with the varying demands of the iron and steel industry and so cannot easily offer an absolutely dependable supply. Thus while the gas companies might be able to buy coke-oven gas on favourable terms, they would also have to maintain reserve plant of their own ready to be brought into use in an emergency. Allowance would have to be made, too, for the loss of revenue from by-products and, in some instances, for compensation to men made redundant (p. 264). Again, there was the question of accessibility: the coke-ovens were concentrated in the iron and steel producing areas and in the absence of a grid could effectively be linked only to neighbouring gas undertakings. In 1929, the Board of Trade set up a Departmental Committee on Area Gas Supply, which concluded that gas supply networks were feasible only in areas, notably South Yorkshire, where coke ovens were concentrated and there was a big industrial load [3]. Some progress was made, but even in 1935 only seven per cent of gas supplied to consumers came from coke ovens [4], and nearly half of this was purchased by one concern, the Sheffield Gas Company. In 1931 this company had acquired powers to construct a high-pressure grid connecting gas-works, coke-ovens, and industrial plants in its area. By 1935, it had cut its price to industrial customers by 30 per cent [5].

An obvious alternative, of course, was for gas undertakings themselves to operate coke ovens and a few did in fact do so. The first were installed by the Birmingham Corporation before the First World War [6]. This installation was inspected in 1913 by representatives of the Gas Light and Coke Company, but not until 1932 did the Company build its own coke-ovens at the Beckton works. In the same year, an agreement was made with the Ford Motor Company to take the surplus gas from a new battery of coke ovens installed at its Dagenham works.

COKE

Ordinary coke, like gas, presented serious supply and demand problems. As has already been noted, it could be sold as a domestic and industrial fuel and the surplus could be used for firing the retorts [7]. Even so, there was often an imbalance. While gas-coke could not be used for metallurgical purposes, coke-oven coke could be used domestically and was sold for this purpose (2–3 million tons in 1936) when the production of pig-iron dropped. Matters came to a head in 1913. The coal strike of the previous year had boosted sales of coke, but fuel users mostly reverted to coal as soon as it was available again. Coke stocks were high, and in London alone amounted to 275 000 tons. In that year, the London Coke Committee was set up, and was later extended (1931) to cover fifteen counties around London as the London and Counties Coke Association, supplying an area south of a line from Bristol to the Wash. Similar bodies covered the Midlands and North East; they not only publicised the use of coke generally, but promoted the design of coke-burning appliances. Domestic coke boilers of improved design were introduced in 1921, and by 1934 were selling at the rate of 120 000 a year; it was estimated that each burned, on average, three tons of coke annually [8]. The success of this campaign—which led to more than half the gas coke in Britain being sold for use in the home—depended upon the introduction of effective screening methods to provide a uniform product. Considerable quantities of coke (800 000 tons in 1937) were exported but, by arrangement with an International Cartel (Britain, Germany, Poland, Belgium, Holland), at prices lower than those ruling in the home market.

CARBURETTED WATER-GAS

From 1890 an important new use for coke began to develop in Britain: this was the manufacture of carburetted water-gas for admixture with the mains supply. One of the first manufacturers of plant in Britain was Humphreys and Glasgow. Their first plant—made for Belfast in 1892—had a daily capacity of nearly two million cubic feet: by 1949 they had manufactured 1332 plants with a total daily capacity of 2000 million cubic feet. The process was not new, having been used in France since 1865, and in the United States—where there were 300 plants in 1889—since 1873; indeed, the basic principles were known as early as 1823 [9, 10]. It depends on two simple chemical processes. Firstly, if steam is blown through incandescent coke a mixture of carbon monoxide and hydrogen is formed: this is known as blue water-gas because it burns with a pale blue flame. This reaction is, however, self-extinguishing, because it absorbs heat. The coke therefore cools off, but can be restored to incandescence by blowing air through it; this provides, in a two-stage chemical reaction, what is known as producer gas, which consists of approximately two-thirds nitrogen (from the air) and one-third carbon monoxide. The alternation of steam- and air-blast can be avoided by using a continuous blast of mixed air and steam, in the right proportion to keep the coke glowing steadily. The product, semi-water-gas, consists of about 50 per cent nitrogen, 25 per cent carbon monoxide, and 15 per cent hydrogen, together with small amounts of carbon dioxide and methane.

These mixtures, rich in carbon monoxide and hydrogen, can be burned—for example, to raise steam—but their calorific value is lower than that of normal town gas. Blue water-gas, for example, has a calorific value of only about 300 Btu per cubic foot. It could, therefore, be mixed with ordinary gas (around 500 Btu per cubic foot) in only small proportions without reducing the calorific value to an unacceptable level. Moreover, it burns with a non-luminous flame. These considerations led to the introduction of carburetted water-gas in Britain when supplies of cannel coal—used to raise to the required standard the illuminating power of gas derived from ordinary coal—were becoming scarce and expensive. To make carburetted water-gas, ordinary water-gas is treated with vaporised oil in a carburetter, from which it passes to a superheater. In this the big hydrocarbon molecules in the oil are 'cracked' to give more volatile inflammable products.

Carburetted water-gas has three important characteristics. Firstly, the plant can be brought into operation at short notice; secondly, it requires little labour; thirdly, it requires relatively little space. Nevertheless, it made only slow progress in Britain. The first to introduce it was the Gas Light and Coke Company at the Beckton works in 1890; this had an initial daily capacity of 10 million cubic feet, but by 1934 this had risen to 40 million cubic feet and the Company had a capacity of 56 million cubic feet daily at other installations. Belfast soon followed Beckton with an initial daily capacity of 1.7 million cubic feet, soon rising to 4.5 million [9]. However, even in the 1930s it was unusual for works to generate more than about one-third of their total make as carburetted water-gas, and many made a great deal less [11]. The Board of Trade figures indicate how the flexibility of the process enabled the companies to cope with varying situations: thus Bristol, on average made 31.4 per cent carburetted water-gas, but at times the proportion was 46.2 per cent. There was some opposition to the process, on the grounds that the gas contained a dangerously high proportion of carbon monoxide, which is a powerful poison. In 1898, the Home Office unsuccessfully sought to limit the amount of carbon monoxide in town gas to 20 per cent, and a further inquiry—again resulting in no action—was held by the Board of Trade in 1921. As we shall see, the toxicity of gas again became an issue after the Second World War.

From the nature of the chemical reactions already cited, it will be apparent that, in theory, coal could be gasified completely, except for its incombustible residue of ash. Although this possibility was closely studied, both in Europe and North America, complete gasification processes at this time made virtually no contribution to gas production in Britain. This can be attributed more to economic than to technological considerations. Provided there was a reasonable market for coke there was no great incentive to introduce complete gasification which, of course, yields no coke at all. After the Second World War, however, the situation was different.

DESIGN OF RETORTS

Brief reference has already been made to the change from horizontal or inclined retorts to vertical ones, and we must now consider some of the implications of this. Gas-making in the nineteenth century was essentially a batch process; that is, the retorts were charged with coal, this was then carbonised by strongly heating them, and the residual coke was discharged. This sequence of operations was then repeated indefinitely. Such an intermittent process is basically uneconomic. Firstly, the constant charging and discharging involves a great deal of labour. Secondly, it is wasteful of energy; a great deal of heat is lost in the cooling of the incandescent coke—usually quenched with water or steam to allow it to be handled—and of the red-hot retorts. Not surprisingly, therefore, attention was early paid to the possibility of developing a continuous process of carbonisation. As far as Britain is concerned, the first successful attempts in this direction were made in the first decade of this century. In 1903, H. W. Woodall and Arthur Duckham installed at Bournemouth an experimental vertical retort in which coal was fed continuously in at the top and coke was removed at the base. It was a failure because, as Woodall stated, 'very little was known about the heating of vertical retorts in those days' [12]. However, a second attempt in the following year was so successful that the directors of the Bournemouth gas undertaking ordered an installation of four 20-foot retorts, which came into operation in 1906 and continued for some years. Capacity was 20 tons of coal daily. Duckham resolved to resign his position as assistant engineer and devote himself fulltime to the problems of continuous carbonisation [13,

14]. Two of his earliest installations, at Nine Elms and Liverpool, were failures, as the gas produced failed to meet the candle-power standard, but a plant put into operation at Poole in 1908 performed very satisfactorily. (See Plate 14.)

Meanwhile S. Glover and John West were developing a similar type of continuous vertical retort [15], based on retorts used for the distillation of oil from shale in Scotland. In 1907, their first plant was working successfully at St Helens. Experience gained there was applied in a second installation for the Droylsden works of Manchester Corporation (1911), and during the construction of this St Helens Corporation placed an order for a 40-retort installation that was operated from 1912 to 1918.

A modification of the continuous vertical retort was to admit steam at the base to generate water-gas in situ [16]. This also cooled the coke before discharge. However, even as late as 1934 it was still being argued whether water-gas was best made in this way or in separate plant [14].

By the 1930s the continuous vertical retort was firmly established in Britain. It was estimated in 1934 [17] that 60 per cent of gas made was produced in this type of retort, and that the total capacity of the two principal types was 800 million cubic feet per day. It had been adopted by over 250 of the 450 largest gas undertakings. Substantial increases in productivity were claimed to result: in 1912 one ton of coal produced on average 13 403 cubic feet of gas but this had risen to 17 290 in 1932 [17]. A further important advantage was in ground space; continuous vertical retorts required only half the area of horizontal ones of equal capacity.

STORAGE AND DISTRIBUTION

The inter-war years also saw improvements in the storage [18] and distribution of gas. In 1927, F. Prentice erected at Ipswich the first waterless gasholder—introduced from Nuremberg—in which the floating roof rises and falls within a metal track. With an increasing demand for dry gas, coupled with the fact that the cost of the foundations was lower, various forms of such gasholders were erected in considerable numbers. One of the most familiar was that of the Gas Light and Coke Company at Battersea, with a capacity of 8 million cubic feet. At Harrow, the Company ran into environmental difficulties. A public protest, led by the Headmaster of Harrow School, complained that the proposed new gasholder would spoil Byron's View from the top of Harrow Hill. Against this, the Company argued that if the size of the holder were curtailed, the inhabitants of Harrow would have to pay more for their gas. In the event, the holder was built as planned, but painted in green and silver-grey to blend with its surroundings: the camouflage may have been optimistic but the price of gas remained unchanged.

The volume required to store a given quantity of gas is proportional to its pressure (Boyle's Law) and where space was very limited, or there were other special circumstances, high-pressure tanks were installed. They were not widely used, however, because of the additional cost involved in compression and the special equipment needed to reduce pressure before it could be used in appliances. The day of high-pressure gas was still far in the future.

Although the distribution of gas showed no startling changes, during the inter-war period steady improvements were made. Consumption, whether measured per consumer or per mile of main, changed rather little. Board of Trade returns show total sales by authorised undertakings as 235 000 million cubic feet in 1920. In the next fifteen years this never rose above 300 000 million, reaching 296 000 million in 1935. By 1939, it was 321 000 million cubic feet. With improved utilisation, these figures under-rate the useful heat available. In these circumstances existing supply systems sufficed, since, on average, they operated at only about 20 per cent of capacity. In a review of the period 1884–1933, S. Lacey remarked:

the majority of present-day distribution systems are more the result of gradual adaptation to changing circumstances than of deliberate planning. While the manufacturing plant of gas undertakings may have been partially or completely reconstructed several times since 1884, the mains laid at that time will still be in use . . . [19]

Nevertheless, it was not by any means a static period. The advent of the prepayment (slot) meter in the 1880s encouraged the use of gas in poorer households and proved a considerable social benefit (see Plate 4). In the South Metropolitan area slot-meter consumers rose from 9794 in 1893 to 155 829 in 1903. In 1911 the Gas Light and Coke Company alone took nearly a quarter of a million coins. By the 1930s nearly 7 million out of 11 million consumers paid for their gas in advance in this way. Extensions of urban areas—and the inclusion of villages in an attempt to obtain more business—demanded extended supply systems. Between 1920 and 1945 the gas-main mileage in Britain rose from 39 000 to 69 000.

More gas can be forced through an existing system simply by increasing the pressure of the gas, but this also increases loss by leakage. Normal practice was to maintain an average pressure of 2–3 inches water, and adjust this—up to perhaps 10 inches, using booster fans—according to the demand expected. For extending the supply area either additional low pressure trunk mains could be laid or high-pressure feeder mains supplying a new low-pressure network. On economic grounds, the latter course was increasingly favoured; widely scattered areas could be supplied by 2–4 inch diameter mains working at 50 lb per square inch pressure. For this purpose, steel pipes were favoured, but cast-iron continued to be used for ordinary purposes.

BY-PRODUCTS

The importance of by-products in the economy of the gas industry has already been stressed. Difficult marketing conditions in the inter-war years led, in this field, to a degree of co-operation closer than was commonly observed: the joint marketing of coke has already been referred to. In 1920 the British Sulphate of Ammonia Federation was set up—later re-inforced by the European Nitrogen Convention—to serve the common interests of producers. This proved valuable in the 1930s when a decline in agriculture— a seasonal market always—and expansion of synthetic ammonia production, led to a situation in which world capacity for nitrogen production was about twice the demand [20]. Between 1926 and 1932 the price of ammonium sulphate exactly halved. It is likely that during these years sales of ammonium sulphate, ranging from 123 000 tons (1928) to 86 000 tons (1937), made no profit, but without the Federation substantial losses would have been probable [21].

In 1919 the National Benzole Company was set up to dispose of another valuable by-product on the best terms possible. Here again the economies were complicated. For small works, it was only marginally advantageous to extract benzole as opposed to leaving it as vapour in the gas, thereby increasing its calorific value. Moreover, its market value as a fuel was liable to be changed at short notice by a change in the duty on imported petrol. In 1938, almost all coke-makers recovered benzole, but only about one-third of the gas industry did so [22, 23], representing about 140 undertakings.

Until almost entirely supplanted by petroleum after the Second World War, coal-tar was the basis of the rapidly expanding organic chemical industry. The main coal-tar constituents involved were benzene, toluene, xylene, phenol, cresylic acid, naphthalene, and anthracene. Its many hundreds of products included dyes, pharmaceuticals, insecticides, rubber chemicals, and plastics. However, as we have seen, the direct involvement of the gas industry was relatively small, the extraction of the various by-products being carried out mainly by independent tar-distillers to whom gasworks sold the crude material. The greater proportion of tar was still used for surfacing roads (the British Road Tar Association was formed in 1927); treating roofs and timber; and other applications requiring a relatively unrefined product. From 1936 I C I, at Billingham manufactured petrol by the hydrogenation of coal-tar and creosote [24]. Total production in that year (including hydrogenation of coal) was 33 million gallons.

THE CHARTERED INSTITUTION OF GAS ENGINEERS

The practical development of technological innovation was, of course, the province of the major undertakings, assisted to some extent by research in the universities. The responsibility fell heavily on gas engineers and for them the Institution served as a valuable forum for exchange of views and the publication of the results of research. In 1929 the national importance of the work of the Institution was recognised by the granting of a Royal Charter and from that year its formal title has been the Chartered Institution of Gas Engineers. The preliminary negotiations owed much to W. T. Dunn, who was Secretary from 1902 to 1928, but J. R. W. Alexander is generally regarded as the main architect of the new structure. A Cambridge graduate, he was called to the bar in 1925 and was Secretary 1929–37. He later had a distinguished career in the gas industry, latterly as general manager of the British Gas Council 1945–49.

REFERENCES

[1] South Metropolitan Gas Company. *A Century of Gas in South London*, p. 16, London (1924).
[2] CHANTLER, Philip. *The British Gas Industry: an Economic Study*, p. 39, Manchester University Press, Manchester (1938).
[3] BOARD OF TRADE. *Report of the Departmental Committee on Area Gas Supply*, London (1929).
[4] BOARD OF TRADE. *Annual Return Relating to All Authorised Gas Undertakings in Great Britain*, London (1935).
[5] CHANTLER, Philip. op. cit., p. 41.
[6] MEADE, Alwyne. *Modern Gasworks Practice*, 2nd edn, pp. 196–1, Benn Bros, London (1921).
[7] FOXWELL, G. E. Coke—the Principal By-product of the Gas Industry, *Gas World*, 28 April 1934, pp. 499–502.
[8] Ibid., p. 502.
[9] Ibid., Fifty Years of Water-Gas Plant, pp. 442–6.
[10] STONE, T. W. *History of Water Gas*, Canadian Gas Association (1926).
[11] Board of Trade Return (1932).
[12] WOODALL, H. W. *Gas World*, **48**, 798 (1908).
[13] WEST, M. J. The Rise, Progress and Development of Carbonisation in Continuous Vertical Retorts, *Gas World*, 28 April 1934, pp. 437–41.
[14] Idem., 'Carbonisation', *West's Gas*, **13**, No. 7, **6** (1935).
[15] MEADE, Alwyne. op. cit., pp. 155–60.
[16] BLUNDELL, J. E. *Gas World*, **67**, 322 (1917).
[17] WEST, F. J. op. cit., pp. 440–50.
[18] SCOTT, J. Winson. Some Historic Landmarks in Gasholder Design, *Gas World*, 28 April 1934, pp. 462–7.
[19] LACEY, Stephen. The Distribution of Gas (1884–1933), ibid., pp. 468–71.
[20] READER, W. J. *Imperial Chemical Industries: a History*, Vol. II, pp. 111–15, Oxford University Press, London (1975).
[21] PEP (Political and Economic Planning). *Report on the Gas Industry in Great Britain*, pp. 177–9, PEP, London (1939).
[22] MORGAN, G. T. and PRATT, D. D. *British Chemical Industry: its Rise and Development*, pp. 216–17, Edward Arnold, London (1938).
[23] PEP (Political and Economic Planning). *Report on the Gas Industry in Great Britain*, pp. 179–81. PEP, London (1939).
[24] READER, W. J. op. cit., pp. 162–82.

BIBLIOGRAPHY

BRADLEY, J. N. *Flame and Combustion Phenomena.* Methuen, London (1969).

CHANDLER, Dean and LACEY, Douglas. Milestones of Gas Progress as Recorded in 256 Volumes of the Gas Journal, *Gas Journal Centenary Volume 1949*, p. 95, King, London (1949).

Development of Engineering Science in the Manufacture and Treatment of Gas between 1924 and 1939, *Journal of the Institution of Gas Engineers*, Oct. (1968).

LLOYD, Peter. *Theory of Industrial Heating*, King, London (1938).

MEADE, Alwyne. *Modern Gasworks Practice*, 2nd edn., Benn, London (1921).

PATRICK, E. A. K. *Watson House 1926–1976* (now Central Laboratory of British Gas Corporation). Institution of Gas Engineers, London (1976).

PEP (Political and Economic Planning), *Report on the Gas Industry in Great Britain*, PEP, London (1939).

REES, T. *Theatre Lighting in the Age of Gas.* Society for Theatre Research, London (1978).

SMITH, Norman, and LE FEVRE, R. N. *Domestic Utilization of Gas*, Pts. I and II, King, London (Pat. I (1932): Pt. II (1936)).

SMITH, Norman. *Gas Manufacture and Utilization*, British Gas Council, London (1945).

STEWART, E. G. *Town Gas—Its Manufacture and Distribution.* HMSO, London (1958).

STOTZ, L. and JAMISON, A. *History of the Gas Industry.* Ste Hiner, New York (1938).

WEBBER, W. H. Y. *Gas and Gas Making: Growth, Methods and Prospects of the Gas Industry*, Pitman, London (n.d.).

10

Changes in the Structure of the Industry

THE principal organisational changes in the industry during the first century of its existence have been referred to in earlier chapters; it was from this that the modern nationalised industry was to evolve. We cannot, however, study the gas industry in isolation, but must consider it in relation to the other established industries that were major sources of energy: of these the most important were coal, electricity, and petroleum.

Electricity and petroleum were comparatively new arrivals; although both were introduced well before 1900, it was really only in the twentieth century that they began to make substantial contributions to the overall energy pattern. In a sense they were both rivals and allies. Both the gas and the electricity industries were major customers of the mines. Thus in 1937, out of 182 million tons of coal used in Britain, 125 million were burnt raw, 41 million were carbonised, and 15 million used to generate electricity. While demonstrating that coal remained the most important fuel, these figures do not represent the useful energy derived from the principal sources. To elucidate this, note must be taken of the efficiency of utilisation of various fuels. For domestic heating purposes generally, electricity had an estimated overall efficiency of 75 per cent, compared with 50 per cent for gas, 25 per cent for coke and anthracite, and 15 per cent for house coal [1]. For the householder, of course, factors other than efficiency—notably cost, convenience, and incidental benefits—were relevant. Thus in wintertime the fact that the coke-fired domestic boiler wasted heat was an advantage rather than otherwise, for it meant a warm kitchen. In summer, on the other hand, it would make the kitchen uncomfortably hot. Again, more than a marginal difference in cost would be necessary to justify the cost of removing existing appliances—say a kitchen range or gas lighting system—and installing different ones.

By the 1930s, the British gas industry was the largest in Europe, and in the world second only to America. In 1935/6 there were about 11 million consumers in Britain (approximately 1 in 4 of the population) against 17 million in the USA (1 in 7), though the position in America was distorted by the fact that natural gas was used more extensively than coal gas. Similarly, the basic figures for Germany (1 in $3\frac{1}{2}$) are misleading because of the extensive use of coke-oven gas [2]. The importance of the gas industry in the British economy is indicated by the fact it gave employment to about 230 000 people, or about 1 in 50 of all workers in insurable employment. Of these about 125 000 were in the supply industry itself; 75 000 in coal mining (the industry used about 10 per cent of all coal mined); and about 30 000 in the manufacture of plant and appliances. The capital assets of the industry were estimated at £200 million [3, 4, 5].

Up to the outbreak of the Second World War the domestic market was much the largest, representing 60–70 per cent of all gas consumed. By far the greater part of this (some 90 per cent) represented heating and cooking, the domestic lighting market having been largely lost to electricity. Rather surprisingly, however, gas had fully held its own in the field of public lighting, gas sold for this purpose roughly doubling between 1920 and 1937, when more than half of all street lights were still supplied by gas; this accounted for some 5 per cent of all gas sold. Commercial and industrial use accounted, in roughly equal proportions, for the balance of gas produced. Commercial use included shops, hotels, offices, and catering establishments. Gas for heating was being increasingly used over a wide section of industry, ranging from iron and steel to pottery and food. Industrial use naturally varied geographically. Thus, Sheffield estimated that more than 60 per cent of its gas went to industry: this was a far higher proportion than undertakings serving non-industrialised areas.

Bearing in mind that the industrial world is always a dynamic one, with some sections expanding and prospering as others decline, and that readiness to adapt to change is essential for success, the gas industry of the 1930s seems at first sight to have been in a reasonably healthy and stable state. The quantity of gas sold rose fairly steadily between 1920 and 1937, the overall increase being about 34 per cent. Electricity was becoming a serious rival in the heating market, but co-existence seemed perfectly possible. There was encouragement to be found in the fact that even Switzerland, with no indigenous coal, still had a flourishing gas industry supplying 1 in 4 of the population. While petroleum had undeniably made startling progress as a fuel in the first four decades of the century, it had mainly done so in fields which did not bring it into direct competition with gas: its main application had been in transport. Labour relations on the whole were satisfactory: demand for the industry's product did not fluctuate wildly—and security of employment was good. Co-partnership had provided, as well as its direct benefits, a valuable link between management and workers.

PROBLEMS OF FRAGMENTATION

Nevertheless, the industry did have some real and intractable problems. In the main, these arose from the fragmented nature of the business and reluctance to resolve internal differences in order to present a united front to the outside world. We have already noted the large number of gas undertakings in existence before the First World War. By 1936 the total had increased to over 1200, varying greatly in size, organisation, and mode of operation.

Board of Trade returns for 1936 show that these undertakings supplied approximately 1500 million therms. Of this, rather more than half (760 million therms) was supplied by only twenty undertakings, of which the original Gas Light and Coke Company was by far the largest (240 million therms as compared with 81 million therms for its nearest rival, the South Metropolitan). At the other end of the scale, 425 undertakings supplied less than 0.5 million therms [6]. Among these last would be miniscule undertakings like Debenham in Suffolk and Wedmore in Somerset (9000 therms each) and Rhayader in Wales (15 000 therms).

It might be expected that the small units would be relatively uneconomic, but available statistics give no support to this. Thus an analysis [7] of some forty undertakings in 1932 shows (in terms of total working expenses per therm sold) a figure of 7.68 (old) pence for the largest (253 million therms) and 6.92 pence for the smallest (312 000 therms). The best performer (5.33 pence) was an undertaking producing only 1.5 million therms. The strictly financial incentive to amalgamation—in the sense of having a relatively small number of large works—was therefore not strong.

Even if there had been demonstrable and widely accepted benefits in amalgamation, purely practical difficulties would have limited its extent. In the economic and technological circumstances of the day, it was not practicable to transmit relatively small quantities of gas over long distances; it was better to convey coal to small local works. In supplying densely populated urban areas, however, the argument was quite different: for one thing, land in central areas is far more expensive than in outlying ones. We have noted that as early as 1868 the Gas Light and Coke Company had started to build its great works at Beckton on marshland a dozen miles from its main supply area. The gas had to be conveyed through a 48-inch main (subsequently duplicated) to the City, with an extension to Westminster. Computations made in 1928 showed that the following general considerations applied:

For quantities of gas up to 5 million cubic feet per day (the average output of Bradford or Southampton) it is cheaper to transmit gas and coke than to rail coal up to a distance of 5 miles from the works. For quantities of the order of 25 million cubic feet (the average of Glasgow or Sheffield) the distance for which transmission is cheaper increases to 35 miles. For quantities of 50 million cubic feet the corresponding figure is 100 miles or more [8].

We have already noted that in 1930 a Board of Trade Committee had argued against anything in the nature of a national gas grid—comparable with the grid initiated by the Central Electricity Board in 1927, and largely completed in 1935—except in areas of high industrial demand in which coke-oven gas was available. In effect, South Yorkshire was the only area judged suitable.

These arguments did not go unchallenged: critics pointed to what seemed to be successful attempts at long-distance transmission on the continent, especially in the German Ruhr. In fact, however, like was not being compared with like. In the Ruhr, the coke-oven industry was completely reorganised in 1926 and fully integrated with the steel industry. The economic viability of the scheme depended upon the profitable sale of the very large volume of coke-oven gas produced (about 250 000 million cubic feet per year). In these circumstances, as the British experts agreed, pumping to distant areas was a practical proposition. An additional factor was that German gas undertakings, unlike those in Britain, had no statutory obligation to maintain supply to consumers: there was, therefore, no necessity for them to maintain stand-by plant in case of failure of coke-oven supply [9]. A further difficulty, already referred to in a different context, was the variability in the nature of the gas made by different undertakings, as regards both composition and calorific value.

In the country at large, therefore, as opposed to densely populated and highly industrialised urban areas, there was no great enthusiasm for closing small works and concentrating production in a much smaller number of large ones. The industry was, nevertheless, conscious of the weakness inherent in its highly fragmented nature and was by no means reluctant to consider organisational changes that might have a unifying effect.

MOVES TOWARDS RATIONALISATION

While there was naturally much diversity of opinion, it is probably true to say that the industry thought mainly in terms of regionalisation, and of rationalisation rather than nationalisation. Yet the possibility of the latter was clear for all to see. A major report on the industry, published by Political and Economic Planning—an independent non-party group of specialists—spelled out the hard facts most explicitly in a report published just before the outbreak of war in 1939:

The industry is at present free to make its own plans for reorganisation and development: but it may not always be in such a position. As an extremely important element of the national fuel resources, its working in time of emergency would almost certainly come under State Control. . . . It must also be remembered that the nationalisation of the gas industry is projected in the short-term programme of the Labour Party, and the industry may therefore at any time find its future a matter of political controversy. The risks of such controversy will be very much enlarged if it can be suggested that the structure of the gas industry is unsuited to modern needs and that its outlook is unprogressive. People of all political views would probably agree that it is an unsatisfactory process for Parliament to have to enforce on a backward or recalcitrant industry adjustments demanded by national economic needs. . . . The gas industry can only expect to avoid being subjected to it sooner or later by spontaneously carrying out whatever measure of reorganisation is needed [10].

A similar note was struck by Philip Chantler, of the Economics Research Section of Manchester University, in an admirably full and lucid economic

study of the gas industry completed in 1938. He visualised a small body of
Gas Commissioners, appointed by the Board of Trade, who would supervise
an industry organised by a small number of area gas-supply authorities:

. . . even if the internal problems of the gas industry did not justify the institution of a
planning and directing authority, it is clear that if Great Britain were to adopt a
national fuel policy some time in the future, the establishment of an authority with
such powers as those suggested for the Gas Commissioners would be necessary. This
condition is, of course, hypothetical, but is of great importance in the long run. Any
national fuel policy must co-ordinate the coal, gas and electricity industries. The coal
industry is at the present time being induced to take measures of co-ordination which
may be the prelude to positive national direction, and the electric supply industry has
been subjected to a developed system of control by Commissioners. The Gas
Industry would not fit into any general fuel policy until it was positively directed [11].

By the time these proposals were made the industry had in fact moved some
way towards meeting them, though not, as events were to prove, far enough
to avoid eventual nationalisation. Although, for the reasons given, very
little was done to reduce the number of works, a good deal had been
achieved by way of administrative reorganisation to gain the benefits inherent in larger working units, facilitating bulk buying on favourable terms,
easier raising of capital, better co-ordination of commercial and technical
policy, and the recruitment of better qualified staff.

The question of staff was of great importance. While the relatively few
large undertakings—such as the Gas Light and Coke Company, with over
20 000 employees—could hold out the promise of rewarding careers to able
and well qualified men, the situation with regard to the multiplicity of small
concerns was quite different. They were of necessity staffed by a few
jacks-of-all-trades, among whom there might not be even one able to
understand the significance of the technical and managerial developments of
the day.

The situation with regard to staff was substantially improved in 1926 with
the foundation of Watson House by the Gas Light and Coke Company. The
beginning of this can be seen in the appointment in 1922 of (Sir) Harold
Hartley as a director of the Company. During the war he had been Controller of Chemical Warfare and subsequently returned to Oxford as Director of
the Balliol–Trinity Laboratory. He clearly saw the need for more intensive
application of science in the gas industry and for an adequately equipped
laboratory for research. Watson House, adjacent to the Nine Elms Works,
provided the necessary facilities, especially for the testing and development
of appliances; not least of Hartley's contributions was to attract to Watson
House some of his abler students from Oxford. Additionally, there was a
useful training school for apprentices, who underwent a five-year course; in
1936 they numbered 250. From 1933 the Watson House facilities were made
available, on a subscription basis, to the industry generally, by establishing a

Development Centre. This was initially concerned with industrial applications, but in 1936 domestic applications, too, were brought within its remit. Its importance was quickly realised and by 1934 there were 74 subscribing undertakings.

Some degree of physical amalgamation of resources was feasible when undertakings served contiguous or closely adjacent areas, and we have noted already that many of the London companies joined forces in the latter half of the nineteenth century. This tendency continued in the inter-war period. Thus, between 1922 and 1935 the Gas Light and Coke Company absorbed six further companies (Ilford, Brentford, Grays and Tilbury, Pinner, Southend, and Brentwood). This gave them a supply area of over 500 square miles, extending from Windsor to Southend. It is interesting to note that at this stage the Company took a formal decision to attempt no further expansion by amalgamation, believing that any larger unit would be unmanageable without major organisational changes. Overall, the number of statutory gas undertakings reporting to the Board of Trade fell from 798 to 716 between 1920 and 1935, but this can hardly be regarded as spectacular as many of the concerns were very small.

More significant was the growth of the holding company movement in the 1930s. From the outset, it was possible for an independent company to acquire control of a gas undertaking by the purchase of its shares. As early as 1824 the British Gas Light Company, with a proposed share capital of £1 million, was formed to supply gas throughout England, Wales, and Ireland. A century later it owned 14 gas-works and had a controlling interest in 24 others. The Gas Undertakings Act of 1932 extended the facility to existing gas undertakings in respect of small neighbouring concerns and in the following year the Board of Trade's Gas Legislation Committee was urging the desirability of this. In 1939, there were eighteen holding companies controlling 242 gas undertakings: this represented about 9 per cent of all gas produced. Additionally, some local authorities rationalised their organisations.

Within the gas industry, and among independent observers, the holding company movement was viewed with mixed feelings. At its best, it certainly provided the advantages that accrue from large organisations generally. The companies could, and often did, provide specialist managerial and technical staff and had means of raising capital not open to small individual undertakings. But often the units of a holding company were widely scattered [12] making effective liaison difficult, and were regarded by the parent company strictly as an investment; short-term profitability, and even the possibility of re-sale at a profit, could override long-term policy. There is some doubt whether the formation of holding companies led to general price reductions, but some certainly improved the service to customers and promoted the sale of appliances, especially cookers.

Another difficulty arising from the multiplicity of independent undertakings was that of formulating common strategies and policies. There were, of course, a number of national organisations representing various interests within the industry, some of which have already been mentioned, but there was no single body which could, over a broad front, represent the industry with executive authority, as opposed to presenting a consensus opinion. The most that was achieved was the British Gas Federation, set up in 1934 and representing five existing bodies. These were respectively the Institution of Gas Engineers (founded 1863); the Gas Companies Protection Association (1898); The Society of British Gas Industries (1905), representing makers of plant and apparatus; the British Commercial Gas Association (1912), a publicity agency for the industry; and the National Gas Council of Great Britain and Ireland (1916). On the eve of war, the Gas Research Board was set up—under the auspices of the Institution of Gas Engineers and the Society of British Gas Industries—to conduct co-operative research in the industry. By 1943 gas undertakings representing 76 per cent of national output had allied themselves with it.

The British Gas Federation must be distinguished from the Federation of Gas Employers (1919), set up as a collective bargaining agency *vis-à-vis* the National Joint Industrial Council for the Gas Industry. National wage agreements were interpreted by Regional Joint Gas Industrial Councils in accordance with the character, size, and general circumstances of local undertakings (p. 263).

PRICING POLICY; TWO-PART TARIFFS

The lack of a satisfactory co-ordinating body in the pre-war industry was reflected in substantial variations in commercial policy and marketing that often left the consumer, and potential consumer, bewildered. He did not really know what he was getting for his money: some undertakings quoted prices in shillings per 1000 cubic feet, others in pence per therm. Appliances might be available in one supply area on terms quite different from those offered in another only a few miles away. The general price structure, too, was not conducive to encouraging greater use of gas by existing consumers, though here the suppliers faced difficulties not of their own making.

Briefly, early legislation had been based on the fact that gas was sold almost entirely for lighting, and in this field it long enjoyed an essentially monopolistic position. In such circumstances, strict price control was understandable, but these circumstances simply did not apply in the inter-war years. The sale of gas for domestic lighting was of almost negligible importance though the street-lighting market survived; almost all gas was sold for heating, in competition with coal and electricity. Yet up to the 1930s most gas was still sold on a flat-rate basis, large and small consumers being treated alike. Gas Acts commonly permitted no more than a 15 per cent discount for large consumption. Yet in 1934, 188 undertakings did not give any discount even to consumers requiring up to 5000 therms annually. Not until the Gas Act of 1934, were the statutory limitations on discounts to large consumers repealed, and the way opened to more venturesome price policies. Even so, the industry failed to obtain authority to impose a minimum charge for very small consumers—a right commonly exercised by suppliers of electricity. This they wanted because the gas purchased by such consumers, whose custom could not be refused, failed to cover fixed costs. Much was made of 'well-to-do people who use a gas-ring to make a cup of tea and whose custom may not pay for the cost of reading their meter'. From 1934, two-part tariffs became increasingly popular. This comprised a standing quarterly charge, and consumption beyond the limit set by this was at a reduced rate. In some cases the quarterly charge was fixed; in others, it was related to the supposed capacity of the consumer to pay, being determined by such factors as the rateable value of his premises and the number of rooms in it. A variety of schemes were introduced by different undertakings and the years 1934–9 must be regarded as essentially experimental. Not the least of the problems was a somewhat surprising resistance on the part of some consumers, who were reluctant to enter into contracts committing them to fixed charges. The whole question of variable tariffs is one of great complexity, and the interested reader must be referred elsewhere [13]. Basically, of course, it was part and parcel of a campaign to win more business, and a complementary campaign had to be waged to improve appliances and make them more readily available.

The general, but certainly not universal, weakness of the commercial side has been attributed to the undue importance then given to the engineering side. In 1939 it was recorded:

It is not uncommon to find that a gas undertaking has no trained sales manager; no adequate sales staff; no showrooms; little or no means for adequate publicity; and no reliable information as to the possibilities of its market. Where such a situation exists there is little cause for surprise if the undertaking makes no progress year after year, and, where electrical competition is vigorous, actually loses ground. There are many exceptions to this inadequacy on the marketing side, but the backwardness is sufficiently common to justify anxious consideration by the industry as a whole [14].

Interestingly, the Weir Committee set up in 1925 to make recommendations on the future of the electrical industry, had encountered a similar difficulty:

A third restriction (on expansion) arises from a tendency prevalent in this country to regard the engineering side as necessarily being of higher status and greater importance than the commercial side . . . We consider this policy to be unsound . . . the interests of the consumers and the success of the undertaking depend as much, if not more, on the efficient and enterprising management of the commercial side as on the technical management of the stations . . . The freeing of officials from the dual task of engineer and manager should be regarded, not as a lowering of status, but as opening up a possibility of even more fruitful endeavour [15].

The Second World War, like the first, profoundly changed the whole climate of public opinion on social, political, and economic matters and this powerfully affected the future of the gas and other public service industries. It was clear in 1939, however, that the gas industry, either voluntarily or by imposition of some substantial measure of public control, would have to undergo a very substantial reorganisation. But for the war, this change might have been less radical, in the nature of rationalisation rather than nationalisation, but major change there would undoubtedly have been.

REFERENCES

[1] PEP (Political and Economic Planning). *Report on the Gas Industry in Great Britain*, pp. 187–91, PEP, London (1938).
[2] Ibid., p. 200.
[3] Ibid., p. 44.
[4] Fifth Census of Production (1935) Preliminary Report, *Board of Trade Jnl., Suppl.*, 18 November 1937.
[5] Board of Trade Return Relating to All Authorised Gas Undertakings in Great Britain for 1935.
[6] CHANTLER, Philip. *The British Gas Industry: an Economic Study*, pp. 28–31, Manchester University Press, Manchester (1938).
[7] Ibid., pp. 45–7.
[8] SMITH, E. W. *World Power Conference 1928*, quoted in CHANTLER, op. cit., p. 120.
[9] PEP. op. cit., p. 121.
[10] Ibid., p. 159.
[11] CHANTLER, Philip. op. cit., p. 136.
[12] PEP. op. cit., pp. 192–9.
[13] Ibid., pp. 107–32.
[14] Ibid., p. 143.
[15] *Report of the Weir Committee on Electricity Supply*, para. 107 (1926).

BIBLIOGRAPHY

CHANTLER, Philip. *The British Gas Industry: an Economic Study*, Manchester University Press, Manchester (1938).
CURTIS, H. *Correlation of Costs and Gas Charges*, I.G.E., London (1934).
DIMOCK, M. E. *British Public Utilities and National Development*, Allen and Unwin, London (1933).
EVETTS, G. *The Administration and Finance of Gas Undertakings*, Benn, London (1922).
FINER, Herman. *Municipal Trading. A Study in Public Administration*, Allen and Unwin, London (1941).
HAYNES, J. T. *The Two-part Tariff as an Aid to Gas Sales*, I.G.E., London (1936).
PEP (Political and Economic Planning). *Report on the Gas Industry in Great Britain*, PEP, London (1939).

Transactions Third World Power Conference, Washington, DC (1936).

See particularly:

1. Stamp, L. F. Organisation of Private Gas Utilities, Paper W, 42, Vol. V.

2. Idem., Public Regulation of Private Gas Utilities, Paper W, 44, Vol. V.

3. Idem., Organisation, Financing, and the Operation of Publicly Owned Gas Utilities, Paper W, 45, Vol. VI.

4. Evetts, G. Rationalisation of Distribution of Gas in Great Britain, Paper W, 133, Vol. VIII.

5. Hunter, R. W. and Anderson, G. W. Organisation of the Production, Transportation, and Distribution of manufactured Gas and Gas By-products, Paper W, 98, Vol. IV.

Upton, E. *Organisation and Administration of Gas Undertakings*, Pitman, London (1925).

Willis, H. I. and Stamp, L. F. (ed.). *Michael and Will on the Law Relating to Gas and Water*, 8th edn, Vol. I (Gas), Butterworth, London (1936).

PART IV

THE SECOND WORLD WAR AND MOVES TOWARDS NATIONALISATION

11

The Gas Industry and the Second World War

THE outbreak of war in 1939 found Britain in some respects a great deal better prepared than she had been in 1914. Many of those in control of affairs had had experience of working in, or with, the Ministry of Munitions in the First World War and, as we have noted, the experience was to stand them in good stead. Government and industry were much more conditioned to working together in the common interest. In May 1934, the Committee of Imperial Defence accepted the principal of 'shadow' factories, which entailed the establishment, from 1936, of government-owned factories, to be managed by industry on an agency basis. This system was both politically and economically sound. If, in the event of hostilities, private industry was required to establish, at short notice, specialised factories whose products would be required for a relatively short time, they would be saddled after the war with a load of expensive property and equipment for which there was only a problematical further use. To obviate this risk, and yet remain solvent, they would be bound to charge very high prices and could unfairly be represented as war profiteers. The shadow scheme had the further advantage of dispersing industry more widely and thus rendering it less vulnerable to the heavy air attacks which seemed inevitable. Until required, the factories would be on a stand-by basis, being used only for training purposes.

EFFECT OF AIR-RAIDS

This scheme greatly facilitated a smooth transition from a peacetime to a wartime economy, especially as, in the event, there were no major hostilities or aerial attacks until the sudden, and catastrophically successful, German onslaught in May 1940. Thereafter, the war began in earnest and was to continue for five long years. For British industry the familiar problems of 1914–18 reasserted themselves: shortage of labour, shortage of equipment and of many raw materials, lack of facilities for renovation, and great transport problems. Superimposed on all this was a new factor: severe and highly destructive aerial attacks on major industrial centres. Although the actual duration of these was relatively short—mainly August 1940 to May 1941, with a resumption in the flying-bomb raids in the south-east in 1944— air raid precautions, and particularly the black-out, had to be maintained, as a very considerable burden, until the last months of the war in Europe. The

immediate physical destruction was enormous: between 1940 and 1946 some
£450 million pounds were spent on repairs, demolition, and debris clearance
directly attributable to air-raids [1]. This figure takes no account of the
enormous consequential cost of lost and delayed production and the disruption of national life generally. These problems and anxieties affected industry generally, and although in the pages that follow we shall be considering
those peculiar to the gas industry, this does not imply that its services to the
nation were exceptional. It is fair to note, however, that—in common with
the manufacture of ammunition, some chemicals, and certain other special
products—the gas industry did face particular hazards because of the inflammable and potentially explosive nature of its products.

The history of the gas industry in the Second World War can best be told
by following several distinct threads. Firstly, there was the response to direct
enemy action. Secondly, there were the day-to-day problems of maintaining
the business amidst the uncertainties of a wartime economy. Finally, there
was active consideration of the future of the industry, when, as none
doubted, victory was won and life began to resume its normal pattern. In
recounting this story we must be careful to recall that we are still dealing with
a fragmented industry in which the experience and practice of some undertakings were very different from those of others.

In the days of preparation before the war it was realised that gas-works
would figure high on the enemy's list of targets. Firstly, they were large and
easily identified targets which, if hit, could cause great local havoc. Secondly,
the disruption of the important public service they provided could have
far-reaching industrial consequences, besides disheartening the civilian
population.

As far as the works themselves were concerned, rather little could be
done, except rely on anti-aircraft precautions generally, and devise procedures for minimising disruption in the face of various possible contingencies.
The general black-out precautions eliminated the rosy glow of the retort
houses, which would have made them a conspicuous target at night. But the
works were only the outward and visible manifestation of the industry:
underground lay some 68 000 miles of gas mains vulnerable to attacks
directed against quite different targets. These ranged from great trunk
mains, bringing gas into large supply areas, to quite small ones supplying
local needs. As far as the main systems were concerned, a valving system
was installed, so that damaged mains could be isolated for repairs and
appropriate diversions made. A special group of valve locators was formed
to be first on the scene. Where practicable, adjacent undertakings made
provisions to connect their systems if the need arose. Special mobile repair
gangs and workshops were organised to deal quickly with emergencies,
especially those requiring road breaking. It was foreseen that as gas, water,
and electricity mains were normally laid in close proximity, problems would
arise due to a need to work in flooded conditions, with the possible risk of

electrocution, though naturally the water and electricity supply industries had made similar plans to isolate damaged sections of their own systems.

Although incidents naturally had to be dealt with on an *ad hoc* basis, and changes made in accordance with the pattern and intensity of the raids, the plans made sufficed to meet all contingencies. Generally speaking, gas supplies were maintained—though sometimes at reduced pressure and of somewhat variable quality—with remarkably little interruption. Where continuity of supply was particularly vital, cylinders of compressed gas were made available until a mains supply could be restored. The Gas Supply (War Damage) Order 1942 absolved gas undertakings from their obligation to maintain a supply to all consumers, but was really no more than a technicality. The undertakings did their utmost to repair damage as quickly as possible, but if a temporary interruption of supply was unavoidable no amount of statutory orders could put matters right.

We cannot here recount the wartime experiences of even the largest undertakings, but must content ourselves with a few examples. London, of course, was the prime target. There the biggest of all undertakings, the Gas Light and Coke Company, dealt in all with 20 500 incidents, involving damage to 5953 mains and 65 000 service pipes. The Company established in the basement of its showrooms in Kensington a Gas Centre to deal with emergencies. This was manned continuously from the outbreak of war until April 1945. It operated in liaison with the London Regional Gas Centre, a voluntary association of all the undertakings in the London area, which in November 1940 became officially a part of the London Region Civil Defence. Shortly before the war, the Company had made plans for the demolition of their premises in Horseferry Road, which included the Court Room, and to build a large modern office block on the site. The demolition involved removal of the old gas-holders, last survivors of the original Westminster gas works. In the event, the outbreak of war prevented completion of these plans: the site was requisitioned by the government and the deep tanks of the holders formed the basis of a steel and concrete Rotunda from which government business was conducted during the raids [2].

As an example of a big provincial undertaking in an industrial area exposed to air attack we may take Liverpool, with a supply area of 120 square miles. The city was raided on 68 occasions, in all but three of which mains and services were damaged. Over 600 mains, ranging from 42-inch trunk lines to 3-inch service mains were damaged; 30 000 domestic installations required attention and 10 000 were permanently disconnected because the houses they served were totally destroyed. The Company's war damage claim was finally settled at £487 000 in 1948. There were some spectacular incidents. In November 1940, all four holders at Wavertree were fired, with a loss of 1.5 million cubic feet of gas. At the end of the same month, at Garston, a parachute mine fell straight through the top of No. 1 holder, containing at capacity 4 million cubic feet of gas. Fortunately it failed to explode, and after most hazardous operations by the military, the fire brigade, and the company's employees, it was eventually defused and dragged out through a hole six-feet-square cut in the side of the holder. In another raid a 24-inch main was fractured and ignited: for the rest of the night it remained a tempting target for later raiders. As in the London area, arrangements for mutual help were made, with Manchester and other Lancashire undertakings [3].

As the war and the raids continued, major problems of storage developed. Whereas in most instances gas production could be restarted fairly quickly, the repair of gasholders was a lengthy operation. Thus at Liverpool, the No. 1 holder at Garston, blitzed in 1940, was not in operation again until September 1944. As a palliative, producer gas plants, capable of being brought into operation at short notice, were installed at some works.

PRODUCTION PROBLEMS

Despite such catastrophes, and the general difficulties of the time, the industry managed not only to maintain, but to expand production, which rose by 18 per cent—from 321 000 million cubic feet to 379 000 million cubic feet—between 1939 and 1944 [4]. This was a national average, however, and concealed great local variations. In one industrial district consumption rose by 250 per cent; others reported a diminution of 70 per cent. This variation produced some unforeseen complications. Since the production of coke went strictly in step with the production of gas, some areas had more coke than they knew what to do with; at the same time, the government was not only urging a general reduction in solid fuel consumption but enforcing this through the Fuel and Lighting Order (1939). By 1943 people were being urged to take coke to eke out their coal, and merchants were asked to take 10 per cent of their supplies as coke or anthracite [5].

Problems of disposing of coke were matched by those of acquiring coal. Supplies were inadequate and increasingly expensive, transport was slow and erratic, and the wartime system of pooling rolling stock deprived the gas undertakings of many of their specially designed wagons. If an opportunity was taken to bring more into stock than usual, the coal was liable to deteriorate before it was used. Coal supplied was not always of good gas-making quality. These problems were a good deal alleviated from 1942 when Sir Andrew Duncan, President of the Board of Trade, appointed a Public Utilities Coal Committee. This endeavoured to ensure that every gas undertaking had enough coal in hand to meet six weeks maximum demand [6].

In peacetime, coastal shipping had long been an important part of Britain's transport system. In 1939 the annual traffic totalled about 35 million tons and approximately half this represented the carriage of coal from the north-east coast to the south. In wartime this traffic would clearly be vulnerable to enemy attack, as in 1914–18, and as the threat mounted, much attention was devoted to formulating government policy in respect of coastal shipping. In theory much of the traffic could be diverted to the west coast or to the railways, but it became clear that in practice every effort would have to be made to keep the east coast sea lanes open. As far as the gas industry was concerned, many of the largest undertakings were designed to receive their coal at waterside frontages. The assumptions made proved not too well founded, and were complicated by the fall of France, but in the event the coastal trade was surprisingly well maintained in the face of great difficulties. In the summer of 1944, despite the demands of the D-day landings, an average of 1½ million tons of coal was being carried monthly. This forms part of the history of inland transport in wartime Britain and has been recorded in detail elsewhere [7].

The price of coal rose relatively a little more than the price of coke. Durham gas coal was on average 19 shillings per ton in December 1938, compared with 31 shillings in April 1943 (63 per cent increase). Over the same period the price of coke rose from 32s. 5d. to 49s. 8d. (53 per cent increase) [5].

The production of gas in wartime followed a pattern familiar to industry generally. Existing plant had to be worked to its limit and war-damaged equipment repaired and put back into operation as quickly as possible. But superimposed on these special wartime requirements was a programme of maintenance, replacement, and extension of the sort that would normally have occurred in peacetime, albeit more slowly and erratically. Thus the winter of 1939–40 saw the completion of new carbonising plant at places as far apart as Bedford, Liverpool, and Londonderry. As Londonderry became an important naval port and a main point of disembarkation for American troops, further extensions were made later (1942, 1945). At Coventry, the Foleshill works escaped serious damage in the blitz of April 1941, and 56 new 50-inch retorts were brought into operation there in October 1942, with a capacity of 5 million cubic feet per day, primarily to meet the needs of shadow aircraft factories in the neighbourhood. In the autumn of 1943, 32 new retorts were installed at St Helens, birthplace of the original Glover–West vertical retort. During the war West's Gas Improvement Company Limited, one of the largest contractors, installed more than 800 new retorts and reset more than 4000 others, requiring some 60 000 tons of refractory materials and 7000 tons of mild steel and cast iron. This surpassed anything in the previous history of the company [8].

THE BALLOON BARRAGE

Although the heavy engineering firms whose normal task was to supply equipment for the gas industry were to a considerable extent diverted into making and assembling military equipment, the gas industry was on the whole left to concentrate on supplying its own product. To this, there was one major exception, namely the supply of hydrogen gas for the balloon barrage [9]. A minor exception, as in the First World War, was the manufacture of charcoal for gas-masks (p. 53), which were in fact not needed. For many people in Britain the appearance of the balloon barrage—controlled by a separate military command from November 1938—was the first visible sign of the imminence of war. At the outbreak of war its strength was 600 balloons; by the end of 1940 this had multiplied fourfold. Balloons were used not only to protect London and the large cities, but later also in the European theatre of war, including the D-day beaches of Normandy. Hydrogen, the gas to fill them, is not easily stored; it had to be kept available for use, on a short-term and unpredictable basis, in 3-cwt cylinders of high tensile steel, each containing no more than 3 pounds (600 cubic feet of hydrogen at atmospheric pressure). These cylinders had to be available at strategic points and recharged at short notice. In an emergency, a certain amount of the topping-up could be done with coal gas, but although lighter than air, this was relatively so much heavier than hydrogen that it could be used only very sparingly.

The technicalities of hydrogen production need not concern us here, except to note that it involves blowing a reducing gas (usually water gas) alternately with steam through a glowing bed of iron-ore (oxide). Approximately one ton of iron-ore was required to make 1000 cubic feet of hydrogen per hour. This is the kind of process with which gas engineers are familiar, and normal plant can be adapted for the purpose; it is known as the steam/iron process. As the war developed, increasing reliance was placed on the gas industry as a source of hydrogen. In 1940 only 7 per cent of the total came from gas works, but by 1944 this had risen to just over 70 per cent. In all, the industry supplied approximately half the total hydrogen required for the barrage (3500 million cubic feet). It may be noted in passing that the production of gas for balloons was no novelty for the industry. Even before the beginning of this century it was often provided for balloon enthusiasts and in 1908 the Gas Light and Coke Company even laid a special main from Fulham to Hurlingham for this purpose. In the First World War, more than 200 million cubic feet of hydrogen were supplied for military use, using the steam/iron process.

Apart from hydrogen, gas undertakings were mainly concerned with the production of fuel-gas (and associated by-products) with increasing emphasis on its use in war industries. In the peak year (1943) industrial sales totalled 470 million therms, almost exactly one-third of all gas sold. The percentage of gas used in industry varied considerably, ranging from 20 per cent in London to nearly 60 per cent in the West Riding of Yorkshire [10]. A detailed account of how gas was used in Britain's principal wartime industries may be found elsewhere [11, 12]. The engineering firms supplying the gas industry had, of course, to divert a considerable amount of their capacity to government contracts, thus correspondingly reducing their ability to provide gas equipment. West's, for example, who had built some 1500 tanks in the First World War, in the Second undertook the assembling of hundreds of Centaur tanks, and later Crusaders. Other military items made included gun shields, components for Bailey bridges, minesinkers, buoys, and invasion craft. W. C. Holmes and Company, of Huddersfield, provided prefabricated decks for 'Loch'-class frigates, bomb cases, components for Churchill tanks, and more than a million 2-inch rocket projectiles.

COMMERCIAL PROBLEMS

So far in this chapter, we have considered gas as an industry. To conclude, we must consider gas as a business for, as much in war as in peace, proper commercial management is essential. Here again the story must be told in terms of generalisations and examples, for the experience of different undertakings varied very considerably. Some problems, of course, were common to all: the overnight loss of sales for street lighting, still important, because of the black-out; the rising cost of coal, and the less than proportionate increase in the price for coke; and rising wages (37 per cent between October 1938 and January 1943). The biggest variable factors were the shift in population and the changed pattern of industry as the shadow factories came into operation and others stepped up production. A substantial part of the population of London was evacuated, and other vulnerable areas were affected. In September 1944 the number of officially billeted evacuees totalled just over a million, and there were many thousands of others who had made private arrangements. In evacuation areas such as London, the south-east coast, and East Anglia, demand for gas fell catastrophically, in some places by as much as 70 per cent. Elsewhere, of course, there were corresponding rises. Thus Liverpool experienced a drop of 5 per cent in 1940, compared with 1939, but an increase of 28 per cent by 1945—a demand which they were hard-pressed to meet. In the fragmented state of the industry there was little opportunity to average things out by transfer between undertakings.

The undertakings had little opportunity of balancing their books by increasing prices, as the government exercised strict control. In November 1939 the London companies increased the price of gas by $2\frac{1}{2}d$ per therm to meet increased costs and a drop of 26 per cent in consumption. Many provincial undertakings made comparable increases though a few, in favourable circumstances, actually made reductions. In 1941, the Board of Trade introduced an Order prohibiting any increase in the price of gas to the general public except under licence. Even though this was offset to some extent by increasing the price of coke, some areas suffered real hardship. Some undertakings actually operated at a loss; generally speaking, the government refused to permit increases of more than 30 per cent as long as an undertaking had reserves on which to draw. In 1940, for the first time since 1816, the Gas Light and Coke Company failed to declare a dividend. Not until 1942 was it allowed to increase the price of gas, by $1\frac{1}{2}d$ per therm [11].

Despite these many difficulties both the industry and government found time to give serious consideration to the nature of the industry in the post-war world. The substance of their deliberations will form the subject of the next chapter.

REFERENCES

[1] *Annual Abstract of Statistics*, No. 84, 1935–46, HMSO, London (1948).
[2] EVERARD, Stirling. *The History of the Gas Light and Coke Company 1812–1949*, pp. 354–64. Benn, London (1949).
[3] HARRIS, Stanley A. *The Development of Gas Supply on North Merseyside 1815–1949*, pp. 149–64, North Western Gas Board, Liverpool (1956).
[4] *Transactions of the Institution of Gas Engineers*, **94**, 296 (1944/5).
[5] PEP (Political and Economic Planning). *The Gas Industry in War-time*; Broadsheet No. 210, p. 11, London (1943).
[6] Ibid., pp. 8–9.
[7] SAVAGE, G. I. *History of the Second World War: Inland Transport*, HMSO & Longman Green, London (1957).
[8] *West's Gas*, **18**, 5, 1945.
[9] HUTCHISON, W. K. The Gas Industry and the Balloon Barrage, *Transactions of the Institution of Gas Engineers*, **94**, 390–431 (1944/5).
[10] *Transactions of the Institution of Gas Engineers*, **94**, 434 (1944/5).
[11] HEMS, H. R. Gas—an Industry at War, *Transactions of the Institution of Gas Engineers*, **94**, 431–80 (1944/5).
[12] PEP. op. cit., pp. 6–7.

12

Plans for Post-War Reorganisation

As has been noted earlier there was general agreement by the later 1930s that the gas industry was too important a public utility to continue in its existing fragmented state. There was, however, no consensus of opinion about how reorganisation should be achieved. Within the industry a process of rationalisation was favoured, leading to a relatively small number of autonomous, but closely collaborating, regional undertakings; we may see some analogy here to the policy of 'districting' that the competing London companies agreed upon in the latter half of the nineteenth century. Outside the industry, however, much more radical proposals were being aired: the Labour Party, in particular, had been committed since 1918 to outright nationalisation of gas, as part of a general policy of bringing about 'common ownership of the means of production, distribution, and exchange and the best obtainable system of popular administration and control of each industry or service'. The outbreak of war in 1939 precluded any major change although, as we have seen, the gas industry was subjected to very strict government control. It did not, however, preclude the preparation of various policy documents against the day when peace was restored, the coalition government was ended, and party political strife was resumed.

PRE-WAR PROPOSALS

Two important pre-war commentators [1, 2] were agreed on one point: the lack of any central authority in the industry was in itself a serious obstacle to reorganisation. Although there existed several national bodies, these lacked the authority to enforce changes, as opposed to recommending them. If change was to come, the industry itself would have to create its own governing body or one would have to be imposed by government.

Political and Economic Planning [3] made some quite detailed proposals for the functions of a National Gas Authority:

(1) To promote the grouping of undertakings within gas supply regions, defined by means of an initial survey, which might be carried out by regional commissions.

(2) Through the regional groups to promote the rationalisation of production and co-ordination of technical policy on the basis of evidence obtained in the survey.

(3) To supervise nationally the marketing of coke; and to co-ordinate

and extend national policies with regard to the marketing of other by-products.

(4) To guide the general line of commercial policy in the industry as a whole.

(5) To collect information and gain advice on economic problems affecting the industry.

(6) To be responsible for the public relations of the industry.

(7) To put forward schemes for recruitment and training of personnel.

Chantler also proposed reorganisation along regional lines and envisaged:

A small body of Gas Commissioners, appointed by the Board of Trade, from the most competent men available, and given powers and resources to secure area co-ordination, would seem to be the appropriate authority. Under their supervision, integration and co-ordination might be achieved by means of amalgamation, joint boards, or the creation of area gas-supply corporations of a public nature. A small number of area gas-supply authorities, supervised by the Gas Commissioners, should be able to secure operating economies, and meet competition more effectively than the industry can with its present atomistic organisation [4].

As general proposals these were sensible enough, but they did not amount to a workable plan. They ignored, for example, the various fringe activities in which gas undertakings were involved, such as transportation. It was not indicated how 'the most competent men available' were to be found and engaged as Gas Commissioners. Were they to be experienced leaders of the industry, men of wide business experience in other fields, political nominees, or what?

Although both Chantler's book and the PEP report embodied much information and comment originating within the gas industry, they certainly had no formal endorsement by it.

PROPOSALS WITHIN THE INDUSTRY

They were, nevertheless, generally approved in another document to which we must now direct our attention. This is a lengthy memorandum submitted by E. V. Evans to the Post-War Planning Committee of the National Gas Council in October 1941 [5]. Evans had had a long connection with the gas industry: in 1907 he had been appointed chief chemist to the South Metropolitan, and at the time of preparing his memorandum he was Managing Director of that company and Chairman of the Gas Research Board. He was, therefore, well qualified 'to incorporate the views of certain members of the Gas Industry'. Of Chantler and PEP he says: 'Much of what follows in this Memorandum is in line with the general conclusions of these valuable works, and the years that have passed since their appearance have served only to confirm and strengthen their major deductions.'

The form of this memorandum was clearly dictated by the circumstances of the day. The first part is concerned not with organisation but with the possibility of substantially increasing gas sales after the war in competition with coal, electricity, and oil. Completed in the latter part of 1941, after the blitz, the author is clearly conscious of the opportunities for gas in the rebuilding programme that must follow the war. He notes that 'it can be assumed that in certain towns some 10% of all dwellings might need to be rebuilt entirely after the war. Such extensive rebuilding could hardly be completed in less than 5 years and, in the extreme assumption that every one of these new buildings used gas exclusively, the rate of increase in gas output would be about 8% per annum.' Pursuing this argument, he foresees problems in disposing of the additional coke produced, but believes that these might be overcome technically by increasing the gas-to-coke ratio. He finds some difficulty in his advocacy of coke because it is a solid fuel, like coal; at an earlier stage he is, understandably, stating as forcefully as possible the arguments against the use of raw coal as a fuel. While coke is undeniably a cleaner fuel it is, like coal, not very efficient when burnt in ordinary domestic appliances, as opposed to steam-raising boilers. The attractions of a bigger post-war domestic market for gas and coke had not escaped the attention of the industry generally: in 1945 a long and detailed examination of the possibilities appeared in the *Transactions of the Institution of Gas Engineers* [6].

Regardless of organisational changes, Evans saw clearly that the gas industry had to make up its mind whether to expand substantially or be content with a relatively minor competitive role:

The first, and fundamental, decision to be made is whether the gas industry is to accept the policy of cheap and abundant gaseous fuel, or whether a limited and costly supply of gas is to remain as a competitive alternative to electricity in the home, and to coal, coke and oil in commercial and industrial premises.

An adventurous and progressive policy was possible only on the basis of a reorganisation setting up some sort of central authority. 'It would not be feasible', Evans points out, 'to submit a document to the Ministry of Works and Buildings, setting out the possibilities of improvement by an extended use of gaseous fuel if there were any doubt as to the willingness of all gas undertakings to play the part assigned to them'. What he calls the 'incoherence' of the gas industry is its greatest weakness. He contrasts this with the relatively strong position of the electricity industry which had already achieved co-ordination in generation and was considering, even before the war, the desirability of further legislation to extend this unity to distribution. The coal industry, with its ownership of many coke ovens, was in a favourable position to influence the policy of coke-oven gas producers. He remarks:

The Gas Industry alone has relied upon voluntary co-operation of its numerous units: often with noteworthy success, but always with the limitation that no Central

Authority can commit its members to any definite course of action to meet the Central Bodies of the other branches on equal terms. If the development of fuel preparation and supply is to proceed on planned lines with full co-operation between the various branches, a radical change appears necessary.

In its conclusion, making specific proposals for organisational change, the memorandum returns again to this theme. Evans visualised a regional organisation by which there would be four or five Regions for England and Wales and one for Scotland. Each would have both a nucleus of dense population and a rural system; roughly speaking, each would supply about two million consumers with 200 to 300 million therms annually. Competition between the Regions would provide an incentive to efficiency and progress but could not be expected wholly to eliminate extravagance on the one hand or apathy on the other. Much could be done by joint consultation but still, in the last analysis, it came back to the need to have 'some overriding power to be used in case of necessity. A National Authority would carry out the final responsibility for the financial, technical and commercial efficiency of the industry.' Deliberately, political responsibility was excluded. Evans and his colleagues recognised the crucial importance of this and proposed a Govern-ment Body—'a small body of men acting for and appointed by the appro-priate Government Department'—to look after relationships between the industry and Parliament, as representing the public interest in general.

Such a central authority caused Evans no undue concern, though he recognised that its creation might not be welcomed universally:

Voluntary methods with no centralized authority have revealed their weakness in the past, and other services and industries have recognised this weakness. Centralised authority with delegated executive powers holds no terrors for efficient undertak-ings, or individuals but gives them greater scope for development.

In effect, this important memorandum on policy bluntly warns the industry of two dangers. First, it will lose out to the better organised sectors of the energy industry. Secondly, if it does not put its own house in order, radical reorganisation will be imposed by government. It argues that a measure of co-operation with the coal and electricity industries is preferable to cut-throat competition. As far as coal was concerned, a jointly agreed price policy 'could avoid the absurd, but by no means improbable, position of a divided gas industry being forced to subsidise the domestic raw coal market'.

In retrospect, this memorandum was a sensible, unprejudiced evaluation of the future prospects of the gas industry. It can be faulted in only one major respect, namely its assessment of the future role of oil, which is cursorily dismissed because it 'requires to be imported from abroad, and cannot, on economic grounds, play a large part in post war fuel utilisation'. Related to this was an undue optimism about sale of by-products, notably coal-tar, to the chemical industry. However, this was largely an excusable fault. Even in 1945 S. E. Whitehead, as President of the Institution of Gas Engineers, remarked [7] that 'we must face the reality that for a considerable time the Gas Industry will continue to use the existing methods of producing and dealing with gas and coke'. As far as the chemical industry was concerned, however, the rapid growth of the petrochemical industry in the USA might have sounded a warning note. In the event, the British chemical industry changed the whole basis of production of organic chemicals from coal-tar to petroleum soon after the war, and long before the availability of domestic oil became apparent. In any event, however, the gift of prophecy could only have reinforced the arguments in favour or reorganisation around a central authority.

Apart from this organisational incoherence, Evans's memorandum reveals another serious weakness of the gas industry, namely 'the serious lack of precise information of a statistical type'. He attributes this mainly to the multiplicity of small units, but, whatever the reason, the consequences were serious: 'Only too often decisions of importance have to be taken with no stronger evidence than the opinion of individuals for guidance.' This serious omission was made good in a further report [8], completed in 1943. This was commissioned by the Post-War Planning Committee of the British Gas Federation. It was proposed by a committee under the chairmanship of A. E. Sylvester. His first important contact with the gas industry had been in 1930, when, as a chartered accountant, he was a partner in Barton, Mayhew and Company, who had been commissioned by the Gas Light and Coke Company to make recommendations for a thorough reorganisation of that undertaking. Sylvester eventually joined the Company and in 1941 became General Manager; in the following year he was made Managing Director. Finally, in 1945, he was appointed Governor, but in the following year ill-health, attributable to wounds received while serving with the Sherwood Foresters in the First World War, obliged him to retire on medical advice. As we shall see, however, his health was soon sufficiently restored to enable him to become, in 1949, the first Chairman of the Gas Council, established after nationalisation.

The remit of Sylvester's committee was strictly a fact-finding one, namely:

To make a comprehensive survey of the Industry designed to provide material upon which a scheme of reorganisation can be based, having in mind the need for ensuring the greatest possible degree of efficiency in terms of service to the consumer.

However, the Report thought fit to remark, on its first page, that:

the mere setting out of facts must give rise to certain lines of thought, and it will be found that the facts point clearly, not to a complete detailed solution of the problem, but unmistakably in the direction in which solutions may be found.

What this direction may be is not explicitly stated, but it is clear that elimination of the fragmentation of the industry, which in itself was a serious obstacle to fact-finding, was an important issue. The Report states bluntly that 'the first stage in the enquiry was to establish the facts of the ownership of the Industry' and it was admitted that in doing this information provided by the Gas Division of the Ministry of Fuel and Power had proved a welcome supplement to that available from individual undertakings. Even so, certain obscurities remained. At the time of the inquiry (1943) the last year for which official statistics were available was 1937; this was, moreover, the last year in which the industry was unaffected by preparation for war and the war itself. Board of Trade Returns were another important source, but had certain inherent defects: they related only to statutory undertakings, though this was relatively unimportant, since by far the greater part of all gas sold was produced by them. The Report did, however, reveal a significant difference in this respect between England and Wales, on the one hand, and Scotland on the other (Eire, Ulster, the Isle of Man, and the Channel Islands were not considered). In England and Wales only 1.3 per cent of gas was sold (1937) by non-statutory undertakings, whereas in Scotland it was 11.3 per cent. The difference was attributable to the fact that in England and Wales any undertaking selling more than 30 million cubic feet per annum had to have a Parliamentary charter: in Scotland, no such size limit applied.

Much more serious was the lack of detail in the Returns. On the production side, sales of gas and of by-products were distinguished, but there was no indication of the size of the industrial load. On the financial side even less distinction was made. Capital structure was shown, but revenue was given as a whole, regardless of how far it derived from gas or from by-products. The variation within the industry was such that no simple formula could reliably be used to estimate the relative contribution of the two sources to revenue.

Within these limitations, however, Sylvester's Report was thorough and useful. A general survey of the industry was followed by an analysis of seven principal areas of gas supply: London, South Lancashire, the West Riding, Birmingham, industrial Scotland, the North-east Coast, and industrial Wales. Much of the Report consists of detailed statistical tables for individual undertakings which need not concern us here, but the overall analysis of ownership is relevant. Briefly, it was shown that the industry consisted of no less than 1079 supply undertakings, with a total of 788 owning interests. The breakdown was as follows:

- 496 undertakings owned by independent companies, supplying 44.9 per cent of all gas sold;
- 19 holding companies controlling, or directly owning, 310 supply areas and supplying 9.5 per cent of gas;
- 268 municipal undertakings, supplying 33.6 per cent of gas;
- 5 undertakings owned jointly by municipalities and supplying 1.0 per cent of gas.

The detailed information gained in the compilation of Sylvester's report was of great value to the Post-War Planning Committee of the British Gas

Federation. This had been set up in September 1941 under the chairmanship of Sir David Milne-Watson, Governor of the Gas Light and Coke Company and Sylvester's immediate predecessor. While accepting the need for thorough reconstruction after the war, the report concluded that nationalisation was not necessary. In an exchange of correspondence with the Minister of Fuel and Power [9] Sir David announced that three sub-committees had been set up, dealing respectively with manufacture and distribution (G. Dixon); utilisation (E. V. Evans); and methods of charge and statistics (A. E. Sylvester). This correspondence was accompanied by a short memorandum outlining the existing function and structure of the gas industry and making certain proposals for its post-war development. In retrospect, it reads somewhat platitudinously; the Federation is against sin and in favour of virtue, but nationalisation is not comprehended within the latter:

Post-war conditions will attach added significance to the part the gas industry can play in the national well-being. A substantial extension in the fuel services it provides may be anticipated in conformity with a national fuel policy which shall so guide developments as to reconcile conflicting fuel interests. The Gas Industry must prepare itself with that objective in view and steps are in progress to that end.

In fairness to Sir David and his colleagues it must be recalled that in 1943 the end of the war was not in sight, nor was a successful outcome assured; day-to-day problems of maintaining supply were severe; and the nature of the post-war world was, to say the least, obscure. In a fuller report [10] circulated for comment in 1943, the need for a considerable degree of integration is accepted, as is the need for some body within the industry powerful enough to enforce it if the undertakings concerned were recalcitrant. The mechanism of control is visualised as a Central Council which, in the last resort could 'report' the matter to the Minister. What action the latter would then have authority to take was not made clear. However, the Committee thought that such ungentlemanly behaviour would be rare: it refers to 'the unusual event of inability or refusal to co-operate'. In short, it was confident that in the long run the industry could manage its own affairs.

The Committee realised that no far-reaching reorganisation was possible within the existing complex framework of legislation. In 1944, the Gas Legislation Committee of the British Gas Council issued a report on 'the form and nature of the gas legislation deemed necessary to further the progressive development and expansion of the Industry' [11]. This is prefaced by a useful historical survey and an account of various official and semi-official enquiries carried out in the inter-war years. As an example of the difficulties under which gas undertakings laboured, it complains in connection with the laying of mains and works in highways, that they are still bound by sections of the Gas Works Clauses Act 1847;

An Act which was passed 97 years ago naturally contains no reference to many of the problems which, in modern practice, arise in the dealings of Public Utility Undertakings with Highway Authorities.

The Committee made some sensible and far-reaching recommendations for reform, especially in relation to gas charges, but these are largely irrelevant in the present context. As we shall see, the Gas Act 1948 effectively repealed all earlier legislation and made a fresh start.

THE HEYWORTH REPORT

While the industry itself was thus occupied in planning its own future, the government had not been idle. In June 1942, a Ministry of Fuel and Power had been created. In June 1944 the Minister, Major G. Lloyd George, appointed a five-man committee 'to review the structure and organisation of the Gas Industry, to advise what changes have now become necessary in order to develop and cheapen gas supplies to all types of consumers, and to make recommendations'. The chairman was Mr Geoffrey Heyworth (later Lord Heyworth), Chairman of Unilever, an industrialist of wide experience. His team included a chartered accountant; a senior civil servant; and an eminent professor of chemical engineering. The Heyworth Committee took its task seriously, and collected a large volume of evidence. It received written evidence from 82 bodies or persons, and from 43 it took oral evidence. It visited various gas undertakings and the works of several manufacturers of appliances. It achieved a great deal for very little: a note on the fly-sheet of the report states that the total expense in connection with its preparation was £634, of which printing and publishing represented £347.

These activities took time and, in the event, the Committee reported [12] not to Major Lloyd George but to Mr Emmanuel Shinwell, Minister of Fuel and Power in the post-war Labour Government. By that time the content of the report was, in a sense, irrelevant in that the Labour government was firmly committed to a programme of nationalisation which the gas industry would escape only if the new government was short-lived, which seemed unlikely in view of size of its Parliamentary majority. The Heyworth Committee advocated the compulsory purchase of all existing undertakings, and the subsequent division of the country into ten Regions, each under a Regional Board consisting of a chairman and six directors. All directors would be appointed by the Minister, but all lower appointments would be made by the Boards themselves. All this uncompromisingly amounted to public ownership, though not to direct public control.

Careful thought was given to the financing of this major operation. The existing capital of gas companies consisted of debenture, preference, and ordinary stock, of which the last was subject to some form of dividend limitation. Municipal undertakings were financed by municipal loans. The

Committee advised against refinancing by equity capital, partly because it involved control by shareholders and partly because it was thought desirable to dispense with the price controls traditionally associated with it. The recommendation of the Committee was that capital should be wholly of a fixed-interest kind. Depending on how the valuation was made, it was estimated that the cost of acquisition would be between £203 million and £272 million. This was to be paid for by fixed-interest stock guaranteed by the government, who would receive a commission of ¼ per cent from the Boards on the amount guaranteed. This was to be a *quid pro quo* to the government for accepting 'less tangible instruments for protection than are normally demanded by guarantors'.

ATTITUDES TOWARDS NATIONALISATION

In the following chapter we shall consider how nationalisation was effected and its immediate consequences for the industry. We may conclude the present one by considering the attitude in the industry towards changes that, after Heyworth, were increasingly seen as inevitable. Again we can only generalise, for widely differing views were held and expressed. Sentiment, of course, played a considerable part, though it pulled in opposite directions. For the workers, with a strong preponderance of Labour supporters, nationalisation was a long-awaited political goal. Management, predominantly middle-class, and with a tendency towards Conservative sympathies, disliked the thought of nationalisation in principle. Possibly the very fragmentation of the industry, causing managers to assume a wide range of responsibility and to act on their own initiative, was a contributory factor towards an independent attitude.

But what of the higher levels, those at which policy is formed and decisions taken? There, there were few illusions about the problems looming ahead. Whatever the complexion of the post-war government, some form of public ownership seemed inevitable: the most that could be hoped for was some arrangement that fell short of full nationalisation, but even this hope was dashed on 15 August 1945, when the Speech from the Throne at the opening of the new Parliament expressly stated that:

A Bill will also be laid before you to nationalise the coal-mining industry as part of a concerted plan for the co-ordination of the fuel and power industries.

While this did not explicitly refer to nationalisation of gas, no one had any real doubt that a Bill to effect this would be introduced as soon as the legislative programme permitted. There could be no doubt, too, that electricity—already to a considerable extent in public ownership—would be similarly brought within the fold. How, it had to be asked, would gas fare in this situation? The industry needed not only reorganisation but, like industry generally, extensive modernisation, for which very large sums of money would be essential. In the political euphoria of the day these sums would certainly be available for the nationalised coal and electricity industries— the principal rivals of gas—but a privately owned gas industry would not be very attractive to investors: government alone could provide what was needed, and obviously it would not do so without acquiring effective control. In the circumstances, a public campaign of resistance was imprudent, and it seemed better to concentrate on securing a form of reorganisation as close as possible to that proposed by the industry itself and under the best terms possible for shareholders and employees alike. R. Kelf-Cohen, a senior government official who was closely concerned with the nationalisation of the power industries in the crucial years 1945–55, goes so far as to state that: 'In fact one may surmise that the gas industry was even anxious to be nationalised' [13].

Largely under Sylvester's initiative, the several central bodies of the industry had formed themselves into the British Gas Council and this, in 1947, gave an assurance to the Minister that it would 'co-operate with the Ministry of Fuel and Power in the detailed implementation of the Government's proposals, so as to ensure that the nationalised structure and organisation of the Gas Industry are such as to maintain an efficient gas service to the public.'

Individual companies made appropriate noises of disapproval but all, in effect, undertook not to be obstructive. Thus Mr Michael Milne-Watson, thirteenth and last Governor of the Gas Light and Coke Company, shortly after his election in 1947 put before the Court a statement of the Company's view of nationalisation [14]:

Firstly that the view of the Court remains unchanged, namely that in the present unsettled state of the country the nationalisation of the Gas Industry is inadvisable and unlikely to benefit the consumers of the Gas Light and Coke Company.

Secondly that in the event of the necessary legislation being passed to bring nationalisation about, the Company will not attempt to be obstructive but in the meantime reserves the right of taking all proper steps to ensure the inclusion in any Act of Parliament of suitable provisions covering the future organisation of the Gas Industry, and compensation to the shareholders, including, in the case of the Company, the co-partner shareholders whose holding is now in the neighbourhood of £1,000,000 of the Company's ordinary stock.

Thirdly that the position of the Company is already that of a Regional Gas Undertaking.

In the event, opposition to the nationalisation of gas was stronger within Parliament—where it was hotly contested—than outside. The industry made its protest, and gained certain important concessions, but was not obstructive.

REFERENCES

[1] CHANTLER, P. *The British Gas Industry: an Economic Study*, Manchester University Press, Manchester (1958).

[2] PEP (Political and Economic Planning). *Report on the Gas Industry in Great Britain*, PEP, London (1939).

[3] Ibid., p. 161.

[4] CHANTLER, P. op. cit., pp. 134–5.

[5] EVANS, E. V. *The Place of the Gas Industry in Post-War Reconstruction and Development.* A Memorandum Incorporating the views of certain members of the Gas Industry and Submitted for the Consideration of the Post-War Planning Committee of the National Gas Council. October, 1941. Privately circulated.

[6] ANDREW, L. W., DUNNING, E. W. B., and HOLLIDAY, G. C. *Transactions of the Institution of Gas Engineers*, **94**, 308–89 (1944/5).

[7] WHITEHEAD, E. S. ibid., p. 302.

[8] 'Report on a Survey of the Gas Industry in Great Britain', British Gas Federation, London (1943).

[9] 'Correspondence between Sir David Milne-Watson and the Minister of Fuel and Power and Memorandum on the Gas Industry', British Gas Federation (1943). Unpublished.

[10] 'Draft Report of the Post-War Planning Committee of the British Gas Federation', British Gas Federation (1943). Unpublished.

[11] 'Report of the Gas Legislation Committee', National Gas Council, London (1944).

[12] *The Gas Industry: Report of the Committee of Enquiry* (The Heyworth Report), Cmd 6699, HMSO, London (1945).

[13] KELF-COHEN, R. *Nationalisation in Britain: the End of a Dogma*, p. 110, Macmillan, London (1958).

[14] EVERARD, Stirling. *The History of the Gas Light and Coke Company*, p. 383, Benn, London (1949).

PART V

NATIONALISATION AND ITS AFTERMATH: THE MODERN INDUSTRY

13

The Post-War Nationalisation Programme

NATIONALISATION was the greatest single event in the history of the gas industry in the first century and a half of its existence. It gave it for the first time a structure based on units, each large enough to develop technologically and commercially, and an over-all organisation that put it on a footing comparable with that of its major rivals, coal and electricity. Further, it provided the framework for the remarkable renaissance of the industry that followed the discovery of North Sea gas, a renaissance made possible only by the availability of large and well-organised technological and financial resources. Clearly, therefore, any history of the gas industry must devote considerable attention to nationalisation, not only in the gas industry itself but in other industries—notably coal and electricity—to which it is closely related.

It must be said at the outset, however, that at this stage the historian's task is exceedingly difficult. Nationalisation was essentially an intellectual and political concept, from which great social and economic benefits were confidently expected to flow. Unfortunately, the nature and consequences of these benefits were by no means fully considered before the event and, as a result, the nationalised industries have developed not in accordance with a long-term strategy laid down at the outset, but rather pragmatically in response to changing circumstances. They have had to co-exist with governments formed by a political party that has cherished them, and with others formed by a party which once bitterly opposed their creation. Such basic problems as the relationship of the industry to Government, through the responsible Minister; to Parliament, as representatives of the public at large; to Local Authorities; to private industry; and to each other are still by no means resolved. This evolutionary process has, of course, many historical parallels, for it is the exception rather than the rule for new movements to be born fully-fledged. The Trade Union movement, for example, is now very different from that conceived by its originators. While it is clear in retrospect that far too little preparatory work was done before nationalisation, it is arguable that this was preferable to excessively detailed schemes leading to a rigidity of policy inimical to change. The post-war years have been turbulent ones, not only in Britain but throughout the world, and the future course of events was certainly not foreseeable in the late 1940s when the nationalisation programme was being effected. Industrial strategy formulated then would inevitably have had to be very substantially modified later.

While this is not the place to trace the history of the nationalisation of industry in Britain, which has already been the subject of several major works (see bibliography at the end of this chapter), it is impossible to understand the changed role of the gas industry without considering the chain of events that led up to it. To do so, we must for a moment go back considerably on our tracks.

Nationalisation, for present purposes, may be regarded as originating from the activities of the Fabian Society in general, and of Sidney and Beatrice Webb in particular. It would be wrong, however, to regard it as solely a socialist concept. In 1882, the very year in which the Fabian Society was founded, the then Liberal government brought forward the first Electricity Act, which provided that franchises granted to this novel and unpredictable industry should revert to the appropriate local authority after 21 years. Seven years later, when this was found too discouraging to private investors, a Conservative government doubled this period, but left unchanged the principle of reversion to public ownership. We have already noted the many statutory restrictions to which the gas industry, as a public utility, were subjected from its beginning. The British public generally, and not merely those with socialist leanings, distrusted private monopolies. Equally, however, they were distrustful of state monopolies and, paradoxically, this concern was not held only outside socialist circles. The Webbs themselves, in their *Constitution for the Socialist Commonwealth of Great Britain (1920)* argued that the individual might find himself powerless against an industry effectively owned and administered by Government Ministers. They feared, for example, that if workers were employed directly by the government, like the police or armed services, they might lose the right to strike [1]. From this concern arose the concept of state-owned industries subject to government directives on general policy but self-governing in the day-to-day running of their businesses. A strike within such a body could not be construed as rebellion. As we shall see, this concept was, in fact, embodied in the various British Nationalisation Acts, but in practice great difficulties arose—and still arise—in interpreting what constitutes directives on policy and what is to be regarded as interference in day-to-day administration.

Until 1945 nationalisation remained largely, but not entirely, an intellectual, and highly emotive abstraction, to be brought about by political means effected by a socialist government. The fundamental belief was that if only capitalist exploitation of the workers could be eliminated by the common ownership of the means of production and distribution, the whole industrial scene would be transformed. Workers, conscious of working for the common good, would recognise that 'no more can be shared among the producers than is produced' [2]. Waste and inefficiency could be eliminated once British industry was freed from 'a jostling crowd of separate employers with their minds bent, not on service to the community, but by the very law of their bodies, only on the utmost possible profiteering'. Such naivety is explicable on the ground that policy documents were, in the main, the product of intellectual groups with neither experience nor understanding of the problems of management and decision-taking in industry; it was not clear to them that, leaving aside all other considerations, a state-owned industry is subject to the same economic constraints as private ones, and that many of these originate outside the country and thus are outside government control. Perhaps the most realistic view at the time with which we are now concerned was that of the trade unions, expressed in the *Interim Report on Post-war Reconstruction (1944)*, in which they expressed themselves as being content with 'the gradual transition of the economic system from unregulated private enterprise to public ownership and public control'. The distinction made between ownership and control is significant. The TUC regarded nationalisation of transport, fuel and power, and iron and steel as being of paramount importance [3].

To a considerable extent, of course, this lack of understanding can be attributed to lack of case-histories on which to draw. If we except municipally owned undertakings, pre-war Britain was almost devoid of public corporations from whose experience lessons might be learned. In 1926, the Conservative government had introduced the Electricity (Supply) Act, establishing the Central Electricity Board. This, however, concerned itself only with the production of electricity and not with its distribution, which remained the concern of several hundred supply undertakings, though many of these were municipally owned. In the following year the British Broadcasting Corporation came into being, but this could scarcely be taken as a model for a production industry. The Labour government of 1929–31 established the London Passenger Transport Board. Apart from the fact that it was concerned only with the London area, this too was not really a nationalised industry. The new Board was not greatly different from the old London Underground Group and it had to pay compensation, and raise capital, by means of London Transport stock, which was not guaranteed by the government. Finally the Conservative government had nationalised coal royalties by the Coal Act (1938). The ownership of all coal was vested in the Coal Commission, a public board appointed by the Minister of Fuel and Power. In 1942 this took over colliery leases.

THE LABOUR PROGRAMME

In July 1945, Labour had its first real opportunity to put its ideas into practice. A convincing Parliamentary majority ensured it, barring accidents, a life long enough to put through a fairly massive programme of legislation, including nationalisation of certain key industries. Nevertheless, despite the fact that this had been a major part of Labour policy since 1919, it is clear now that on assuming office they were ill-prepared to put it into execution. Mr Emmanual Shinwell makes a startling, and often quoted, statement in his autobiography (1955):

I immediately took up the task of preparing the legislation for nationalisation of the mines. . . For the whole of my political life I had listened to the Party speakers advocating State ownership and control of the coal mines, and I had myself spoken of it as a primary task once the Labour Party was in power. I had believed, as other members had, that in the Party archives a blue print was ready. Now, as Minister of Fuel and Power, I found that nothing practical and tangible existed. There were some pamphlets, some memoranda produced for private circulation, and nothing else. I had to start on a clear desk. [4]

It is a statement that demands a pause to consider it. At the most, it is demonstrably a half truth: there certainly existed a number of substantial and authoritative reports relating to all the major candidates for nationalisation, which certainly cannot be dismissed as mere 'pamphlets and memoranda'. The preparation of Parliamentary bills is a highly complex operation, especially when it involves the nationalisation of great industries with multiple interests, and is a task beyond the resources of anybody save a government in office who can call on all the resources of the departments concerned, and in particular of skilled Parliamentary draftsmen. Clearly, no government can be expected to come into office with fully drafted versions of all the legislation it has proposed in its election manifesto. But the Labour Party had certainly had opportunity to go further along the road than it had done according to Mr Shinwell. Even in opposition, a major political party can command very considerable resources. Its supporters, who will give their services for little or nothing, are to be found in positions commanding great knowledge, experience, and influence. They will include ex-ministers, senior academics, lawyers, economists, financial experts, trade-union officials, and many others. Collectively, they could not draft a Parliamentary bill—the details of which would in any event be determined by the conditions of the day—but they could certainly provide a future minister with something better than 'a clear desk' when he had at last the opportunity to fulfil the aspirations of thirty years.

COAL

Nevertheless, lack of preparation was no deterrent to the politicians in power, and the Coal Industry Nationalisation Bill was published in December 1945, only four months after the King's Speech. In retrospect, it is clear that this hasty cobbling together of such an important measure was undesirable; its promoters were conscious of its defects but hoped that the worst of these might be eliminated during the passage of the Bill through Parliament. This was all very regrettable, but we must remember the circumstances of the time. Firstly, the coal industry was in a poor state, and a long period of uncertainty about its future was highly undesirable. Secondly, the government had to demonstrate to the electorate that it was losing no time in putting into effect measures which, in its Manifesto, it had stated to be of great urgency. Thirdly, and by no means least, the miners were a powerful political force. Preparation or no preparation, the government had no option but to press on. Inevitably, the Bill was inadequate and did little more than provide the necessary machinery for transferring to public ownership the assets of the industry—the very identification of which proved to present unexpectedly great difficulties because of the range of outside interests. The hated coal-owners had been shown-off, but little else was achieved. When the nine men appointed by the Minister to form the National Coal Board formally took office on 1 January 1947 they faced appalling difficulties. The gas industry may count itself fortunate that it was not at the top of Labour's shopping-list for nationalisation. Late-comers materially benefited from the experience gained with their predecessors.

The problems of the coal industry need not for the moment concern us further, but before leaving it we should note certain features of its nationalisation that differ from that of other industries. Firstly, the owners were compensated with Government stock. This was largely for psychological reasons: the government was anxious to demonstrate to the miners that their industry really belonged to the nation and not to some corporate body which might bear even a remote resemblance to the dispossessed colliery owners. Similarly, future developments were to be financed directly by the Treasury through the responsible Minister. In later nationalisation operations payment was made in stock issued by the Boards themselves. The system of valuing the coal industry assets acquired was exceedingly cumbersome and took some ten years to complete, at a cost of some £6½ million to the tax-payer [5]. In later nationalisation operations, the simpler procedure was adopted of making the basis of compensation the market value of shares in the undertakings concerned.

ELECTRICITY

Although the nationalisation of the coal industry had been carried out rather crudely, there was no ignoring its reality. The gas industry had to face the fact that its principal rival in the supply of fuel, and the source of its basic raw material, had been reorganised—even if the details might take some considerable time to work out—and was assured of very substantial and cheap government finance. Very shortly, under the Electricity Act (1947), another rival—and one already growing very rapidly, in contrast to the gas industry itself—was similarly brought under public ownership and control. As we have noted, some steps towards this had already been taken even before the war. As early as 1919, Electricity Commissioners, responsible to the Minister of Transport—'free from political control and untrammelled by past traditions'—had been appointed: this now somewhat surprising choice of Minister had been made because it then seemed that the greatest opportunity for expansion of the electricity supply industry lay in electric traction on the railways. The original intention was that the Commissioners should have powers to enforce reorganisation, but this was rejected by the House of Lords, who left them with only limited powers. Their task was that of 'promoting, regulating and supervising the supply of electricity'.

In the early 1920s, it became apparent that there was an urgent need for an electricity transmission network covering the whole of Britain, so that generation could be restricted to the most efficient stations and electricity conveyed to wherever it was needed. In 1925, the government set up a committee, under the chairmanship of Lord Weir, to advise it on this matter. The Weir Committee recommended that a Central Electricity Board should be set up to construct a national 'grid' of high-voltage (132 000 volts) transmission lines to link the principal existing power stations and distribution systems, thus making it easier to spread the load and avoid difficulties arising from the closing of individual stations through accident or for maintenance. This important development was put into effect with the passing of the Electricity (Supply) Act (1926). By 1935 nearly 3000 miles of primary transmission lines, and 1200 miles of secondary lines, had been built. By 1946, these had been extended to 3700 miles and 1500 miles respectively.

The satisfactory completion of the electricity grid involved the solution of two associated problems. Firstly, it was necessary to standardise the frequency of the supply. In 1926 three-quarters of the electricity generated was 50 Hz, three-phase. As this was general throughout most of Europe (except Italy) it was accepted as the national standard: the cost of effecting the change was about £17 million. Secondly, it was necessary to standardise the supply voltage, where even in 1935/6 (when the situation was investigated by the McGowan Committee) there was a wide variation. Of 642 undertakings, 282 supplied A C current only; 77 supplied D C only; and 283 supplied both A C and D C. There were 43 different supply voltages, ranging from 100 to 480 volts. Not until 1945 was a standard 240-volt A C supply established for the whole country.

The relationship of the Board to individual undertakings was complicated. The Board owned the grid, and controlled the undertakings, but it was not concerned with supply to consumers. Effectively, the Board bought the total output of individual stations, and then sold back to them, on favourable terms, the amount of electricity they actually required. Needless to say, the determination of the proper rate was difficult, and often the cause of controversy.

By this sequence of events the electricity industry relieved itself of the principal problems that still faced the gas industry after the Second World War. It had a national distribution system, whereas gas had nothing approaching a grid save in one small densely populated industrial area in the north-east. It had standardised its frequency and voltage, so that appliances could be used without modification anywhere in the country: in the gas industry there were considerable local variations in pressure, composition, and calorific value. The Electricity Act (1947) really did little more than complete a gradual process of nationalisation that had been going on for some thirty years. The transition was naturally less painful and complicated than it was for industries which were nationalised in a single operation.

The nationalised electricity industry became operative on 1 April 1948. Organisationally, it consisted of a British Electricity Authority (later the Central Electricity Authority) responsible for the power stations and the grid. Fourteen Electricity Boards (twelve in England and Wales and two in the South of Scotland) were responsible for distribution. The Central Electricity Authority was responsible for all financial matters. It submitted to the government, after its own scrutiny and amendment, the requirements of the Boards, together with its own requirements for production and distribution. It had effective control over the policy of the Boards who, in the terms of the Act, 'shall give effect to any direction (necessary or expedient for the purpose of coordinating the distribution of electricity) given to them by the Central Authority'. This organisation remained in force until 1958, when a new three-tier structure was introduced.

Certain points of detail in the Electricity Bill are of interest in the present context. Unlike that for coal, the full title of the Bill did not include the word nationalisation; nor did any of the other later nationalisation Acts. The government had reached the conclusion that the public, whose fickle interest in nationalisation was already waning, found this a somewhat cold and uncomfortable word; between themselves, but not in the public arena, Ministers preferred to call it socialisation. It is questionable, however, whether more than a very small fraction of the public knew, or even cared about, the full titles of the nationalisation bills that went through the House with bewildering rapidity; for most, the abbreviated forms used in the newspapers, and on radio and television, sufficed and for these nationalisation was the operative word.

The method of compensation was argued to and fro almost up to the time the Bill was published [6]. The enormous amount of work involved in valuing the coal assets was beginning to be appreciated. Not only was it doubtful whether there were sufficient competent valuers available for a further massive operation of the same kind, but it had become apparent that many mining engineers were being lost to the Coal Board because their services were being retained by the former owners to advise them on compensation. After misunderstandings due to ignorance of the financial structure of the industry—the Ministry had no accountant experienced in the affairs of electricity undertakings [7]—it was finally accepted that a practicable scheme could be devised on the basis of Stock Exchange share values. In the event, the complete valuation was effected in seven months at negligible cost, a marked contrast to coal. The amount of compensation stock issued by the British Electricity Authority was £342 million.

Like the gas industry, the electricity distribution industry could not operate without statutory powers to lay its mains under public highways. As with gas, however, there were a few non-statutory companies and provision was made for these to apply for compulsory acquisition if they satisfied certain criteria. In the event, 25 such undertakings did apply, and were compensated on the basis of what they might have been expected to fetch on the open market.

TRANSPORT

The nationalisation of transport under the Transport Act 1947, is less relevant to our present study than that of the much more closely related coal and electricity industries. Nevertheless, the gas industry relied heavily on outside transport organisations to convey coal to its works and take away coke, tar, and other products, and the terms on which it could do business with these was of great importance. As we have seen, the nationalisation of coal and electricity presented the government with difficulties enough, but these paled almost into insignificance in comparison with transport. Although they had certain fringe interests, the acquisition or otherwise of which presented problems, coal and electricity were on the whole fairly well defined industries. Transport was a very different matter. The government, under the Act, set up a British Transport Commission 'to carry goods and passengers by rail, road, and inland waterway within Great Britain'. Subsumed within their broad definition was concealed such considerable matters as the provision of port facilities; the running of certain hotels and catering services; and certain warehouse activities. The upheaval was enormous and the progress of reorganisation correspondingly slow. One of the Commission's major assignments was the preparation of a comprehensive Charges Scheme covering all three forms of transport; for this two years were initially allowed, subsequently extended for a further two years, and then yet again for two years more. Those familiar with the extraordinarily complex system of charges evolved by the four main-line railways alone will not be altogether surprised by this. A still older generation recalled that when, under the Railway Act 1921, 120 railway undertakings were merged to form these four major companies the process of reorganisation took seven years to complete. When it is considered that revolutionary changes were simultaneously going on in road transport the problems appear, and indeed were, almost overwhelming. The 1949 Report of the Commission records that it employed 895 000 people with an annual wage bill of £300 million. Its total assets were around £1600 million. Yet the Commission itself consisted initially of only five men, and this was shortly reduced to four for most of the period 1948–51 by the death in 1948 of Lord Ashfield, the former chairman of the London Passenger Transport Board. It is true that the Commission operated through a series of boards but the ultimate responsibility to the Minister was laid upon it. Their task was not aided by the optimistic speeches of Labour Ministers who virtually ignored the fact that the whole of Britain's transport system was—as any traveller could see—in a poor state as a result of unavoidable wartime neglect. Nationalisation was no magic wand that could quickly put this right nor, it must equally be stated, could this have been achieved by radical reorganisation under private ownership.

The second readings of the Transport Bill (16 December 1946) exemplifies this euphoria. Mr Alfred Barnes, the Minister of Transport, told the House:

There are no physical or financial reasons why we should not have the most efficient, comfortable, speedy and cheap systems of transport in the world. . . . A small body with time to think and plan, and the vast resources it will have behind it, will work a revolution in the efficiency of the transport system of the country.

Even allowing for Parliamentary licence at a moment of political triumph, this was an ill-considered speech. The Minister and his colleagues knew full-well the physical and economic reasons why rapid improvement was totally impossible, and that while Britain was putting her transport system in order other countries would not be standing still. Equally he must have realised that the five-man Commission responsible for the mammoth task of reorganising the system could have little time to think and plan. Nationalisation might be a useful preparation for a long journey, but it did not in itself make the way ahead less arduous. However, an important electoral pledge had been honoured, and in political terms this was a major achievement; the public would learn in the fullness of time that progress must inevitably be slow whatever government was in power. In 1949, in their annual report, the Commission had to concede that it had done no more than keep the transport system in 'reasonable working condition' and that they found it 'impracticable' to submit plans for reorganisation and development.

After long argument [8] it was agreed that railway and canals compensation should be paid on the basis of Stock Exchange quotations in November 1946, which covered some 98 per cent of the assets acquired. Payment was made by issue of British Transport 3% Stock 1978–88. There was considerable, but certainly not universal, dissatisfaction with this settlement. Firstly, it was argued that because of the measure of control it had itself exercised over the railways during the previous seven years, the state was buying at a price that it had itself largely determined. Secondly, the very threat of nationalisation on terms unknown—but unlikely to be very generous—had depressed the value of railway stock at the relevant date. Thirdly, and undeniably, many investors would suffer a considerable loss of income. This last argument the government countered by pointing out that railway company dividends had been erratic, whereas the regular payment of interest on the new Transport stock was assured. This, of course, cut both ways: the nationalised transport undertakings would have to pay interest on their stock regardless of their financial performance. This aspect was rather lost sight of in the excitement of the time, but the harsh reality became increasingly important as the years went by.

Some loose ends remained to be tied up. Although passenger rolling stock was largely owned by the railway companies, a large proportion of goods wagons—totalling some 5–6 million—were privately owned, about one-third of them by the newly nationalised coal industry. Many of these were old and in disrepair, some going back to the beginning of the century. The valuation of this rag-bag of assets presented considerable difficulties, but was eventually set at £43 million, of which £12 million went to the Coal Board. As before, payment was made in 3% Transport Stock.

Whereas the acquisition of the railway and canals was immediate, that of road transport was gradual. Initially the take-over was voluntary, with compensation for vehicles on a complicated basis involving the cost of replacing with a new vehicle, less depreciation; annual profits; and severance [10]. In its first year the Commission thus acquired 248 undertakings, bringing with them some 8000 motor vehicles, 1700 trailers, and—perhaps surprisingly at so late a date—nearly 2000 horse-drawn vehicles. In October 1948 the Commission began to exercise compulsory power of purchase, and by 1951 had acquired 432 undertakings by voluntary agreement; 1880 by notice of compulsory purchase; and 1409 demanding to be compulsorily acquired.

But in the event all this effort was wasted. In 1951 a Conservative government took office and proceeded to put into effect its declared intention of denationalising road transport. The vehicles laboriously acquired by the Commission were sold. At the same time, however, the railways were given powers to compete more freely with road transport. In particular, they were required to publish only maximum charges and were free to quote more favourable terms, in confidence, to particular customers. Naturally, this dispensation was of particular interest to the coal and gas industries, whose bulk transport requirements were measured in millions of tons annually. At the same time the Railway Executive was abolished in favour of a decentralised regional system.

GAS

As the programme of nationalisation developed a very great strain was put upon both Parliament and the Ministers and departmental officers concerned; this tended to limit consideration of major issues, both in the preparation of Bills and in their debate, and lead to the taking of decisions that were later seen not to be the wisest possible. On the other hand, growing experience generated a certain proficiency both in settling fundamental principles and in drafting the bills to give effect to them. Moreover, even brief experience of nationalisation in practice was beginning to reveal certain problems that could not be ignored. On balance, therefore, the gas industry gained some advantage from being brought into the fold later, rather than earlier. Apart from iron and steel—which was to be denationalised before the new organisation could get into its stride—gas was the last industry to be nationalised by the post-war Labour government.

As we noted in the last chapter, the gas industry's attitude to nationalisation was one of resignation rather than enthusiasm. It had itself long accepted the need for reorganisation on a national basis—as distinct from passing into public ownership—but it was clear that in the political climate of the day this was scarcely a possibility. The government, like governments before and since, was intent upon a national fuel policy, in which gas must find a place. It would be illogical, and unacceptable to the bureaucratic mind, to nationalise two legs of the stool and leave the third in private ownership. Little public support could be expected. In the words of Sir Arthur Hetherington, the first Chairman of the present British Gas Corporation [11]: 'In the early nineteen fifties few would have given the gas industry much chance of survival, let alone expansion and hardly anybody outside the industry seemed unduly concerned at the outcome [nationalisation].' Attention was, therefore, directed primarily to securing the best terms possible for the industry and its shareholders. To this end, rather than with any expectation that nationalisation could be avoided, the Conservative Opposition was given all the support possible. If the country at large was apathetic, Parliament seemed to have lost none of its enthusiasm. The Committee stage of the Gas Bill was prolonged, concluding with a marathon session of 51 hours.

In the event, the shape of the new gas industry—as embodied in the Gas Act 1948—was not very different from that which its own leaders had been advocating in principle. It must be doubted, however, whether an industry consisting of such a conglomerate of concerns would in fact have achieved, within a realistic span of time, a self-generated reorganisation of the necessary severity. A decision imposed on it from outside at least left it with no opportunity for delay.

Understandably—because the two industries concerned had much in common—the Gas Bill as originally drafted drew heavily on the Electricity Act [12]. In particular, there was a much clearer view at the outset of the nature of the undertakings to be acquired and of how to deal with composite concerns; that is, concerns which provided not only gas but another service, such as water. At the same time, note was taken of differences between the two service industries. In the electricity industry, non-statutory undertakings were relatively unimportant, in that their customers could almost all be supplied if need be from the national grid. Non-statutory gas undertakings—of which there were some 350—were different. Although they represented only 2 per cent of sales in 1946, many of their customers had no alternative source of gas. Furthermore, unlike electricity undertakings, gas undertakings did not automatically pass into the ownership of a Local Authority after a certain lapse of time. In fact, there were two kinds of non-statutory undertaking. Firstly, there were those (the great majority) which provided a general public supply: these were taken into public ownership. Secondly, there were 35 such undertakings which generated gas for their own use or for the use of closely associated concerns: thirteen of these were owned by existing nationalised industries, six by the Coal Board, and seven by the Transport Commission. These 'ancillary gas undertakings' were excluded from the Bill, though provision was made in the Act for the nationalised gas industry to acquire any surplus gas they might have.

A problem of much greater magnitude, in terms of the quantity of gas produced, was that of the coke-ovens. As we have already noted, these were an important source of supplementary supply for the gas industry. A large part of the coke-oven industry was associated with collieries, already acquired by the Coal Board. At first, it was proposed to transfer the colliery coke-ovens to the gas industry, but this was opposed by both the National Union of Mineworkers and the Coal Board. Eventually a compromise was reached in the Act (Section 51), by which the gas industry was required to consult with the Coal Board, at a local level, in order to submit to the Minister agreed schemes for co-ordinating their carbonisation activities.

The steel industry, still in private ownership, also owned many coke-ovens. Much of the gas produced was used in steel-making, but the surplus was commonly supplied to the gas industry. The Act excluded such coke-ovens from its provisions, but gave the nationalised gas industry the right to distribute and sell spare gas. Later, when iron and steel were nationalised (1949), provision was made for the gas industry to co-ordinate with the Iron and Steel Corporation its schemes for the use of surplus coke-oven gas.

Composite companies were treated on the basis that only those parts of their business directly related to the manufacture and supply of gas were compulsorily acquired. Such companies could, however, apply—within a statutory period—to be taken over in their entirety. Holding companies were taken over where at least 75 per cent of their assets were in authorised undertakings, as with electricity.

All this was a far cry from Mr Shinwell's blithe and simple statement to a subdued annual meeting of the Institution of Gas Engineers (4 June 1946) that the government would 'take over the Industry lock, stock and barrel'. He had slightly tempered this in a subsequent speech at Lincoln in which he assured the industry that it would be run by people who knew all about it. But who else could?

The assets to be acquired being at last defined, it was necessary to legislate for their purpose. Again, the basis was the share market value which, in effect, the Heyworth Committee had recommended (p. 96). A Treasury minute [13] noted that 'any attempt at a separate valuation of over 1000 undertakings on a physical assets basis or by reference to net maintainable revenue would be hopelessly complicated and wasteful of time and man-power'. The fact that the coal industry consisted of some 800 companies, many owning several collieries, had not deterred the government from embarking on this very exercise in 1946; but it was not one they were anxious to repeat. Examination showed that the complexity of the gas industry, in terms of its financial structure, was greater than that of electricity. Neverthe-less, after careful study it was discovered that only about £10 million gas stock, out of about £165 million, was unquoted in either the Daily List, the Monthly List, or the lists of provincial stock exchanges. It was reasonable to hope that a substantial part of this residue could be valued by informal agreement, leaving only a relatively small sum to be the subject of arbitra-tion [13].

As measures had already been passed to acquire two industries (electric-ity, transport) on this basis, this aspect of the Bill met with little opposition in principle, but there was much debate about detail. As with electricity, it was argued that government control of the price of gas during the war had depressed the price of shares. The Heyworth Report had had a disturbing influence. Again, the industry was still suffering from the effects of bomb damage and this too might be reflected in the share prices. It could certainly be argued that in this respect the gas industry was different from electricity. As an old industry, gas-works tended to be located in city centres, the main targets for enemy attack. By contrast, the much newer electricity generating stations tended to be situated further out and were less vulnerable. The point was taken and the Act provided that allowance should be made for loss of business demonstrably attributable to war damage or shift of population. Again, it was remarked that Stock Exchange quotations could be mislead-ing. Although daily quotations might be published these might be notional—no more than a jobber's mark—no actual purchase of shares need have been made on that day, nor for weeks, or even months, previously. This objection was largely met in the Act by stipulating that valuations might be based on quotations on six stated days in 1945 or six days in 1947, whichever was most advantageous to the dispossessed shareholder. Local Authority undertakings, generally financed by loan stock, were compen-sated on the basis of the cost of redeeming the loan, including any interest due. In the event, the task of valuation was completed within a year, at a total administrative cost of about £350 000. Total compensation amounted to £220 million, paid in British Gas 3% Guaranteed stock 1990/95.

Apart from defining the assets to be acquired, and how they were to be paid for (Part II), the Act had to specify the way in which the newly unified industry was to be run (Part I). Broadly speaking, the Act followed the recommendations of the Heyworth Report, which had concluded:

. . . there are no important problems in the Industry which are by their very nature country-wide. It is not economically possible for gas to be provided everywhere; a national grid is not practicable; nor can selling price usefully be determined on a national basis . . . Complete centralisation can therefore safely be rejected as inappropriate . . . Division of the country into regions has obvious attractions and is the solution we recommend. [14]

Under the 1948 Act, twelve Area Boards (Heyworth had recommended ten) were set up, including one for Scotland and one for Wales and Monmouth. These Areas were defined on the general principle that each should include, and not divide, some major urban and industrial district and that regional loyalties, as in Wales and Scotland, should be respected [15]. Generally speaking, these Boards were autonomous. In particular, they were permitted to fix their own prices, insofar as this was compatible with the general direction that 'every Area Board shall reduce, so far as practicable, the price of gas and coke, and avoid undue preference in the supply of gas and coke'. At the same time, the Area Boards were required 'to secure that the revenues of the Board are not less than sufficient to meet their outgoings properly chargeable to revenue account, taking one year with another'.

The Heyworth Committee set its face against any central body, and in its early consideration of the Bill the government accepted this. Subsequently, the view was accepted that some central organisation, with limited powers, was necessary. This would serve as a channel of communication with the Minister; for negotiations with labour; for carrying out research; and for acting as spokesman for the industry generally. To this end, the Act provided for a Gas Council (Section 22), whose duties were defined as:

(a) to advise the Minister in questions affecting the gas industry and matters relating thereto; and
(b) to promote and assist the efficient exercise and performance by Area Boards of their functions.

The powers of the Gas Council appeared considerable. It could demand financial and other information from the Area Boards; it could (with the approval of the Minister and the Treasury) borrow money up to a limit of £250 million by issuing British Gas Stock; it would maintain a central guarantee fund to assist any Area Board (or the Council itself) in the event of their 'being unable temporarily to discharge their obligations'; it would negotiate wages; and the Minister would consult with Council before approving Area Boards' plans for substantial reorganisation and development. Nevertheless, the constitution of the Gas Council was such that control lay effectively with the Area Boards. It consisted of a chairman and deputy chairman, both appointed by the Minister, and the chairman of each of the twelve Area Boards.

In debate on the Bill, the Council came in for some criticism. Some thought that as it was essentially an advisory body, the gas industry would be put at a disadvantage compared with coal and electricity. Yet, it was pointed out, the Council had imposed on it the task of negotiating wages and conducting research, neither of which could properly be described as advisory. Colonel Walter Elliot regretted the departure from the Heyworth proposals and remarked prophetically, that:

Inevitably, the Minister, having departed from the Heyworth scheme that there should not be a central body, is being driven towards a central body which will assume greater and greater powers . . . we are departing from the original conception . . . of a decentralized industry, and the power and authority will lie inevitably at the centre and less and less at the periphery [16].

These then, were the main provisions of the Gas Act 1948 (vesting date 1 April 1949) as far as the reorganisation of the industry under public ownership was concerned. We must not leave it, however, without noting certain other features.

As has been remarked in earlier chapters, the gas industry suffered from a super-abundance of legislation. One of the tasks of the Ministry of Fuel and Power, in the course of preparing the Bill, was to go through all existing Gas Acts in order to extract significant points from them. The fourth Schedule of the Gas Act 1948 formally repealed all previous enactments that were irrelevant, and thus the Act itself became the new legal basis. A similar attempt to wipe the legal slate clean for the electricity industry had been less successful.

In distinction from earlier nationalisation Acts, the Gas Act 1948—as a result of Opposition proposals made in debate—made special provisions for taking over, as though they were gas undertakings, the industry's existing national bodies (Section 62). These were the British Gas Council; the Federation of Gas Employers; the National Federation of Gas Coke Associations; and the Association of Gas Corporations. The employees of these bodies thus became the responsibility of the Gas Council which, incidentally, acquired a London headquarters.

At the time of the Act, only the most prescient would have regarded it as applying to anything but coal gas. Nevertheless, its provisions did not exclude the supply of gas of quite a different kind, it being explicitly stated (Section 55) that:

The Minister shall, after consultation with the Gas Council, prescribe standards of pressure, priority and uniformity of calorific value . . . and may . . . prescribe other standards with respect to the properties, condition and composition of gas supplied . . .

Such then, was the new shape of the gas industry, in Britain. The change was relatively smooth, in that the majority of top management elected to remain within the industry. A. E. Sylvester—a former Governor of the Gas Light and Coke Company—was the first chairman of the Gas Council (remaining until 1951), and eight of his thirteen colleagues had previously held senior managerial positions.

Shinwell's promise that the industry would be 'run by people who knew all about it' had certainly been fulfilled, and it is worth pausing for a moment to consider some of the members of this first team [17]. Sylvester's deputy, and later successor, was Mr (later Sir) Harold Smith who had been in the gas industry since 1906. The offices he held included the presidency of the Institution of Gas Engineers and the chairmanship of the Federation of Gas Employers. Mr (later Sir) Michael Milne-Watson, appointed Chairman of the North Thames Gas Board, was the last Governor of the Gas Light and Coke Company. Mr W. K. Hutchison (later Sir Kenneth) (South Eastern) was a product of Edinburgh Academy and Corpus Christi, Oxford. He had joined the Gas Light and Coke Company as a research chemist, and became its managing director in 1947: during the war he had been given responsibility for all hydrogen used in the balloon barrage, and oxygen used in high altitude flying for the British and American Airforces. Mr (later Sir) Henry Jones (East Midlands) had been educated at Harrow and Pembroke College, Cambridge. His family had had a long connection with the gas industry and at the time of his appointment he was director of several gas companies, including the South Metropolitan. He was later to be Chairman of the Council (1960–71). Different interests were represented by such men as Sir John Stephenson (Eastern), prominent in the labour movement and General Secretary of the Plumbing Trades Union since 1939; Mr T. Mervyn Jones (Wales), a Cambridge graduate who had turned to law and had been Town Clerk of Newport since 1946; Dr Roger Edwards (North Eastern), a physics graduate of Imperial College who, after a career in research, had become a director of the Co-operative Wholesale Society; and Sir Andrew Clow (Scottish), another Cambridge graduate, who had been Governor of Assam.

Money was now available, if not for the asking, at least on a scale and with a facility previously unknown. Area Boards, through their own chairman, submitted ideas to the Council who in turn referred them to the Minister. In the political climate of those days, when nationalised industries were the pride of the Labour government which had created them, they mostly got what they wanted: disenchantment lay in the future. A programme of modernisation could be confidently embarked on without the tedious process of submitting proposals successively to Local Authorities or Company boards; to the Board of Trade; and to committees of the House of Commons scrutinising private bills. In the first decade after nationalisation some £500 million was invested in capital developments. Old and inefficient gas works were closed and the remainder modernised. In 1949 the Gas Council had inherited 1050 separate works: by 1958 this number was reduced to 536 [18]. Increased efficiency was measured by an increased yield of gas—from 71.6 therms per ton in 1950/1 to 76.7 in 1959. This would have been welcome in any event, but particularly so in view of the steep rise in the cost of coal (from £2 per ton on average in 1947 to £4 in 1957). Additionally, there was a considerable extension to the system of gas mains—from 77 000 miles in 1950/1 to 90 000 in 1956/7.

Unfortunately, this considerable expenditure of time and effort was not matched by an increase in the sale of gas. Total sales were 2400 million therms in 1950/1 and had risen to only 2546 million in 1956/7. Over the same period the number of domestic consumers rose slightly—from 11.2 million to 12.1 million—but the number of industrial consumers actually fell, from 114 000 to 95 000.

Over roughly the same period electricity, the main rival of gas, was going ahead rapidly. Power generated almost doubled from 43 000 million units in 1948/9 to 85 000 million in 1959; domestic and industrial consumers contributed roughly equally to the increase. Whereas the price of electricity rose by only 17 per cent between 1950 and 1957, that of gas rose 51 per cent.

It has been argued [19] that these comparisons are unfair to the gas industry, which had long stressed that in no field did it have a monopoly. By contrast, electricity did have such a monopoly in the field of domestic lighting and small power-units. It was claimed that the Electricity Boards used this monopoly to supply electricity at an uneconomic rate for other uses, notably cooking and space heating, in which they competed directly with gas.

Undeniably, the first fruits of nationalising the gas industry were not impressive as far as the general public was concerned. Fortunately, this period of relative stagnation was comparatively brief. To understand the factors that brought it to an end, and gave new life to a seemingly old and tired industry, we must now direct our attention primarily to new technological developments.

REFERENCES

[1] WEBB, Sidney and WEBB, Beatrice. *A Constitution for the Socialist Commonwealth of Great Britain*, p. 140, London (1920).
[2] Ibid., p. 186.
[3] *Report of Trades Union Congress*, p. 436 (1944).
[4] SHINWELL, E. *Conflict without Malice*, p. 172, London (1955).
[5] CHESTER, Norman. *The Nationalisation of British Industry 1945–51*, pp. 240–57, HMSO, London (1975).
[6] Ibid., pp. 277–95.
[7] Ibid., p. 287.

[8] *Economist*, 23 November 1946.
[9] CHESTER, Norman. op. cit., pp. 261–77.
[10] CHESTER, Norman. *The Nationalisation of British Industry 1945–51*, pp. 275–6, HMSO, London (1975).
[11] BRITISH GAS CORPORATION. *Annual Report and Accounts 1975–6*, p. 7.
[12] CHESTER, Norman. op. cit., pp. 261–77.
[13] CHESTER, Norman. op. cit., p. 296.
[14] *The Gas Industry Report of the Committee of Inquiry*, HMSO, London (1945).
[15] *Gas Supply Areas*, Cmd 7313, HMSO, London (1948).
[16] CHESTER, Norman. op. cit., p. 440.
[17] *Gas World*, 13 November 1948, p. 710.
[18] *Gas Council Annual Report 1957/8*, Para. 327.
[19] LITTLE, I. D. M. *The Price of Fuel*, p. 88.

BIBLIOGRAPHY

CHESTER, Norman. *The Nationalisation of British Industry*, 1945–51, HMSO, London (1975).

KELF-COHEN, R. *Nationalisation in Britain: the End of a Dogma*, Macmillan, London (1958).

KELF-COHEN, R. *Twenty Years of Nationalisation: the British Experience*, Macmillan, London (1969).

PRYKE, Richard. *Public Enterprise in Practice: the British Experience of Nationalisation Over Two Decades*, MacGibbon and Kee, London (1971).

ROBSON, William A. *Nationalised Industry and Public Ownership*, 2nd edn, George Allen and Unwin, London (1962).

14

Introduction of New Manufacturing Processes

As we have seen, small quantities of gas were at a very early date prepared by carbonising oil; carburetted water-gas was introduced towards the end of the last century; and natural gas was widely exploited in North America well before 1900. Nevertheless, at the time of nationalisation the British gas industry, like its European counterparts, was firmly based on the carbonisation of coal by traditional methods. It was, however, apparent that the existing coal-based industry had inherent disadvantages that would become increasingly serious as the pressure of competition from rival fuels, especially oil and electricity, increased. If the industry was to survive, let alone prosper, improved gas-manufacturing processes were essential. In the event natural gas was to sweep the board, but even at mid-century the very existence of this in substantial quantities in Northern Europe was virtually unsuspected, though some minor discoveries had been made (Ch. 15). The move away from dependence on coal began long before the discovery of North Sea gas and oil, and there was a brief period during which new processes of gas manufacture were developed and introduced. This change of policy was prompted by the big increases in the price of coking-coal demanded by the National Coal Board, which presumably thought that in gas it had a captive customer.

Before we can evaluate these new processes, however, we must consider the reasons why the traditional gas-making process, with all the technical improvements effected in it, had become inappropriate for current needs. Basically, the factors making changes mandatory were economic. The high quality coking-coals necessary for making gas by direct carbonisation were becoming scarce and expensive. By contrast, the electricity industry could fire its boilers with relatively cheap inferior coal. Further, the handling of coal and the operation of rather complex purification processes demanded a large labour force at a time when wages were rising. Revenue from the sale of coke, an important factor in keeping the price of gas competitive, was uncertain. The process produced large quantities of waste, some of it noxious, the disposal of which presented problems. Only in exceptional circumstances was distribution through a grid feasible, so that a multiplicity of relatively small manufacturing units had to be maintained. Last, but by no means least, working conditions in gas works were unattractive compared with those in many other branches of industry.

These considerations directed research and development into three main channels. Firstly, there was interest in the complete gasification of low-grade coal, to which the Ridley Report [1] of 1952 directed particular attention, thus simultaneously reducing the cost of the raw material and eliminating the production of coke. Secondly, attention was directed to the use of petroleum as a raw material in place of coal. Thirdly, there was the possibility of importing liquefied natural gas into Britain from sources where it was cheap and plentiful. Overall, there was a particular interest in processes that would provide gas at high pressure, as compared with the very low pressures of carbonisation. This could not only radically affect the economics of operating a gas grid but very substantially increase the carrying capacity of existing mains.

The cost of transmitting gas generated at, say, 25/30 atmospheres is less than half that of transmitting gas initially at low pressure and—very significantly—only about a quarter the cost of transmitting the equivalent amount of electricity over similar distances.

Although a separate operation, the importation of liquefied natural gas is most appropriately considered in relation to the exploitation of North Sea gas. For the moment, therefore, we will consider processes based on complete gasification of low-grade coal, and the use of petroleum as a raw material. To understand the introduction of these, we must first briefly note the organisation of research in the gas industry up to the time of nationalisation.

RESEARCH IN THE GAS INDUSTRY

In 1939 the Institution of Gas Engineers and the Society of British Gas Industries had set up a Gas Research Board to replace the Research Executive Committee established by the Council of the Institution in 1934, 'to be responsible to the Council for the initiation and organisation of all research on behalf of the Institution'. The principal aims of the new Board were:

(1) To promote and finance research and other scientific work.
(2) To establish and maintain an information bureau.
(3) To encourage invention and improvement.
(4) To co-operate in research work done by kindred organisations.
(5) To establish research laboratories, if and when thought desirable.
(6) To issue detailed reports for the confidential use of members.

The Gas Act 1948 charged the Gas Council with responsibility for research but the Board remained independent, even though more than 90 per cent of its subscription income came from the Council as successor to the old independent undertakings. Meanwhile, the Council appointed (1950) a Research Advisory Committee, which recommended the establishment of a new research station, somewhere in the Midlands, to be administratively responsible to the West Midlands Gas Board. This was to be part of a general plan for three principal research centres, the other two to be situated in London and the North respectively. The London Centre developed from the existing Watson House and the London Research Centre near by at Fulham. The Northern Centre was not finally set up until 1964, and was located at Newcastle upon Tyne.

The rather anomalous position of the Gas Research Board was resolved by acceptance of an offer by the Gas Council to take over all its assets and personnel. A suitable site for the new Midlands Research Centre—concerned primarily with the development of high-pressure catalytic processes of gas manufacture—was found in an obsolescent, but still operational, gas-works at Solihull. The Council were fortunate in appointing as its first director F. J. Dent, a very distinguished scientist who had initially embarked on his academic career in the Department of Fuel at Leeds University, which had already a close connection with the gas industry. Dent did brilliant work at Solihull which led to his election as a Fellow of the Royal Society, a highly prized distinction, in 1967. His remarkable career has been recorded at some length by Sir Kenneth Hutchison and D. H. Hebden [2]. Sir Kenneth himself was closely identified with major developments in the technology of the new gas industry and was also elected a Fellow of the Royal Society (1966); he was Deputy Chairman of the Gas Council 1960–66.

Thus the nationalised gas industry's acquired and created research facilities were established in four main centres, each complementing the other but having different fields of work. Watson House (1926) concerned itself with the use of gas in the domestic, catering and commercial fields. The London Research Station (1928) looked after scientific aspects of the manufacture, storage, and distribution of coal-gas. Both these were inherited from the old Gas Light and Coke Company. The Midlands Research Station became responsible for the use of gas in industry and for the development of high-pressure gasification processes, especially those involving catalysis. Later, the Engineering Research Station at Killingworth, Newcastle upon Tyne, was developed to deal with problems arising in connection with oil reformers.

COMPLETE GASIFICATION

The idea of utilising low-grade coal for gas manufacture by processes that gasified it completely, instead of leaving a residue of coke and tar, was not novel; as early as 1898 C. B. Tully and V. B. Lewes patented a 'methane–hydrogen' plant which used coal tar as a carburetting medium in a modified water-gas generator. Between 1918 and 1921 Tully built some 150 small complete gasification plants in Britain [3]. On the Continent, the Semet-Solvay Company introduced plant in which low-grade coal was interspersed between layers of coke to overcome difficulties due to coking: however, such processes made little impact because, apart from technical difficulties of operation, the gas produced was of too low a calorific value to be directly useful.

The first successful complete gasification process was that developed by Lurgi in Germany in the 1930s [4]. This differed from its predecessors in certain important respects. Firstly, the coal was gasified by a mixture of superheated steam and oxygen. Secondly, it was a high-pressure process producing gas at 300–450 lb per square inch. Thirdly, it was a continuous process. In Germany the Lurgi process was used to gasify brown coal. To apply it to the black British coals required considerable modification. However, this was by no means foreign territory to British gas technologists. As early as 1920, at an Annual Meeting of the Institution of Gas Engineers, H. J. Hodsman and J. W. Cobb had presented a paper on 'Oxygen in Gas Production', which attracted a great deal of interest [5]. In this they discussed the possibility and economies of using oxygen and steam in the carbonisation of coal and in complete gasification.

In the Lurgi process two principal chemical reactions occur simultaneously. In the producer gas reaction carbon and oxygen combine to form carbon monoxide. In the water gas reaction carbon and steam combine to form carbon monoxide and hydrogen. The raw gas leaving the Lurgi reactor consists largely of hydrogen, with about 25 per cent of carbon monoxide, together with a little methane formed as a result of secondary reactions. The presence of carbon monoxide in gas is objectionable because it is a dangerous and insidious poison, a disturbing frequent cause of death by suicide or accident in the days of coal gas manufacture. The removal of carbon monoxide from the low-pressure gas produced by conventional carbonisation was not feasible, but high-pressure Lurgi gas was quite a different proposition. In the presence of a catalyst at about 800°C the carbon monoxide will combine with steam to form carbon dioxide and hydrogen: this is known as the water gas shift reaction. The carbon dioxide, an incombustible diluent, can be removed by passing the gas through an alkaline solution. The gas must also be dried and treated for removal of traces of hydrogen sulphide and for recovery of benzole. While the Lurgi process gives a good clean gas at high pressure it could not, for two reasons, be used as a simple alternative to town gas produced by the traditional carbonisation process. Firstly, its high hydrogen content gives it a rather low calorific value, about 400 btu per cubic foot. Secondly, it has, for the same reason, a very low specific gravity, about 0.28. The calorific value can be increased by admixture of liquid petroleum gas (LPG) such as butane (calorific value about 3000) available from petroleum refineries, or natural gas (calorific value about 1000). The addition of these gases increases the specific gravity but not to the 0.5 level necessary to give the right Wobbe number (p. 58). To achieve this, some 'ballast' gas must be included. This may be nitrogen, available from the air-liquefaction plant that normally provides the oxygen, or carbon dioxide, provided by simply not removing all that present in the original gas.

The successful operation of the Lurgi process demands the availability of oxygen in tonnage quantities, which was not easily attainable in pre-war years. After the war, with the wider demand for oxygen, especially in steel making, the situation was very different. In 1952 the Ministry of Power pointed out to the Gas Council and the Scottish Gas Board that there was in Scotland a large deposit of open-cast coal (Bogside coal) that might be suitable for use in a Lurgi plant. Preliminary trials at Lurgi's test plant at Oberhausen-Holten in Germany were successful and a contract was made with the National Coal Board for the supply of coal to a site at Westfield adjacent to the Scottish coalfield, on which the construction of a Lurgi-type plant began in 1958. It consisted of four Lurgi gasifiers, three of which were in use at any given time, and had a capacity of 40 million cubic feet per day. It required 200 tons of oxygen per day for its operation, and there was a storage capacity for 550 tons of liquid oxygen. The plant became operational at the end of 1960 and continued until June 1974, when the area it served was converted to natural gas [6]. (See Plate 13.)

The active role of Westfield was not ended, however. As early as 1972 its facilities and expertise had led a consortium of American companies to choose it as a centre for an experimental study of the manufacture of substitute natural gas (SNG) by a modification of the Lurgi process. This reflected a fundamental difference between the American and British fuel situations. By 1970, the USA was concerned about the availability of natural gas to supply the growing demand of her million-mile transmission and distribution system. Vast quantities of natural gas were being used to generate electricity and for other non-premium purposes inappropriate in the circumstances. It was clear that one possibility for making up the deficit would be the gasification of coal by a process capable of yielding gas rich in methane (SNG).

In Britain, a second Lurgi plant was built at Coleshill, near Birmingham, but in 1969 it was decided to close this down as oil gasification proved to be more economic. The Lurgi period, was therefore, a relatively brief one but processes of this type may well be revived when, as is ultimately inevitable, supplies of North Sea gas prove inadequate to meet demand. Under present circumstances it has certain disadvantages, though these may be less relevant two or three decades hence. Basically it is a relatively expensive process, both in terms of capital cost of plant and of the steam and oxygen required to run it. Although it does not demand the high quality coking-coals required for conventional carbonisation, it is not the case that any kind of cheap coal can be used. Further, the coal used must be crushed and graded. Finally, the large amount of steam results in very dilute effluents, the disposal of which presents problems. Research at Solihull and Westfield, however, indicates that in the so-called slagging gasifier wider ranges of coal quality and size are possible and the volume of effluent can be much reduced.

In the event, gas technology in the post-war years began to move in quite a different direction. Pre-war Britain had rather little petroleum refining capacity but after the war the situation changed rapidly. The refineries could offer very large quantities of volatile hydrocarbons potentially suitable as gaseous fuels. The British chemical industry, long dependent on coal-tar, was rapidly moving away from this and utilising petroleum as its principal raw material for organic substances—dyes, drugs, plastics, and many others. In so doing it was devising new processes and new techniques for handling petroleum feedstocks. The gas and chemical industries were to remain firmly linked, but now the link was increasingly through petroleum and not coal-tar.

At Billingham, Imperial Chemical Industries required enormous quantities of hydrogen for the synthesis of ammonia by the Haber-Bosch process; this ammonia was needed mainly for the manufacture of artificial fertilisers. Originally, the hydrogen was made by passing steam over coke, but after the war a completely different steam-reforming process was introduced. In this, the raw material was light distillate, consisting of volatile hydrocarbons obtained as a product of petroleum refining. At a pressure of 20–30 atmospheres, and a temperature of 700–900°C, in the presence of a catalyst, the light distillate will combine with steam to produce hydrogen, carbon dioxide, carbon monoxide, and small amounts of methane. As in the Lurgi reaction, the carbon monoxide can be removed by converting it to dioxide in the water-gas shift reaction. The reaction is strongly endothermic; that is to say, it requires heat to keep it going. This heat can be provided by burning some additional light distillate.

The final product is a 'lean' gas rich in hydrogen. For the purpose of ammonia synthesis this is just what is required, but as an alternative to coal gas the calorific value and Wobbe number are both too low, as with Lurgi gas. Two solutions to this problem are possible. Firstly, as with Lurgi gas, the appropriate degree of enrichment can be achieved by addition of butane or propane (LPG). Alternatively, the hydrogen can be used in a further process, the catalytic rich gas (CRG) process, first operated at the Bromley-by-Bow gas-works of the North Thames Gas Board. (See Plate 18.) Other plants were subsequently constructed in Britain and also built under licence in foreign countries—including Italy and Japan.

The CRG process, developed at the Midlands Research Station, resembles the ICI continuous reforming process but is carried out at a lower temperature, around 500–550°C. A consequence of this is that whereas the ICI process requires small diameter reformer tubes heated in a furnace the CRG process can be carried out in a vessel of very much larger diameter with no external heating.

Alternatively, the rich gas can be weakened by subjecting it to steam reforming, or to what is called the pre-heat/re-heat process. In the latter the methane-rich gas is first subjected to some catalytic reforming at about 750°C, and then to further reforming at a slightly lower temperature (720°C) in a separate reactor.

Basically, all the above processes depend upon the gasification of light petroleum distillate by reaction with super-heated steam in the presence of a catalyst [7]. An alternative is to combine the distillate with hydrogen—which might be lean gas from a reformer—at high pressures and temperatures (750°C). Under these conditions the hydrogenated distillate molecules will break down into simpler gaseous ones, mainly methane and ethane. Under properly controlled conditions this so-called gas recycle hydrogenerator (GRH) process, also developed by Dent at the Midlands Research Station, will produce a rich gas that can be blended with lean ones to produce a satisfactorily burnable mixture. The first GRH plant in Britain was built at Avonmouth, near Bristol, in 1965, and was followed by others. Three were built under licence in Germany.

This determined move away from coal towards petroleum had far-reaching consequences which the National Coal Board cannot have foreseen. Even without the advent of North Sea gas it was rapidly changing the whole face of the industry. The new processes had very important intrinsic advantages [6]. They were both technically better and provided a cheaper gas. On the first count, we may note that the exclusive use of gas and liquid feedstocks, and the absence of solid by-products, enabled full advantage to be taken of the highly sophisticated techniques of the chemical and petroleum-refining industries. The new plants were much more compact than those based on coal, occupying little more than one-tenth of the space. The low carbon monoxide content made the gas much safer. Overall the economics were very favourable: gas could be made from oil at approximately half the cost of that made from coal.

The implications for the gas industry's nationalised partner—the National Coal Board—were serious. In 1947, the last year before nationalisation, the gas industry carbonised $22\frac{1}{2}$ million tons of coal, costing £57 million [9]. Far from having a more or less captive customer, the Coal Board now faced the prospect of losing (on 1947 figures) nearly one-eighth of its total sales. Indeed, the prospect was rather worse. Cheaper and better gas could eat into other markets. The domestic consumer would turn away from the open coal fire and solid-fuel boiler; if gas were preferred to electricity, less coal would be required by the power stations. The nationalised electricity industry, too, had cause for concern. Thus not overnight, but over a relatively short period of years, the seemingly moribund gas industry was showing remarkable signs of vitality.

Nevertheless, the way ahead was not easy. Technical improvements in the manufacture of gas had to be matched by comparable improvements in salesmanship and promotion and the development of efficient and attractive appliances. Further, the industry was constrained by its own past. As we have noticed earlier (p. 44) gas had to be produced to a strict specification: essentially a calorific value of at least 500 Btu per cubic foot, a Wobbe number of about 730, and a flame speed factor of about 40. The tens of millions of existing appliances would function satisfactorily only if supplied with gas complying closely with this specification. As we have seen, the new processes required modification and blending of their products to make them conform to these standards: Lurgi gas was too lean and CRG gas too rich. The problem was to become more acute, and call for a major policy decision, with the advent of North Sea gas.

The distribution of gas produced from a variety of sources presented the gas industry with difficult technical and administrative problems. Initially, it had to provide gas made by coal carbonisation, yielding coke as a disposable by-product, with a growing contribution from Lurgi and oil-based gas which produced no coke. As late as 1960, 90 per cent of gas still came from coal. Then it had to make provision for utilisation, from 1959, of a certain amount of imported natural gas. In the 1960s an increasing amount of gas came from new CRG and GRH processes. Then North Sea gas began to flow into the system. Not until the late 1970s was the industry back in a situation where it was based virtually entirely on one type of gas only.

But these relatively golden years lay far ahead. Of gas manufacture in the early 1950s it has been recorded that:

the industry was in a difficult situation. Its image was honest but old-fashioned, dull and dirty. Its competitive position was critical, with costs rising as a result of a selective coal pricing structure. Its primary product was regarded as expensive, and its secondary fuel, coke, looked upon as a second-rate substitute for coal despite the capability of the new coke grates to burn it outstandingly well. The need was for a new breed of appliances, with a new standard of efficiency and of convenience, and for new processes for gas production to break the stranglehold of coal upon the industry [10].

In 1952 an unforeseen, and unforeseeable, event gave unexpected encouragement to the gas industry in general and its research and development activities in particular. In December of that year London—long notorious for its peasoup fogs—was stricken with a dense smog lasting 45 hours. In this, the ordinary discomfort and inconvenience of fog were accentuated by an accumulation of irritant chemicals largely attributable to the burning of raw coal. The smog caused many human deaths, especially among elderly people subject to asthma and bronchitis, to say nothing of animals brought to London at that time for the annual Smithfield Show. This disaster led to the setting up of the Beaver Committee on Pollution (1953/4) and subsequently to the Clean Air Act (1957) which gave a considerable incentive to the use of smokeless fuels. Its cleanliness was a feature of gas that the industry had always stressed, and this episode directed public attention to the importance of this.

WATSON HOUSE

In 1954 the death of G. C. Holliday, who had been Manager of the Watson House Laboratories since 1950, led to the appointment of L. W. Andrew as his successor, with somewhat increased responsibilities. At the same time, changes at Fulham necessitated, in 1954, re-location of the Coke Laboratory, still busy enough, though, for those who could read the writing on the wall, the transition from coal to oil meant that eventually there would be no more coke. For the moment, however, the Clean Air Act had helped to promote the sale of coke. The new Coke Laboratory was adjacent to Watson House, and plans were made for further expansion on the same site to give extra accommodation for the Industrial Laboratory and for an Aerodynamics Laboratory which would work on the design of flues and other problems of gas-flow. In the event, these plans did not materialise, as the North Thames Board, which was administratively responsible, decided to move Watson House to a new building to be erected on a site at the junction of Carnwath Road and Peterborough Road. The plans for the new laboratory were completed by the beginning of 1958 but last-minute changes—resulting from the decision of the North Thames Board to utilise some of the space for a new computer centre—meant that staff, by then numbering over 150, could not begin to move in until the autumn of 1961. The new laboratory was not formally inaugurated until November 1963, when the Duke of Edinburgh performed the opening ceremony.

In passing, we may note that in accordance with its improved prospects and new nationalised status, the gas industry was exercising a mild patronage of the arts. For the design of the new exhibition centre at Watson House in 1951 they called on the services of an independent industrial design consultant, Mr Misha Black, who subsequently had an exceedingly distinguished career in this field. In 1959 he was appointed Professor of Industrial Design in the Royal College of Art and he was knighted in 1972. The exterior of the new Watson House was embellished by 29 large mural panels designed by the versatile artist John Piper, whose many outstanding achievements include the windows for the new Coventry Cathedral (1962), and the King George VI Memorial Chapel, Windsor (1969). The percipience of the industry's leaders was clearly not limited to trends in gas technology.

The move to new premises was quickly followed by an internal reorganisation, which formed part of the Gas Council's re-appraisal of the role of research and development within the industry. Three Divisions were established at Watson House—Research, Development, and Approvals Testing. Only the Coke Laboratory, whose days were numbered, was excluded from the new organisation.

By this time, the first small shipments of liquid-methane gas had arrived in Britain from Louisiana (1959), and the discovery of vast deposits of natural gas at Slochteren in Holland in the same year presaged the exploitation of the North Sea. Increasingly, gas utilisation research concerned itself with natural gas, to which we shall come in the next chapter. We may perhaps appropriately conclude this reference to Watson House by quoting its own assessment of its major achievements [11] even though this takes us a little beyond the period of our present concern:

1. A detailed understanding of the factors affecting the safe and satisfactory combustion of a wide variety of gases and hence the ability to predict for other gases with a fair degree of certainty. This achievement has made us world leaders in knowledge of the inter-changeability of gases, and has played a major part in our own industry's discussions on conversion to natural gas and on the acceptability of gas-making processes.
2. A knowledge of the fundamentals of ignition—whether by pilot, hot wire or spark—so that gas can be safely and satisfactorily ignited, and proprietary devices assessed.
3. An understanding of flues, and particularly of natural gas flues, leading on the one hand to the safe and successful evacuation of products in a wide variety of buildings and on the other, to keeping the majority of dwellings in gas supply areas available to the domestic gas sales force.
4. The evolution of appliance standards and installation Codes, and the establishment of a sound body of knowledge on appliance design have raised the norm of appliance construction and performance to a high standard and have led to an Approval/Certification role which is the envy of every other fuel industry in this country and of every Gas Industry in the World.
5. The technical basis for converting Great Britain from manufactured to natural gas was developed in a very short time, and this—coupled with education of Regions and appliance makers, schemes for appliance identification, and the testing and approval of our 5,000 conversion sets—made speedy and successful conversion possible.

Lest this catalogue of success should seem unduly complacent, the same report [11] lists a number of failures. One was the attempt to evolve a reliable cold-start ignition catalyst. Another was the effort to develop a thermostatically controlled multipoint water heater: technical success was achieved but the equipment never reached the market. Another failure was in developing gas-fire radiants that were not fragile to handle and easily broken in use. Last, but not least, it is recorded that:

One of the greatest shocks ever received by the domestic utilisation side of the industry was the realisation that conversion to natural gas meant abandoning the non-aerated flame upon which so much of the market success of manufactured town gas in the 1950s had been built. Intensive efforts were made to provide a similar flame from natural gas, and a moderate level of technical success achieved. However, it eventually became clear that any new non-aerated burner would have limited tolerance to variations in gas quality, and moreover demanded production tolerances that even the most modern techniques could not economically meet.

These developments in gas technology have been considered at some length because they were an essential factor in restoring the fortunes of the industry. Their historical significance is, therefore, very great; but while such achievements were a pre-requisite for renaissance, they were by no means sufficient in themselves. Their success could be exploited only by correspondingly vigorous marketing policy and sales promotion, and we must now turn our attention to the situation that the nationalised industry had inherited.

PRICE POLICY

Price policy in the gas industry had always been very complex, mainly because even if the most profitable commercial strategy could be clearly discerned—in itself no easy task—social and political considerations usually made its implementation virtually impossible. We have seen in earlier chapters how, virtually from the beginning, the industry was subject to statutory regulations in respect of the prices it could charge and the dividends it could pay. As a public utility, the gas industry was obliged to fulfil certain social obligations which might run quite contrary to commercial considerations. These difficulties are very real, but they do not fully explain the very diverse pricing policy that characterised the industry prior to the Second World War. The complexities of this in the pre-war industry have been skilfully unravelled by P. Chantler [12].

We need not here concern ourselves with the problems of distinguishing between the various relevant items of cost in the manufacture of gas: basically service or consumer costs, manufacturing capacity costs, distribution costs, and commodity costs. The boundary between these is often difficult to distinguish and this makes it impossible to determine 'the theoretically correct rate' which some analysts sought with almost the same fervour as alchemists sought the philosopher's stone. As Chantler tersely remarks: 'price policy is designed primarily to sell gas, not to mirror costs, allocated in some more or less arbitrary manner'.

As long as the industry had an essentially monopolistic position as a supplier of gas for lighting, a flat-rate system of charging was appropriate, but with the advent and ultimate dominance of electric lighting, and the need to find new and larger outlets for gas as a domestic and industrial fuel, changes were needed to encourage new customers. Nevertheless, the changes—essentially a system of differential charges to encourage greater use—were introduced far too slowly; the flat-rate continued long after the circumstances that had engendered it had disappeared. Up to 1934, admittedly, most Gas Acts had limited discounts for large consumers to 15 per cent, but the Gas Undertakings Act of that year removed most of the difficulty. Under this Act, undertakings were obliged to supply consumers at a 'published price' but they were free to offer two-part tariffs, or other promotional rates, to individual customers. In effect, they were given considerable latitude to revise their charges downwards, but no powers to revise them upwards above the published price. This was a major bone of contention, for all suppliers complained that they had many customers who, for one reason or another consumed so little gas that their bills failed to cover the cost of supply.

To cover such cases, the undertakings wanted to impose a minimum quarterly charge before supply began to be paid for, but the Board of Trade would have none of this. The Parliamentary Secretary, explaining why this concession could not be included in the 1934 Act, made no secret of the reasons for the refusal:

I am not attempting to justify the exclusion of the minimum charge . . . on any ground of logic or technicality. I am doing it entirely on the political argument that the Government are not prepared to face the opposition that would necessarily come from people in scattered places, amounting to millions in total, who would never understand the reasons behind a clause of this kind [13].

This conflict between political expediency and commercial interest continues to bedevil the gas industry, and other nationalised industries, to the present time.

The relatively few undertakings which sought to take advantage of the new Act encountered difficulties. Thus the South Metropolitan, in 1936, introduced a new scale of charges replacing the flat rate of $8\frac{3}{4}d$. per therm by a three-stage scale according to which the consumer paid $11d$. per therm for the first 10 therms, diminishing ultimately to $4d$. per therm. This and similar tariffs were publicised as 'Half-Price Gas'. This, of course, bore hard on the small consumer but though the South Metropolitan argued (though not entirely convincingly) that the small consumer is not synonymous with the poor consumer they had to bow to popular outcry and abandon the new scales, reverting to the old flat-rate. One consequence of this episode was the setting up of a Joint Committee of the House of Lords and the House of Commons on Gas Prices [13], but though this accepted the principle of a minimum charge this was still not sanctioned. The gas undertakings were still obliged to supply many customers who cost more than they paid. This was economically serious, in that although the industrial load was growing, the domestic consumer still took, over the country as a whole, some 80 per cent of all gas made. Nevertheless, the industry persevered with block tariffs, which had the general effect of reducing the rise in price to the householder as he increased his consumption. By 1936/7 some fifty undertakings were offering two-part tariffs, many of them taking account of such factors at rateable value, number of rooms, floor area, and so on [14]. Some included a 'summer differential' to encourage use—for hot-water systems, for example—in the warmer months. There were almost as many variations as there were undertakings involved. With industrial and commercial consumers, taking relatively large volumes of gas, contracts could be concluded on an *ad hoc* basis.

SALES PROMOTION

These tariff variations were, of course, all designed to encourage a greater use of gas. With the same end in mind, the industry began to take steps to promote sales by advertising and various public relations exercises [15]. One of the first to advocate this was the versatile and energetic Sir Francis Goodenough, who entered the service of the Gas Light and Coke Company in 1888; from 1903–31 he was Controller of Gas Sales. Among his many outside interests was the Incorporated Society of British Advertisers, of which he was President 1933–36. As early as 1907, at a meeting of the Institution of Gas Engineers in Dublin, he argued that gas managers were wrong to restrict their interest to the making of gas; they should also concern themselves with promoting sales to the public. Following this, the British Commercial Gas Association (BCGA) was formed in 1911, supported by subscriptions from most undertakings, with the principal objective of promoting gas-heating. Sir Francis was its Executive Chairman from 1912–36. The outbreak of war in 1914 effectively halted the Association's activities, but in the 1920s it became active again and introduced a short-lived advertising character known as *Mr G. A. Service*. This may well have inspired the very much more successful *Mr Therm*, originally devised by the commercial artist Eric Fraser for the Gas Light and Coke Company. This was adopted by other undertakings and by the BCGA; 'Mr Therm burns to serve you' ranks among the best known advertising slogans of all time [15]. Press advertising was supported by practical demonstrations of the use of gas, directed at particular consumer groups. Among the most popular of these were cooking demonstrations for housewives, staged in local gas showrooms. From time to time there were national sales drives, such as National Gas Cooker Fortnight in the late 1930s. Today, such campaigns seem modest to a degree, but we must remember that in the 1930s advertising one's wares was only beginning to be respectable in Britain—though things were very different in the USA—and the uninhibited approach of modern times was undreamt of.

Gas is useless without appliances in which to burn it, and separate publicity campaigns were organised by manufacturers of this type of equipment. On the whole, however, gas appliances were not so well promoted as electrical ones, as has been acknowledged within the industry [15]. One reason, no doubt, lay in the different organisations of the two industries. Though there were familiar names such as New World and Ascot, the manufacturers of gas appliances did not, in general, command the same resources as big electrical companies such as GEC, Hoover, English Electric, and Belling. A second reason was the different organisation of the retail

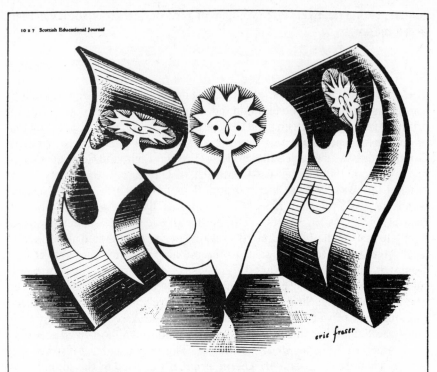

10 x 7   Scottish Educational Journal

eric fraser

'FLEXIBLE' IS MY MIDDLE NAME! says Mr. Therm

The gas and gas-heated equipment that Mr. Therm brings in his train are amazingly flexible in their applications to all sorts of heating problems. What other fuel but gas could give you a tiny — but steady — pin-point of flame or full heat the instant you want it? And gas can be controlled at the flick of a finger — or can be completely automatic if required. It needs no storage space, is smokeless and ash-free, and works unfailingly for you with remarkable efficiency. No wonder Mr. Therm is to be found hard at work in so many industries!

Top class cook

School meals go down well when Mr. Therm's in charge of the cooking! At Manland School, Harpenden, the gas-equipped kitchen has to be capable of serving about five hundred and fifty hot lunches every day. A man-sized job — and Mr. Therm's just the man for it!

MR. THERM BURNS TO SERVE YOU   THE GAS COUNCIL · I GROSVENOR PLACE · LONDON · SWI

Fig. 18. Mr Therm—devised by Eric Fraser—was one of the best known characters in British advertising. Introduced by the Gas Light and Coke Company, he was equally acceptable to the Gas Council.

markets for the two industries. The main outlets for gas appliances were the local showrooms of gas undertakings, which also undertook installation—a job requiring some skill and experience—and maintenance. The appliance manufacturers tended, therefore, to look to the gas undertakings to take the lead in promotion. In the electrical industry things were very different. Roughly speaking there were about as many electricity showrooms as ones for gas, but in addition there were thousands of important retail outlets ranging from small local shops to big department stores. Most appliances—except large cookers—needed no special installation, being simply plugged into the existing circuit.

The manufacturers of appliances suffered not only from the fragmentation of the industry but from reluctance to co-operate: the technical men of the different firms were not encouraged to communicate with each other. After the First World War some re-grouping occurred, leading, among other things, to the formation of Radiation Limited, a merger of six existing firms under the initiative of James Yates. Outside Radiation were such firms as R. & A. Main of Falkirk; Sidney Flavel of Leamington; Cannon Iron Foundries, near Bilston; and the Vulcan Stove Company at Exeter.

Rather slowly, improvements in both design and performance took place, and increasing attention was paid to the appearance of the products taking advantage, in particular, of stove enamelling processes. Main produced the first completely enamelled cooker in 1927. Among important technical innovations was the rod-type gas thermostat, a German patent annexed by Britain in 1919. Under the name Regulo it was introduced by Radiation, but was not welcomed by housewives: today, of course, no cooker lacking a thermostat would be acceptable. (See Plate 10.) The New World oven had a single burner and a flue outlet at the back. For gas fires the design of the refractory elements was improved and research was undertaken to reduce the hissing noise of the flame, a constant cause for complaint. Gas governors to control the pressure began to be fitted to individual appliances, instead of relying on control at source: variations in gas pressure were a frequent source of trouble, especially on Sunday mornings. A minor, but useful, innovation was the spring-loaded tap.

During the war, advertising generally was reduced to a minimum; mainly to institutional advertising designed to show how gas was assisting the war effort, advice on economical cooking, and so on. In the immediate post-war years the gas industry did little to promote itself. Apart from being in a rundown state, and still with a highly fragmented organisation, the stimulation of demand by advertisement would, in many areas, have been an embarrassment, because it was proving difficult enough to supply even existing consumers. Additionally, the government discouraged promotional advertising. Mr Therm was still a familiar figure, accompanying slogans such as 'Public Servant No. 1'. A good deal of stress was laid on the virtues of gas in preventing atmospheric pollution, to which London's smog disaster of 1952 had directed public attention.

Not until 1957/8 were nationally co-ordinated campaigns launched, with hire-purchase facilities and trade-in allowances the main incentives to the buyer. In the early 1960s Shell made a determined bid to promote central heating in Britain with their 'Mrs 1970' campaign, designed to persuade the public that this was no longer a luxury but a normal domestic amenity. The gas industry was quick to realise the potential of this new outlet and the promotion of central heating was given high priority in marketing. The 'High Speed Gas' campaign was launched in 1963, designed primarily to give gas a new image as an efficient and increasingly popular fuel. The campaign was based initially on newspaper and hoarding advertisements, embodying such cartoon characters as Whizzigas and Get-up-and-go-gas. The following year the resources of television were heavily utilised, with emphasis on gas central heating and radiant convector gas fires [16].

The High Speed Gas campaign was timed to coincide with a change of fortune in the gas industry. In the decade following nationalisation, the price of coal had been steadily increasing—the average price received by the NCB was £2 per ton in 1947, and over £4 in 1957—and the competition from electricity had been severe. Thus from 1950 to 1957 the average price of electricity had risen from 1.346d. to 1.581d. per unit, or $17\frac{1}{2}$ per cent. Over the same seven-year period the average price of gas went up from 14.8d. to 22.34d. per therm, or 51 per cent [17]. Moreover, while sales of gas had been more or less static over these years, sales of electricity had almost doubled, with the highest increase in the industrial field. However, the technological developments we have discussed earlier changed the economic basis. With the development of new methods of gas manufacture, the importation of liquid gas from the Sahara, and a more realistic marketing policy, the gas industry could feel—even before the advent of North Sea gas—that the way ahead was easier.

To understand the recent history of the gas industry in Britain it is essential to realise that in the 1950s it was not being driven into new technologies and new business methods by force of circumstances, but was actively pursuing them as a matter of deliberate policy. North Sea gas was not the crucial incentive. This position was very clearly expressed by Sir Henry Jones in his Presidential Address to the Institution of Gas Engineers in 1957:

If a large supply of natural gas was found in this country expansion in the sale of gas would soon occur. In its absence, there is a challenge to the Members of this Institution, engineers and scientists, to create the processes and build the plants to make it possible for gas made from coal and oil or from imported natural gas to be supplied on terms which ensure a substantial increase in its use and consequently an improvement of fuel utilisation by the nation. [18]

It was this positive drive that put the industry in a position to take full advantage of North Sea gas when the opportunity arose. But for these developments the industry would have lacked credibility. The Continental Shelf Act (Ch. 16) might not have included the requirement to offer gas on a 'first refusal' basis to the gas industry and the producing companies might not have accepted that it could market all the gas contracted for.

REFERENCES

[1] *Report of the Committee on National Policy for the use of Fuel and Power Resources*, Cmd. 8647, HMSO, London (1952).
[2] HUTCHISON, W. K. and HEBDEN, D. *Biographical Memoirs of Fellows of the Royal Society*, Vol. 20, pp. 155–80 (1974).
[3] MARSDEN, A. SCI Jubilee Memorial Lecture, *Chemistry and Industry*, 1678–1731 (1955).
[4] WILSON, D. Scott. *The Modern Gas Industry*, pp. 14–19, Edward Arnold, London (1969).
[5] BRAUNHOLTZ, Walter T. K. *The First Hundred Years: 1863–1963*, p. 101, Institution of Gas Engineers, London (1963).
[6] HEBDEN, D. and BROOKS, C. T. *Westfield—the Development of Processes for the Production of SNG from Coal*, Communication 988, Institution of Gas Engineers, London (1976).
[7] DENT, F. J. *Principles of the New Gas-making Processes*, Gas Council Midland Research Station, Solihull (n.d.) *Idem.* Hydrogasification of Coal, *Coke and Gas*, **23**, 4 (1961).
[8] WILSON, D. SCOTT. op. cit., p. 33.
[9] *The Gas Industry: Facts and Figures*, p. 17, The Gas Council, London (1948).
[10] *Watson House 1926–1976*, p. 67, British Gas, London (1976).
[11] *Watson House 1926–1976*, p. 50, Communication 998, Institution of Gas Engineers, London (1976).
[12] CHANTLER, P. *The British Gas Industry; an Economic Study*, pp. 107–32, Manchester University Press, Manchester (1938).
[13] *Report by Joint Committee of the House of Lords and the House of Commons on Gas Prices*, HMSO, London (1937).
[14] CHANTLER, P. op. cit., pp. 124–5.
[15] CHALK, W. K. Crampton. A Century of Advertising, *Gas Journal Centenary Volume, 1949*, p. 133, King, London (1949).
[16] MAUNDER, C. L. 'Reflections on a Working Lifetime in Gas Publicity'. Paper presented to Yorkshire Junior Gas Association, 10 November 1976.
[17] KELF-COHEN, R. *Nationalisation in Britain*, pp. 118–19, Macmillan, London (1958).
[18] JONES, H. F. H. *Gas World*, p. 1043, 18 May 1957.

BIBLIOGRAPHY

DENT, F. J. Experience in Gasification Research, Melchett Lecture 1965, *Journal of the Institute of Fuel* (May 1966).
ELGIN, D. C. and PERKS, H. R. *Gasification of U.S. Coals at Westfield, Scotland*, Communication 946, Institution of Gas Engineers, London (1974).
LOM, W. L. and WILLIAMS, A. F. *Substitute Natural Gas: Manufacture and Properties.* Applied Science, Barking (1976).

B.P. Trading Ltd., *Gasmaking*, London (1959).

B.P. Trading Ltd., *Gasmaking and Natural Gas*, London (1972).

The Gas Industry and the Environment: a Symposium of the United Nations Economic Commission for Europe (1977). Published for the United Nations by Pergamon Press, Oxford (1978).

HEBDEN, D. and BROOKS, C. T. *Westfield—the Development of Processes for the Production of SNG from Coal*, Communication 938, Institution of Gas Engineers, London (1976).

15

Natural Gas

In the first chapter of this book passing reference was made to the use of natural gas by the Chinese some two thousand years ago, and to Marco Polo's account of the burning of natural gas at Baku. Much later, in the eighteenth century, proposals were made to use inflammable gas (fire-damp) from coal mines to light the streets of Whitehaven. These early uses of natural gas were of negligible importance in themselves; nevertheless, they may have served a useful purpose in promoting the early gas industry by giving a preliminary indication of the possibilities of gaseous fuel. In the event, however, it was the natural product and not the manufactured one that was to dominate the gas industry and we must, therefore, now pick up the threads of this remarkable technological development.

NATURAL GAS OVERSEAS

Although natural gas had long been used in a limited and irregular way in many places, the origin of the modern industry undoubtedly lies in the USA. In the petroleum districts of Pennsylvania and adjacent states gas occurs fairly freely at depths of 500 to 2000 feet. The first utilisation of this was in 1821, when a gas well was drilled at Fredonia some 45 miles south-west of Buffalo and three miles from Lake Erie. It supplied sufficient gas to light the streets and it is recorded that in 1824, when Lafeyette revisited America at the invitation of Congress, this gas was piped to the local inn at which he was staying. Not until 1858, however, was the Fredonia Gas Light and Water Works formally established: this was the world's first natural gas corporation. In 1870, an attempt was made at Bloomfield to convey natural gas through a 20-mile main but this failed, chiefly because of excessive leakage from the pinewood pipes used. Two years later natural gas was fed into the mains of the Rochester Gas Company, but this venture, too, was short-lived. Not until 1873, at Titusville, was natural gas satisfactorily supplied to consumers: this involved an iron main some four miles long. Thereafter, progress was rapid, even though preoccupation with the winning of oil led many petroleum companies to allow associated natural gas to burn to waste in flares. Nevertheless, T. E. Thorpe [1] reported that in 1887 'The neighbourhood of Pittsburg, Pennsylvania, is the most important locality for natural gas. Six companies supply the gas for that city; they have 107 wells and transport the gas through 500 miles of pipes, delivering 250 million cubic feet of gas in one day . . . The amount of coal displaced by gas in

1866 was 6 353 000 tons.' This early reference by Thorpe sounds a warning that has caused increasing anxiety in recent years: 'It has been found that the supply of gas in a reservoir is limited; some of the smaller ones have already been exhausted.' However, he ends on a more cheerful note: 'a gas-well at Cambia, Ohio, has been blowing for twenty years without any apparent diminution in the supply'.

At this time, America had also a well-established coal-gas industry on the European pattern. As early as 1816 the city of Baltimore approved a scheme for lighting the streets by gas. Other cities followed suit, and gas began to be used to light public buildings, but the domestic use of gas lighting made slow progress until about 1865; at about the same time gas began to be used for cooking, especially after the Centennial Exhibition at Philadelphia in 1876. As in Britain, the advent of electric lighting was a severe blow, but one that ultimately proved beneficial by directing the efforts of the gas industry into the profitable fields of domestic, commercial, and industrial heating. In the twentieth century the American gas industry grew rapidly, though natural gas steadily gained the ascendancy over manufactured gas. This was made possible by the development of a nationwide network of high pressure mains. Some features of this, as recorded by a British Gas Industry Productivity Team which visited the USA in 1952, indicates the magnitude of the industry that had been built up on the basis of domestic natural gas.

The dominance of natural gas is indicated by the following figures [2]:

TOTAL GAS UTILITY SALES USA 1935–1950 (MILLIONS OF THERMS)

Year	Natural	Manufactured	Mixed	Liquefied petroleum	Total
1935	10 635	1610	678	–	12 923
1940	14 681	1688	866	–	17 235
1945	22 503	2087	1194	23	25 867
1950	38 500	2217	1284	90	42 090

It will be seen that while sales of natural gas almost quadrupled over the above fifteen year period, sales of manufactured gas rose by only 27 per cent; moreover, natural gas commanded over 90 per cent of total sales. It was reported that in 1955 one new gas well was being brought into production in America every 23 minutes. Against this, 7000 dry holes (over one-third of the total) were drilled in 1951 [3]. Twenty years later, however, the American industry was sufficiently concerned about the exhaustion of natural gas supplies to commission, in Britain, research and development work on improved methods of manufacturing gas from coal (p. 125), and also to build SNG plants using the CRG process.

These vast sales could not have been achieved without a correspondingly large distribution system. The same Report records that in 1951 there existed in the USA 115 000 miles of transmission mains for conveying natural gas from the fields to gas companies; this did not include 35 000 miles of field and gathering mains. Over and above this, the supply companies had their own network of mains to supply consumers; one of these alone had over 7000 miles of pipe. Perhaps the biggest achievement up to that time, however, was the pipeline of the Trans-Continental Gas Pipeline Corporation. This had then been lately completed (1951) to transport natural gas from the vast reserves on the Texas–Louisiana Gulf Coast to the high-demand areas around Philadelphia, New Jersey, and New York. The pipeline was 1840 miles long and 30 inches in diameter. It worked at a pressure of 800 pounds per square inch (nearly seven times the maximum then current for high-pressure mains in Britain) maintained by 19 compressor stations. In urban areas, however, the working pressure was generally limited to 200 pounds per square inch for safety reasons. It was of welded steel construction throughout, and it was claimed that despite the very high pressure, gas losses were negligible. Major engineering problems had to be solved in its construction. These included a 4678-foot suspension bridge in Louisiana, carrying two 30-inch pipelines, and a 6500 foot underwater crossing to supply New York. The Productivity Team remarked that 'if substantial volumes of natural gas at high pressures were found in this country, it would be necessary to follow the American practice of frequent pipeline leakage surveys if pipelines operating at very high pressures were to be used'. In the event, this situation did arise in Britain and the knowledge and experience of the American gas industry was a most valuable guide.

While America thus decisively took the lead, certain other countries well-endowed with resources of natural gas also set about their systematic exploitation [4]. In Russia, for example, the Nobel brothers, Alfred and Ludwig, had set up the Nobel Brothers Naphtha Company in 1878 to develop oilfields around Baku in Azerbaijan, on the Caspian. Until the Second World War this remained the main centre of Russian oil production, accounting for nearly three-quarters of Russian production in 1939. Use was made of the associated gas at an early date, but systematic exploration after the war led to the discovery of tremendous new resources of both gas and oil in many parts of Russia; by 1965 Azerbaijan accounted for only 1 per cent of Russian production. A network of gas trunklines was established, which rose from 2273 kilometres in 1950 to 68 000 kilometres in 1971. In 1970 the output of natural gas in Russia was roughly the same as that in the USA in 1955. This provided a surplus for export not only to Eastern Bloc countries but eventually to Western European countries such as Italy and West Germany. At the same time, Russia began to import natural gas from Iran and Afghanistan, whose gasfields were not directly accessible to the west. Many of the Western European countries had themselves discovered indigenous sources of gas. The St Marcet field, some forty miles from Toulouse, was discovered in 1939, but the economically much more important Lacq field, also in the Aquitaine Basin, a few miles from Pau, did not come into operation until 1957.

NATURAL GAS IN BRITAIN

We need not consider these developments any further at this point, but it is important to note that the development of the natural gas industry in Britain went in parallel with major expansion of the industry in many parts of Europe in the post-war years. For half a century America was the pace-setter, but after the war Europe began to overhaul her rapidly.

From the general tone of their Report it is clear that in 1952 the British productivity team was greatly impressed by American practice. In particular, they were very conscious of the immense advantages conferred by the ready availability of natural gas. They therefore argued [5] that:

Although there are no appreciable known reserves of natural gas in Britain, a discovery of any magnitude would be of immense benefit to our national economy, and it is suggested that *prospecting, where there is any possible hope of success, should continue to receive vigorous support.*

At that time, however, not even the most optimistic and prescient member of the team could have foreseen that in less than two decades Britain would have such an abundance of natural gas that the manufacture of gas would be discontinued altogether. Nevertheless, despite the apparently disadvantageous position of Britain in the 1950s interest in natural gas was sustained. Firstly, trial drilling for underground oil and gas was continued on a modest scale; success had been sufficient to sustain a faint hope that in time commercially viable deposits might be located. Allied with this, some work was done on the possibility of extracting useful quantities of gas from coal mines. Secondly, and more immediately successfully, attention was directed to the possibility of importing liquefied natural gas into Britain in specially designed tankers.

Taking first the search for natural gas within the confines of the United Kingdom, it will be recalled that over a period of some three centuries surface leakages had been noted at various places, but these had been too small for commercial development to be considered seriously. Even before the Second World War, however, systematic exploration by the oil industry had led to some more tangible results. In 1937, for example, a trial bore at Eskdale, Yorkshire, yielded 2.5 million cubic feet of gas daily at a pressure of 1650 pounds per square inch: in 1959 this was purchased by the North Eastern Gas Board for reforming to town gas. In 1939, the British Petroleum Company struck oil at Eakring in Nottinghamshire and commercial exploitation was embarked on. By world standards Britain's oil industry in

1. Diorama of William Murdock's gas-lit house in Redruth (1792).

2. The banqueting hall of the Brighton Pavilion, to which the Prince Regent introduced gas lighting in 1821.

3. Gas cooking in the Reform Club, London, in the 1840s.

4. The pre-payment (coin-in-the-slot) meter was introduced in the 1880s. This glass-fronted model was made for training gas fitters.

5. B. W. Maughan's famous water heater—the 'geyser'—introduced in 1868.

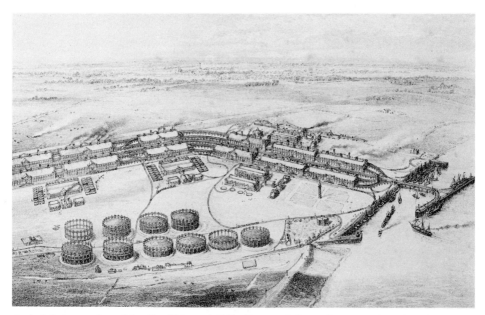

6. Artist's impression of the Gas Light and Coke Company's huge plant at Beckton (1877).

7. Beckton Gas Works, showing the interior of No. 9 retort house (1881).

8. Improved cooker, with double wall filled with insulating material (*c.* 1875).

9. A Black Beauty cooker, 1887.

10. In the 1920s black iron cooking stoves began to be replaced by ones having easily washable enamel surfaces, like this Radiation New World of 1923, with Regulo thermostat.

11. The Main Mayflower of the 1970s was a frameless cooker with electric spark ignition in place of pilot lights, effecting a significant saving in gas consumption.

12. This picture shows how women adapted themselves to the heavy and dirty tasks of gas manufacture during the First World War. Here they are handling iron oxide.

13. Lurgi plant completed at Westfield in 1960. In 1974 it was modified, subsequently supplying parts of Scotland briefly with substitute natural gas (SNG) as part of a development programme, to demonstrate how gas can be made from coal.

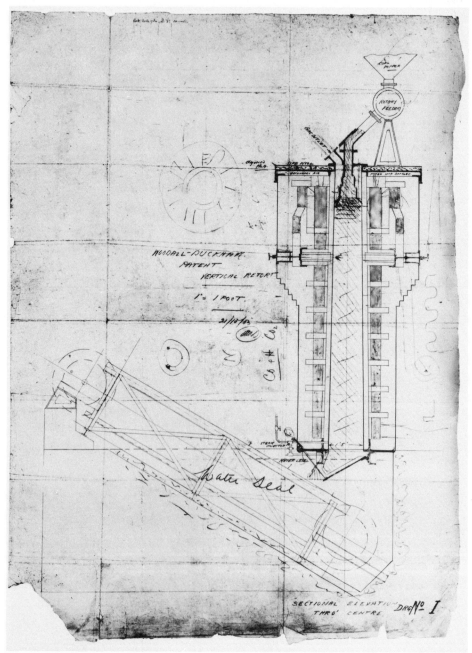

14. Original sketch for the Woodall-Duckham patent vertical retort (1903) as built at Bourne Valley for the Bournemouth Gas and Water Company.

15. The East Greenwich jetty of the South Metropolitan Gas Company in 1924. Direct delivery of coal by water was favoured where practicable. This collier comes from Durham or South Yorkshire.

16. By the early 1920s research and development, and strict monitoring of materials and manufacture, had become very important. This illustration shows the laboratory of the South Metropolitan Gas Company as it appeared in 1924.

the 1950s was scarcely spectacular: in 1953 production amounted to 53 000 tons and a year later had risen to 66 000 tons. The total up to 1954 was no more than 800 000 tons [6]: nevertheless, it was sufficient to keep alive the hope that one day a more important discovery might be made, especially as techniques of prospecting and drilling were constantly improving [7]. The Gas Council's involvement with exploration began in 1953 when, after discussion with the Anglo–Iranian Oil Company (later BP) £1 million was devoted to an extensive search for natural gas on land. This was conducted by D'Arcy Exploration (later BP Exploration) and seismic surveys began in the same year. The first drilling began in February 1954, at Cousland, near Edinburgh, and small reserves of gas were discovered.

IMPORTATION OF LIQUEFIED NATURAL GAS

By far the most important development in this field, prior to the North Sea operations themselves, was the importation of liquefied natural gas in substantial quantities. For the start of this project we must once again turn our attention to the USA. There, the producers and distributors had been directing their attention to the general problem of storage: as with the gas manufacturing industry they had problems of balancing supply and demand. Gas-holders were the obvious solution but, as we have noted, they are both bulky and expensive. Where relatively small quantities are involved the size can be reduced by compressing the gas, the volume of a given mass of gas being inversely proportional to its pressure. For natural gas (essentially methane) there is a third option. If it is sufficiently cooled it can be liquefied and the volume of the liquid is 600 times less than that of the gas. Coal gas cannot, in practice, be treated in this way, because its main constituent, hydrogen, is what is termed a 'permanent' gas; it cannot be liquefied unless it is cooled to $-240°C$, and then only under pressure. While hydrogen can be fairly readily liquefied in the laboratory, and for special industrial purposes, its large-scale storage in this form is impracticable.

As long ago as 1917 a US patent [8] described not only the storage of natural gas in liquid form but its transportation in special insulated containers, and other patents of a similar kind were taken out in the years between the wars. The first important application, however, seems to have been that of the Hope Natural Gas Corporation, West Virginia: in 1940 they built a liquefaction plant capable of dealing with 8000 cubic metres of gas daily, and a storage capacity for about 50 cubic metres of liquid gas. A much larger plant, designed to liquefy and store gas in the summer to meet the heavy winter demand, was built in 1941 by the East Ohio Gas Company. This had storage capacity for no less than 6800 cubic metres of liquid gas, which was increased in 1944. Eight months later disaster struck. The new tank failed, releasing a flood of liquid gas; there was a violent explosion in which 128 people were killed. Shortly after the war (1947) Dresser Industries of

Dallas, Texas, built a natural gas liquefaction and storage plant for the USSR with a capacity—large by the standards of the day—of $4\frac{1}{2}$ million cubic metres. By the middle of the century, therefore, there was a considerable accumulation of knowledge and experience of liquefying and storing natural gas.

In 1951, the Union Stockyard and Transit Company in Chicago faced a problem in meeting its energy requirements. On the one hand, it was finding it difficult to obtain adequate supplies of fuel, at an economic price, for its stockyard activities; on the other, it happened to own a natural gas field in Louisiana. As a solution, it was proposed to liquefy the gas at the field and then convey it by water along the Mississippi to Chicago. The idea was not novel, for it had been envisaged in the US patent of 1917. The temperature of the liquid gas is $-162°C$ or less; if not maintained at this very low temperature it will quickly boil away. Long-distance refrigerated transport of meat and other perishables was, of course, well established—from the 1880s Australia, New Zealand, the Argentine, and other countries had shipped enormous quantities of frozen meat to Europe—but for this trade the temperature had to be maintained at only something like $-10°$ during the voyage. Apart from the need for very effective insulation in transit, considerable constructional difficulties were encountered in handling liquid gas. At the temperature of liquid methane, for example, steel becomes extremely brittle: this was probably the cause of the disaster at the plant of the East Ohio Gas Company. However, Union Stockyard overcame the difficulties—replacing steel by aluminium, which is unaffected in this respect by very low temperatures—and built a barge capable of carrying 2500 tons of liquid methane in five separate tanks.

This project attracted the attention of the oil industry and in 1954 Union Stockyard joined with the Continental Oil Company to form the Constock Liquid Methane Corporation (later Conch International Methane Ltd) who conducted further trials. The project also attracted the attention of the British gas industry, which was no stranger to the possibilities of liquid natural gas. In 1936 A. C. G. Egerton had succeeded W. A. Bone—whose special interest in gas technology we have already noted (p. 46)—as Professor of Chemical Technology at the Imperial College of Science in London. In the following year he directed attention to the possibility of liquefying and storing natural gas. During the Second World War, considerable effort was devoted to utilising natural gas as an alternative to petrol, using as a main source the various natural emanations that have been recorded and the methane gas produced in the anaerobic degradation of sewage. A special type of carburettor had to be designed, and there were practical problems of refuelling and storage, but the project reached the stage of extensive and successful trials with a motor-bus service in the Midlands [10]. This work on the liquefaction and storage of natural gas, as well as that done in America and elsewhere, would as a matter of course have been familiar to gas engineers in Britain. In addition, there was a ready means of communication through Egerton's chairmanship of the Scientific Advisory Council to the Minister of Fuel and Power (1948–53). The Gas Council, in association with Conch, decided to convert a 5000-ton dry cargo vessel into a liquid methane tanker capable of carrying 2200 tons of gas 4000 miles across the Atlantic. The vessel—the *Methane Pioneer* (see Plate 22—was completed in 1958, and after trials in America the first Atlantic crossing was made in February 1959, to a specially constructed terminal at Canvey Island, Essex. This was successful and successive voyages demonstrated that the venture was both technically and commercially feasible. In all, 12 000 tons of liquid gas was imported in this trial venture—the first of its kind in the world—in a period of just over a year.

As a result, the Gas Council decided to embark upon a more ambitious project. This initially envisaged the importation of 300 000 tons of liquid gas annually, enough to supply one-tenth of Britain's need for gas at that time. The Minister of Power approved the scheme in November 1961. Two tankers, each capable of carrying 12 000 tons of gas, were built, one by Vickers at Barrow-in-Furness and the other by Harland and Wolff at Belfast; both were completed in 1963 at a cost of £4.7 million each. They were respectively the *Methane Princess* and the *Methane Progress*. In general, they were built on the same lines as the *Methane Pioneer*, but embodying certain improvements based on experience with the latter. Insulation was improved, but even so it was found impossible to reduce daily gas loss to less than 0.3 per cent. However, this was not wasted, as special provision was made to utilise boiled-off gas as fuel for the ships' engines. The size of these vessels was deceptive. Because the density of liquid natural gas is only half that of crude oil, they had dimensions comparable with that of oil tankers with a capacity of 28 000 tons.

Unlike their predecessor, however, the new vessels did not ply across the Atlantic. Instead they drew their gas supply ultimately from vast reservoirs located 7000 feet below the Sahara at an oasis called Hassi R'Mel. These had recently (1956) been discovered by a French/Algerian survey company: the Société d'Exploitation des Hydrocarbures d'Hassi R'Mel. They have proved to be the third largest in the world after Panhandle in Texas and Groningen in Holland. The gas was piped 200 miles to the small port of Arzew on the Mediterranean for loading into the tankers, which then conveyed it to the Canvey Island terminal. This entailed an ocean voyage of some 1600 miles, as compared with 4000 miles for the Atlantic, and each vessel was scheduled to make thirty trips a year at an average speed of about 17 knots.

Hitherto, we have directed our attention to the specialised tankers developed for this novel trade, but the history of imported natural gas cannot be completed without some account of the very elaborate shore installations that made the venture possible. That at the Algerian end was built by a

specially formed company, the Compagnie Algérienne du Méthane Li-
quide, with French capital [11]. This was commenced in 1962 and completed
in 1964, at a cost of £31 million. Occupying a site of 10 000 acres it was the
biggest industrial project in Africa with the exception of the Aswan Dam. At
its heart was the biggest gas liquefaction plant in the world, capable of
liquefying 150 million cubic feet daily, one third destined for France—
carried to Le Havre in the *Jules Verne*—and the remainder for Britain.
Additionally, provision had to be made for storing up to 36 000 tons of liquid
gas pending shipment, a major technical achievement in itself.

At Canvey Island the whole process had to be reversed. Liquid gas was
delivered from a 750-foot jetty to insulated storage tanks on shore. There
were five tanks in all, each 95-foot in diameter, 62-foot high, and holding
4000 tons of liquid gas. As had been found at sea, gas boiled off steadily
despite the insulation; a gasholder with a capacity of half a million cubic feet
was built to receive this escaped gas. The remainder of the liquid gas was
drawn off from the bottom of the tanks to re-vaporise it and bring it back to
ordinary temperature. In the fullness of time, this would, of course happen if
the liquid gas were simply allowed to warm up slowly by absorbing heat from
its surroundings, just as a drop of volatile liquid—such as ether or petrol—
will do if spilled. In practice, however, the evaporation must be speeded up
and this was done in heat exchangers through which passed water drawn
from the Thames. To a warm-blooded human this water might seem bitterly
cold, but to liquefied gas at $-162°C$ it is almost searingly hot, and it responds
by vaporising rapidly. In practice, heat exchange directly between the liquid
gas and river water was found to introduce technical problems due to
formation of ice. To avoid this, compressed propane gas was used as an
intermediary.

In practice, storage facilities at Canvey Island proved only marginally
sufficient. To enlarge capacity, plans were announced in May 1966 to
provide storage for, ultimately, an additional 84 000 tons of liquid. For this,
a procedure first used in Algeria was adopted: a hollow cylinder of earth
about 130-foot in diameter, and of similar depth, was pre-frozen. The
unfrozen earth was then excavated and the giant circular tank thus formed—
with walls and base of solidly frozen ground—was capped with a gas-tight lid
[12]. In the event, however, this technique ran into serious practical difficulties.

Canvey Island thus became, in effect, a natural-gas well in Britain,
yielding 700 000 tons of gas annually. To be useful, however, this gas had to
be conveyed to the consumer in a form he could use. As we have seen,
methane gas is too rich to be burned in appliances designed for coal gas, but
there was a need for such a gas to strengthen various lean gases—such as
Lurgi gas—to bring them up to the required quality. Equally, the gas
reforming process made it possible to weaken natural gas to provide a
mixture suitable for existing burners. In the event, Sahara gas was used for

both these purposes. In 1962 work began on a high-pressure pipe-line 200 miles long from Canvey Island to Leeds; the maximum operating pressure was 1000 pounds per square inch. This was a joint effort of Board Distribution Engineers. This trunk line had numerous spurs, so that no less than eight of the twelve Area Boards had access to the new type of gas. With the completion of the project, gas burnt in the majority of British homes began to contain a proportion of gas that had originated in the depths of the Sahara Desert. The observable effect was precisely nil so far as the consumer was concerned, but a major step had been taken towards the establishment of a natural-gas industry in Britain. The project provided British gas engineers with valuable experience in handling high-pressure natural gas on a large scale. Apart from this, the venture was significant in marking a development in policy in the nationalised industry. It was the first major development in which most of the Area Boards were involved. While the operation was controlled from the central headquarters of the Gas Council in London, which was in direct touch with Canvey Island, there was also a constant liaison with the eight Area Boards served by the new pipe-line.

The Gas Council's Annual Reports for 1964/5 and 1965/6 record that there had been exploratory talks about importing natural gas from Holland. Negotiations were broken off, however, when the West Sole field was discovered in 1965.

The transportation of liquefied natural gas from areas with little opportunity for local use to those in urgent need quickly became an important factor in the world fuel pattern. Regular runs were established, using larger tankers of improved design, on routes which included Alaska–Japan, Libya–Italy, Libya–Spain, and Brunei–Japan. By 1975 around 30 liquid-gas tankers were in commission and many more planned [13]. For Britain, however, events took a different turn, with the discovery in 1959 of a vast gas field at Slochteren in the Groningen province of Holland.

THE SLOCHTEREN GAS FIELD

In common with other European countries, Holland began to seek oil and gas within her own frontiers even before the last war, but the effort was relatively small—some 800 trial borings—and the result negligible. These exploratory surveys continued after the war. Then, dramatically, the situation changed overnight. A joint Esso/Shell survey team struck gas in enormous quantities at Slochteren on 14 August 1959. Further survey established the existence of a field some 20 miles long and 15 wide, with a potential estimated at well over a million million cubic metres. As a measure of the magnitude of the discovery, it may be remarked that this would have sufficed to meet for a century Britain's need for gas, at the rate of consumption then prevailing. The present rate of gas consumption is, of course, much greater.

It may be asked why the very existence of this vast gas field—almost the largest in the world—was unsuspected for so long. For this, various reasons can be adduced. First and foremost, perhaps, was the fact that these deposits lie relatively deep—2700 metres—below the surface. Secondly, the abundance of cheap oil and gas elsewhere in the world offered the European oil companies relatively little incentive to explore at home. Whatever the reasons that obtained up to that date, the sheer magnitude of the Slochteren discovery demanded an urgent and radical reconsideration of policy.

For Holland the economic consequences were very great. By 1970 natural gas was not only supplying about 15 per cent of Dutch energy requirements but proving a valuable export. NAM Gas Export—a joint Shell/Esso concern operating in association with the Staatsmijnen—was exporting gas to Belgium, France, and West Germany through a 1500 km pipeline system belonging to Nederlandse Gasunie, an enterprise owned jointly by the Dutch government and Shell/Esso [14].

The discovery of the Slochteren field naturally gave great encouragement to prospectors in other countries in northern Europe who had hitherto met with only limited success. Various important questions arose. Was the Groningen discovery an isolated one, or were there comparable associated gas, and perhaps oil, fields to be discovered? If the latter, what clues were there to their location? These questions could be answered only by intensive investigation of the nature of the new field, and evaluation of the results. This involved highly technical considerations which are so fundamental to the whole North Sea project that they cannot be ignored here, even though they can be discussed only in very general terms. Without this, it is impossible to understand the justification for the very expensive and difficult programme of undersea exploration that was embarked on.

As has been noted, the Groningen gas lies more than a mile underground. It is contained in a layer of very porous sandstone (the Rotliegendes sandstone) some 400-foot thick, reminiscent of the oil-bearing structures of the Middle East. Geological evidence indicated that this rock was in fact the remains of a sandy desert laid down some 270 million years ago when the climate of Holland was tropical. This gas-bearing rock became capped with an impermeable layer of salt, some thousands of feet thick, which completely traps the gas, contained at a pressure of some 4000 lb per square inch.

This situation could have been brought about by the following series of geological events. Some 400 million years ago Europe extended far further into the Atlantic than it does now; the British Isles were an integral part of it, and what is now the North Sea was dry land. Then, some 350 million years ago, this land mass began to be invaded by the Atlantic, leaving a swampy area bounded on the south by the Hercinian Continent (comprising most of the middle and south of modern Europe), and on the north by Atlantis, with an island, the London Ridge, standing out from it. Very roughly the London

Ridge extended from the Wash to North Wales and from Ramsgate to Pembroke; in the west it extended over the present Irish Sea and in the east across the North Sea to what is now Belgium. It was a period, the Carboniferous Age, when the climate was hot and humid, encouraging luxuriant plant and animal growth, the accumulated deposits of which formed the great coal measures which have been exploited in modern times. The Carboniferous Age was followed, some 300 million years ago, by the Permian. During this the shallow sea began to silt up, so that the land extended southwards and Britain became joined again with the main European land mass. There were great climatic changes and the Rotliegendes sandstone was created by the weathering of rocks of the Hercinian Continent. Later in Permian times a shallow sea, the Zechstein Sea, covered much of north-west Europe and the solar evaporation of this led to the formation of thick salt deposits [15].

Analysis of the composition of gas from the Groningen Field suggested that it derived ultimately from coal, and this is consistent with the sequence of geological events outlined above. Briefly, it seemed that the gas formed in the coal measures laid down in the Carboniferous Age migrated to the porous Rotliegendes sandstone, and was there trapped by the thick layer of salt formed by the drying up of the Zechstein Sea. On this basis, a general prediction could be made. If other gas fields existed, they were most likely to be found where the salt deposits, or other impermeable strata, overlay coal seams with an intervening layer of porous rock to act as a reservoir. Such a combination might occur in rocks younger than the Permian and therefore relatively nearer to the surface. Clearly, the most promising areas for further exploration were those in which salt deposits overlaid coal deposits. This area could be fairly easily charted but a further requirement—not amenable to easy prediction—was that the salt (or other impermeable deposit) should have a humped structure. Without this the gas would, over a period of tens of millions of years, simply have leaked away. Indeed, what prospectors were really looking for were vast underground gasholders storing gas resulting from the effect of intense heat and pressure on coal seams deep in the earth's crust, akin to the great metal bell-jars which gas engineers had devised for storing gas made by carbonising coal in retorts. Alternatively, gas might be trapped by a fault in the rock strata. Gas working its way upward beneath an impermeable stratum might find its way barred by a transverse layer of impermeable rock.

The greater part of the salt/coal area proved to lie under the North Sea, though it covered parts of north and south Denmark and extended eastward across Holland, into Germany and under part of Eastern England. Within this area a great treasure hunt began, but the task was not an easy one. This might be expected on purely statistical grounds: the total area of the Groningen field, huge though it is in terms of gas content, is only some 600 square miles, whereas that of the North Sea basin is over 200 000 square

miles. Further, although the petroleum industry had developed highly sophisticated methods for detecting the nature of rock structures deep in the
ground, these had in the main been used on land. Where they had been used
in connection with offshore drilling, conditions were generally more
favourable. The Gulf of Mexico, for example, is far less stormy, cold, and
foggy than the North Sea. The methods used we will describe in the next
chapter.

In many parts of the world oil and gas are commonly encountered in the
same field: such gas is called associated gas. Analysis of the Groningen gas,
and evidence that it derived from coal rather than from marine deposits,
originally led geologists to believe that it was unassociated gas and that,
while there might be further vast deposits of this, there was little hope of
further exploration leading to any major discovery of oil [16]. In the event,
of course, this prediction proved incorrect, and the North Sea has proved a
rich source of oil as well as gas.

THE CONVENTION ON THE CONTINENTAL SHELF

For the moment, however, we must turn our attention from scientific and
technological considerations to matters of law. In former times the law of
the sea was relatively simple. Countries possessing a coastline normally
exercised sovereignty over the sea extending three miles beyond low-water
(as acknowledged by The Hague Convention of 1882), allowance being
made for the bays and inlets normally encountered. In such territorial
waters—as distinct from rivers and landlocked seas, which are national
waters—foreign vessels had the right of peaceful passage, but no more. The
high-seas were open to all, though from time immemorial all states claimed
jurisdiction over pirates, and in time of war special conventions might apply
to neutral vessels. Beyond this, restrictions could be imposed only by mutual
treaties between nations who shared common interests. In practice, such
treaties were normally restricted to the fields of fishing and whaling, where it
was advantageous to all concerned to avoid over-fishing, by such measures
as control of the size of mesh in nets, size limits below which fish might not be
marketed, and regulation of the number of whales killed in any given
season. There have also beeen internationally agreed measures to control
pollution resulting from the discharge of oil sludge at sea.

Until recently, the question of undersea mineral rights hardly arose. The
galleries of coal and metal mines like the collieries of North East England, or
the tin mines of Cornwall, might extend out under the sea but rarely beyond
the accepted three-mile limit. But a very different situation arose with the
discovery and exploitation of undersea oil outside unequivocally territorial
waters, as in the shallow waters of the Gulf of Mexico. Again, tin has been
dredged from offshore deposits and there is now considerable commercial
interest in deep-sea deposits of manganese.

To whom should such valuable deposits belong? To the world at large, to the country which has the nearest coastline, or to the first comer who can deploy the technological measures—often complex and expensive—able to exploit them? The developing countries of the Third World, understandably, began to press the first view. It was argued that poor countries, with no access to the high-seas, should not be deprived of a share of the riches that lie beneath them. This debate continues, and has been sharpened by growing interest in the development of Antarctica. For the present historical study, however, we must restrict ourselves to what has already been done to bring some order into a confused situation.

The most important development has been that of the concept of the Continental Shelf. It is argued that the coastline does not necessarily delineate a land mass in the geographical and geological sense. Very commonly, the same rock structures extend outwards below the sea, in comparatively shallow water; only at some considerable distance from the shore does the water deepen, often fairly abruptly, to form the ocean proper. The shallow-water extension of the land is known as the Continental Shelf and the declivity between it and the deep-sea is the Continental Slope. In the years immediately after the last war it became generally accepted that national sovereignty, as far as undersea exploitation was concerned, should extend at least to the limit of the Shelf. There was, however, no clear idea of how the Shelf should be defined in order to allow this concept to be translated into unambiguous international law [17].

From 1953 to 1958 the United Nations, through its International Law Commission, sought to establish a generally acceptable legal definition of the Continental Shelf. In 1958 agreement was reached at a Convention of the Seas in Geneva, but not until 1964 was this ratified by 22 nations, the number required to make it effective. In the present context the following provisions are important.

(1) The Continental Shelf normally extends outwards until a depth of 200 metres is reached.

(2) It may be taken to extend beyond this limit 'to where the depth of superjacent waters admits the exploitation of natural resources'.

(3) Sovereignty extends primarily to mineral reserves, though sedentary living organisms are also included: the latter provision extends protection to, for example, oyster, pearl, and sponge fisheries.

(4) The sovereign state reserves the right to forbid scientific research on the Shelf.

(5) Apart from such general considerations, the waters of the Shelf are international. They are, for example, open to fishing—subject to any separate agreements that may be made—and to the laying of cables and pipelines in the seabed. The needs of navigation were protected by providing that no drilling or other exploratory work, or the establishment of permanent

well-heads, was permissible in recognised shipping lanes. Elsewhere, however, shipping might be required not to approach within 500 metres of an installation.

As with territorial waters, provision had to be made for cases in which the defined sovereignty of one nation overlapped with that of another. In such circumstances the boundary might be defined by mutual agreement or on the basis of a median line lying half-way between the lines (usually the low-tide lines) used to define the limits of territorial waters. As with the latter, allowance would be made for natural irregularities of the coastline. In principle, this is similar to the tradition that the rights of riparian owners extend to mid-stream.

In implementing the Convention of the Sea, the North Sea presented an unusual example of overlapping interests. It is bordered by six states: Belgium, Denmark, Holland, Norway, the United Kingdom, and Germany. It extends from the Strait of Dover to the Shetlands. It is some 600 miles long and 400 miles wide, covering an area of about 240 000 square miles. It is a shallow sea—with an average depth of no more than about 300 feet—especially in the south and east, where great rivers such as the Thames and the Humber, the Scheldt and the Maas, the Rhine and the Elbe, pour in a vast annual tribute of silt. The only really deep water is a trench off the Norwegian coast (the Norwegian Deep) and the Skagerrak between Norway and Denmark. On the basis of depth of water and exploitability of the seabed virtually the whole of it comes within the scope of the Convention and it was divided up between the six states concerned on the median-line principle. This was, on the face of it, particularly favourable for Britain, because by an accident of geography she acquired rights to the whole of the western half of the area. Whether this represented half the available gas and oil—or even whether there were commercially exploitable deposits to be found anywhere—was, of course, still largely a matter of speculation. The northern and southern limits of the area were defined as lying between 61°N and 51°N latitude; the delineation of the eastern borders was arrived at in the negotiations with the Dutch and Norwegian governments.

Norway presented a considerable problem. Technically, it could be argued that the Norwegian Deep effectively set a limit to Norway's sovereignty and that Britain was entitled to exploit the seabed up to the western edge of the Deep. However, it could also be argued that modern technology—and certainly the technology of the fairly near future—did not preclude operations at a depth of 1000 feet, the maximum encountered in the Deep. In the event it was agreed (1965) that in defining the boundary between the two countries, the existence of the Deep should be ignored [18].

NORTH SEA LICENSING

The assignment of rights was, of course, to the nations concerned; it did not confer any rights of exploration and exploitation on private citizens of the countries concerned. Once the limits had been broadly defined, it was therefore necessary for the states themselves to enact their own national legislation to control undersea development by approved organisations. In Britain, this was embodied in the Continental Shelf Act of 1964, the year in which the first liquid gas was imported into Britain.

British policy was to divide its allocated area—some 100 000 square miles in all—into blocks of 100 square miles each. Licences to explore and work these blocks were then issued to approved concerns. In the main these were oil companies, or consortia in which they were strongly represented. This was scarcely surprising, for the oil companies alone had sufficient knowledge, experience, resources, and capital to locate and extract any oil and gas that might lie beneath the North Sea. Even for them, these notoriously inhospitable waters presented a major challenge.

From the outset, it was clear that an enormous investment would be necessary if exploration proved successful, even though its full extent could not be gauged at the outset. Furthermore, it was clear that the investment would not pay a dividend for ever. The total amount of gas and oil that could be economically extracted was uncertain—as, indeed, it still is. Unlike the widow's cruse, gas and oilfields sooner or later become exhausted. From the oil industry's point of view it was therefore essential to have licensing agreements and marketing arrangements consistent with the investment demanded of them and the limited duration of return on it. Equally, the British government, having unexpectedly acquired this potential source of treasure for the nation at a time of mounting economic problems, was determined to issue licences on the most advantageous terms possible. British licensing policy will be examined in the next chapter.

In the bargaining that had to be done the Gas Council was in a fairly favourable position. First and foremost, it had, under the 1948 Act, a virtual monopoly of the supply of gas in Britain; it also had a nationwide distribution system. Secondly, with the start of the Algerian experiment, it was gaining experience in handling natural gas and had constructed a high-pressure trunk-line for its distribution. Against this, however, it had no expertise in the extraction—as opposed to the distribution—of natural gas, so some considerable degree of co-operation with the international oil companies was unavoidable for the foreseeable future. The Gas Council had in fact, already been trying to interest these companies in exploration for natural gas. Further, implicit in the situation was a complete, and fairly rapid, switch to natural gas as the sole source of supply and an overall expansion with emphasis on growth in the industrial market. This would demand either a huge investment in gas reforming plant so that existing appliances could continue to be used, or modification or replacement of every appliance in the country so that it could burn natural gas. Relatively small quantities of liquid gas from Algeria could be absorbed into the existing system but total dependence on natural gas made a major upheaval in the industry inevitable.

In the outcome, as we shall see in greater detail later, the solution reached was that the oil companies formed consortia to prospect for gas, extract it, and deliver it to shore bases operated jointly by the oil companies and the Gas Council. The gas industry then purchased the gas under contract and was responsible for its further treatment (mainly odorisation), distribution, and sale to consumers. To this general rule there was one important exception: one of the major exploration groups was owned jointly by the Gas Council and Amoco. The Council later also had a share in some other groups.

The first licences were issued in 1964, to some two dozen different groups. They covered about 42 000 square miles of the North Sea, rather more than one-third of the British sector. The first major strike was made in October 1965. This was the West Sole field, some forty miles off the mouth of the Humber. Within six months its commercial viability had been established and by the middle of 1967 gas was coming ashore at Easington, just north of Spurn Head: North Sea gas had its foot in the door. Exactly ten years later (September 1977) the Chairman of British Gas, Sir Denis Rooke, was formally to announce the end of the appliance conversion programme: North Sea gas reigned supreme. That it should have fallen to him to make this announcement must have been a cause of great personal satisfaction. He had joined the gas industry at the time of nationalisation and as a professional engineer had been closely associated with the technological problems of utilising natural gas as the industry's main source of supply: he had played a key role in the *Methane Pioneer* project and had sailed as a member of the technical team aboard the vessel on the first voyage bringing liquefied natural gas into Britain.

REFERENCES

[1] THORPE, T. E. *A Dictionary of Applied Chemistry*, Vol. II, p. 163, Longmans Green, and Co., London and New York (1891).
[2] *Productivity Team Report: Gas*, p. 23, British Productivity Council, London (1953).
[3] MARSDEN, A. SCI Jubilee Memorial Lecture—1955, *Chemistry and Industry*, 1678 (1955).
[4] TIRATSOO, E. N. *Natural Gas: a Study*, 2nd edn, pp. 238–82, Scientific Press Ltd, Beaconsfield (1972).
[5] *Productivity Team Report*, p. 117 (1953).
[6] LEES, G. H. *Journal of the Institute of Fuel*, **27**, 209 (1954).
[7] TIRATSOO, E. N. *Natural Gas: a Study*, 2nd edn, pp. 205–7, Scientific Press Ltd, Beaconsfield (1972).

[8] MEDICI, M. *The Natural Gas Industry*, pp. 185–6, Newnes–Butterworth, London (1974).
[9] CABOT, US Patent 1.225.574 (1917).
[10] EGERTON, A. C. G., HALL, T. A., and PEARCE, M. *Journal of the Institute of Fuel*, **19**, 193 (1946).
 EGERTON, A. C. G. and PEARCE, M. Ibid., **18**, 161 (1945).
 EGERTON, A. C. G. 'Methane as a Fuel', Address to Meeting of Fuel Economy Group, 7 November 1950.
[11] MEDICI, M. op. cit., p. 187.
[12] TIRATSOO, E. N. op. cit., pp. 185–6.
 MEDICI, M. op. cit., pp. 225–9.
 WILSON, D. Scott *The Modern Gas Industry*, pp. 42–3, Edward Arnold, London (1969).
[13] TIRATSOO, E. N. op. cit., pp. 202–3.
[14] Idem., p. 261.
[15] WILSON, D. Scott. op. cit., pp. 47–52.
[16] GASKELL, T. F. *Endeavour*, **26**, 140 (1967).
[17] SHAWCROSS, Lord. *The Law of the Continental Shelf, with Special Reference to the North Sea* (Discourse to the 20th International Geographical Congress, London, 1964). Geographical Publications Ltd, London (1964).
[18] Cmnd No. 2626. HMSO, London (1965).

BIBLIOGRAPHY

COOPER, Bryan and GASKELL, T. F. *North Sea Oil—The Great Gamble*, Heinemann, London (1966).

HINDE, Peter. *Fortune in the North Sea*, Foulis, London (1966).

LOM, W. L. *Liquefied Natural Gas*, Applied Science, Barking (1974).

MEDICI, M. *The Natural Gas Industry: a Review of World Resources and Industrial Applications*, Newnes–Butterworth, London (1974).

TIRATSOO, E. N. *Natural Gas*, Scientific Press, Beaconsfield (1960).

VAN MEURS, A. P. H. *Petroleum Economics and Offshore Mining Legislation*, Elsevier, Amsterdam (1971).

WILSON, D. Scott. *North Sea Heritage*, British Gas, London (1974).

16

North Sea Exploration and Development

IN the previous chapter we considered in general terms the way in which the countries bordering the North Sea agreed to divide the ocean bed between themselves and how the British Government allocated the first exploration and production licences on the basis of blocks of roughly one hundred square miles each. As government policy, and the way in which it was put into effect, has profoundly influenced the development of these petroleum resources, which include both oil and gas, we must now examine this in greater detail.

CRITERIA FOR THE ISSUE OF LICENCES

The Convention on the Continental Shelf, signed in Geneva in 1958, delineated the areas of national sovereignty with sufficient precision for Britain to enact the Continental Shelf Act of 1964, as a basis for exploiting oil and gas resources in her portion of the Shelf. The only caution necessary was to avoid, for the moment, any activity on the fringes of the area, which might possibly be sources of dispute later. As we have noted, it was eventually agreed that Norwegian sovereignty would be treated as though the Norwegian Deep did not exist.

In most western countries, exploration for, and extraction of, minerals on public land is traditionally carried out by private companies acting under government licence. This was the course adopted by the Conservative government in 1964 and it was not substantially changed by the Labour government that took office subsequently. In that year Mr F. J. Erroll, the Minister of Power, set out five criteria that would guide the government in allocating exploration and production rights [1]:

(1) The need to encourage exploration and exploitation as rapidly, thoroughly, and economically as possible.

(2) A requirement that applicants for licences should be incorporated in the United Kingdom and taxed there.

(3) Where the applicant was a foreign-owned concern, consideration would be given to the extent to which British oil companies are equitably treated in the country in question.

(4) The programme of work proposed by the applicant, and the evidence that he has the resources and ability to carry it out.

(5) The contribution the applicant has already made towards develop-

ing the resources of the British Continental Shelf and the development of the British fuel economy generally.

If these criteria are examined it will be seen that their general intention was to favour British companies; to ensure that foreign companies make the maximum contribution to the British economy; and to leave sufficient vagueness in interpretation to give the government considerable freedom of action. As the programme developed, the government took advantage of this to impose conditions not by formal legislation, but by the convenient device of letting it be known among those concerned what kinds of proposition were likely to be favourably considered [2]. Those concerned were largely the eight oil 'majors'. Of these, five were American (Standard Oil of New Jersey (now Exxon), Standard Oil of California, Texaco, Mobil, Gulf); one was French (Compagnie Française des Pétroles); one Anglo–Dutch (Royal Dutch–Shell); and one British (British Petroleum). These dominated the world scene in the immediate post-war years, but from the late 1950s were increasingly challenged by a growing number of independent operators working on a smaller, but in many cases very substantial scale. They included some large chemical companies like ICI and Monsanto, whose interest in oil and gas was not primarily as a fuel but as a chemical feedstock. There were even some participants with no direct interest at all such as Northcliffe Developments Limited, a newspaper group, and the Canadian Pacific Railway. Having made these general observations we may usefully consider these criteria in detail, and the way in which they were applied in practice.

The first calls for little comment. It was no more than a declaration that, in the face of growing economic difficulties, the British government—of whatever political complexion—was anxious to see the North Sea making a contribution to the national economy as quickly as possible.

The second criterion recognised the fact that the resources of domestic oil companies, effectively British Petroleum and Shell, would be insufficient for the task. It was, therefore, necessary to enlist the support of major foreign companies, through British subsidiaries, but only on terms that ensured that the British government got the greatest possible share of the profits.

While the intention of this second criterion was good, as far as the British national interest was concerned, its effectiveness has been challenged. It must be supposed that what the government had in mind was that the operators should pay tax on profits resulting from their North Sea operations as such. It appeared to some that in fact they could offset profits made in this area against losses made elsewhere, especially in the Middle East, to such an extent that they might have virtually no UK tax liability until around 1980. In its *Report on North Sea Oil and Gas 1972/73*, the Public Accounts Committee of the House of Commons drew attention to this and recommended that the anomaly should be removed. This was accepted in principle by the Chancellor, the limits of whose discretion appears to have been under estimated; the second criterion asserts that the operators shall be liable for UK tax, but does not make this synonymous with normal corporation tax. It appeared, therefore, that there was no obstacle to allowing North Sea losses—which initially were bound to be heavy and unavoidable—to be set only against later profits generated within the United Kingdom.

The third criterion provided a means of excluding certain foreign companies, if this seemed desirable, and might give some relief to British companies in their overseas operation, but it cannot be regarded as being of great importance.

The fourth and fifth criteria were of very different consequence however, for they gave the Minister considerable power to persuade foreign companies to use their best endeavours in Britain's interest and to favour British companies, at least marginally, if this seemed appropriate. It must be remembered that whereas for Britain, North Sea gas and oil was a wholly novel domestic enterprise, of crucial importance to the future of the national economy, the situation for the big international oil companies was very different. Every mining venture, whether for petroleum or minerals, is risky, and the success of the long-term strategies of the big operators depends upon their careful evaluation of all the factors involved, in order to reduce the element of chance to a minimum. But this is the most that can be done; in the last analysis, the operations of the petroleum industry are based on carefully calculated risks. The general nature of these, and how they are assessed is well understood, and have been clearly summarised by A. P. H. van Meurs [3]. Briefly, there are three principal areas of risk: the economic, the engineering, and the geological risk.

Economic risks include such factors as changes in taxation rates; changes in the world demand for petroleum and the price customers are willing to pay for it; and sequestration of assets by new political régimes. Engineering risks include all the great technical problems involved in exploring for oil and gas: extracting them from the deep deposits in which they occur; and transporting them to consumers by tanker or pipeline. The geological risk is very considerable: modern survey methods can fairly readily identify structures likely to contain petroleum or gas, but whether they actually do so can still be proved only by drilling. In fact, the proportion of dry holes bored in exploratory work is high, perhaps 90 per cent, and even when a hole is not dry it may not yield petroleum in sufficient quantities, or of the desired quality, to be profitable.

All these factors had to be taken into account by the oil companies in determining their attitude to North Sea oil and gas, and the terms on which the British government proposed to issue licences. Even though it soon became apparent that the new field was of exceptional promise, it was equally clear that its development would be unusually difficult and expensive. This had to be weighed against the demands of major existing commitments in other parts of the world and assessment of the relative profitability of proved reserves identified and available elsewhere. It will be apparent, therefore, that both parties—government and industry—had to negotiate with skill and determination. Government's desire for maximum public revenue must be set against the concern of industry—especially foreign industry with attractive opportunities for investment elsewhere—to maximise their own profits. In such circumstances, of course, neither party fully achieves its objectives, but an acceptable compromise is found.

In *A Progress Report on North Sea Gas Contract Negotiations* prepared by the Gas Council in 1967 attention was drawn to problems arising from fundamental differences in attitude between Britain and the USA. In Britain security of supply, termination of service, and price review were matters of vital importance, but these were matters that were of relatively little significance in US gas purchase contracts. Consequently when American producers submitted to the Council their standard forms of contract they were disappointed to find that they were not acceptable. A further difficulty was that collective bargaining was impracticable, as under US Anti Trust and Restrictive Practices legislation, each US company preferred to negotiate separate contracts with the Council. As some companies insisted on being represented by their own negotiators and lawyers this resulted, as the Council wryly reported, 'in large and sometimes confused meetings and a considerable extension of the time required for negotiations'.

Van Meurs [4] has analysed the general considerations that determine the policy of any government, and stresses the importance of pitching the terms at the right level initially:

A crucial period for the government is that moment when the petroleum law applicable to the projects becomes effective. How many companies will accept the terms? How many projects do the companies consider profitable?

He goes on to argue that government must always fall a little short of their target:

There generally exists a contrast in the amount of information that is available and capable of being processed by the industry and the government. If companies must place all relevant information at the disposal of the government, and if the concession areas are small, the government may be able to obtain a better insight into the geology than the companies themselves. Normally, however, the companies are better informed and the conditions pressure [i.e. the influence exerted by petroleum law] can accordingly be calculated more accurately by the companies than by the government. In summary, there exist two sources of governmental uncertainty concerning the value of the conditions pressure: the character of most projects is cloudy, even when the best information is available, and the government is only partially informed of the company's analysis of the project.

The British government's introduction of the 'programme of work' condition was very important. Exploration and production licences are, of course, potentially marketable properties and it was thought desirable to exclude applicants whose interest was purely speculative, merely seeking licences for re-sale. By requiring companies to indicate their intentions in some detail, it was easier to ensure that development was pressed ahead as rapidly as possible and in the desired areas. Speed was a factor of major importance in British government thinking, even before the OPEC price rises of the 1970s. North Sea oil was urgently needed to assist the balance of payments situation. The achievement of this objective was clearly the subject of much discussion: in 1964 Mr Erroll stated [5] that:

. . . a great deal of detailed discussion and negotiation was necessary with each applicant, so that I could be satisfied that it was right to grant licences. In some cases the programme of work first proposed was inadequate and I had to insist on improvements.

By this device, an element of competition was introduced into the system of application. It became clear to the companies that licences would go to those most willing to press on strongly. This served to some extent to answer critics who advocated an auction system, licences going to the highest bidder. This was normal practice, for example, in the United States' offshore-drilling programme in Louisiana and Texas, and on the north slope of Alaska. It is argued that under such a system the more efficient applicants are successful because they can afford to pay more. Against this, however, the companies have to make large cash payments in advance of revenue from production. When Alaskan leases were sold in 1969 the top bid for the most desirable tract was $72 million; the total bid was $900 million. In 1971, the Conservative government then in office in Britain carried out a cautious experiment with the auction system. Of the 450 blocks allocated in that year, 15 were put up for auction and the remainder disposed of according to the discretionary system. Although the government netted £37 million as a result, more than half of which was represented by an astonishing £21 million bid by Shell/ Esso for a block northeast of the Shetlands, it had no immediate influence on policy. The next highest bid for another block was only just over £6 million, and there were only four bids in excess of £1 million. Indeed, there is some evidence that just as Britain was making this tentative move towards the auction system, opinion in the American oil industry was tending to favour the British discretionary system 'which the oil companies consider to be more sophisticated and eminently suitable' [6]. UK policy has been endorsed by the Dutch economist van Meurs who remarked [7] that 'the British government proved to be a master at fishing behind the nets!' However, it must be noted also that other authorities such as K. W. Dam [8] of the University of Chicago and Colin Robinson [9], formerly of Esso and now of the University of Surrey, have expressed themselves in favour, on balance, of the auction system. The Public Accounts Committee of the House of Commons severely criticised the Department of Trade and Industry (within which the old Ministry of Power had disappeared) for relying so heavily on the discretionary system in the fourth (1970) round of allocations, but D. I. and G. A. Mackay [10] of Aberdeen University regarded the Committee's concern as 'greatly exaggerated'. They conclude, however, that the Department of Trade and Industry ought to have placed less reliance on discretionary licensing. A more favourable view has been expressed by two former members of the staff of British Petroleum. They attribute the drafting of the regulations primarily to J. A. Beckett, Under-Secretary in the Ministry of Power. A Cambridge geographer, he had had experience of geological work in the field, had twice served as chairman of the Petroleum Committee of the O E E C, and was for three years Petroleum Attaché at the Washington Embassy. He thus had considerable knowledge and experience of the international oil industry.

With this professional skill behind the scenes there is no wonder that a fair and stimulating set of regulations was produced with speed and thoroughness. The importance of formulating the rules quickly is shown by the fact that Britain's North Sea territory is a year or more ahead in development over the rest of the area, and the reward is that Britain is the first to discover gas in commercial quantities [11].

In the face of such conflicting views it may perhaps be fair to argue that while the two systems differ substantially in principle they may both lead to the desired result. This certainly seems to have proved to be the case in the short-term, though the policy adopted may well engender long-term problems; in speed of development Britain outstripped her continental rivals. If the number of exploration wells drilled is taken as a rough index of activity—though geological factors are naturally also relevant—we may note that of 468 such drillings between 1964 and 1973, no less than 266 were in the U K sector. West Germany came next with 90, followed by Norway (80), Denmark (20), and the Netherlands (12). It was expected that by 1980—only sixteen years after the first licences were issued—Britain would be a net exporter of oil, with remarkable consequences for the balance of trade. Mackay and Mackay predicted in 1975 that in the absence of North Sea oil, the value of crude oil imports in 1980 would have been just over £4000 million. With the advent of North Sea production, they expected that the value of crude oil exports would exceed the value of imports by just over £2000 million, a turnaround of over £6000 million. They concluded that:

It is possible to exaggerate the economic significance of North Sea oil and gas, but these calculations clearly illustrate that the exaggeration, while still possible, is difficult [12].

In passing, attention should be drawn to the phrase 'net exporter' in the paragraph above. It was commonly assumed that North Sea oil, found on Britain's doorstep, would be used directly to satisfy her domestic needs.

This is not so, because petroleum, like coal, is a product of rather variable composition. That derived from the North Sea is of high quality: it has a low sulphur content and yields a relatively high proportion of the lighter fractions, notably petrol (gasoline). It is, therefore, particularly suitable for the American market, supplying millions of large motor vehicles doing big mileages. Britain, in contrast, has a relatively high demand for fuel-oil, for which Middle East crudes are more appropriate. Another relevant factor is that British law is more tolerant of high-sulphur oils than most other developed countries. The general pattern expected, therefore, was of oil still continuing to be imported into Britain, but a greater volume, of a different nature, being exported. These expectations were destined to be fulfilled. In the first nine months of 1977 Britain's North Sea oil exports were worth £750 million, of which 60 per cent went to Western Europe, 30 per cent to North America, and 10 per cent to Sweden and Finland. This situation does not at present apply to gas from the U K sector, all of which is used domestically. When these supplies fail, or begin to fail, and attention is again directed to manufacturing gas, it does not necessarily follow that oil from the North Sea or elsewhere will be the principal raw material. Natural gas may outlast oil and it may be that coal will be the source.

The British scheme has been criticised on the basis of the size of the blocks allocated. These were of approximately 100 square miles each, one degree of longitude and one degree of latitude encompassing thirty blocks. There was some feeling on the industrial side that this was too small. Clearly, the patchwork of equal rectangular blocks into which the seabed was arbitrarily divided would not, except by chance, correspond with the underlying geological structures bearing oil or gas. It could, therefore, very well happen that rival companies made independent bores into the same reservoir and each would then aim for the greatest extraction rate in order to secure the lion's share. The smaller the block, the greater the chance of this happening. To mitigate this foreseeable difficulty, the regulations provided that licensees must exploit each field as a unit and the Minister had power to require them to submit joint schemes to effect this. If they failed to agree the Minister could himself 'prepare a development scheme which shall be fair and equitable' to all parties. If this was unacceptable, there was provision for arbitration. It may be remarked that this difficulty argued in favour of an auction system by which successful bidders were free to sell their rights if they wished. It would then be possible for the operators to make appropriate deals between themselves until they had assembled mutually satisfactory packages of blocks. However, as we have seen, the alternative procedure actually adopted proved reasonably effective.

The problem that existed within the British zone of sovereignty was encountered also along the international boundaries. Geological structures take no account of sovereign rights, and gas and oil fields may lie partly under one country's territory and partly under another's. In such cases no government could dictate to a foreign operator working just beyond its boundary. In the case of Norway, provision was made for this sort of difficulty to be resolved by joint consultation. The British agreement with the Netherlands went a little further, and provided for disputes to be referred to an arbitrator, whose decision would be binding. In the event, a satisfactory arrangement was made to exploit gas from the Frigg field on the median line between Britain and Norway.

Finally, just as judgement had to be exercised in establishing the general principles of allocating offshore licences, so it had to be also in respect of the financial terms. Two kinds of licence are involved here: exploration licences, and production licences. The first of these could be issued at any time to suitable applicants. They were non-exclusive and covered the whole of the British North Sea area. They allowed survey work and exploratory drillings to a maximum depth of 350 metres, but commercial production was forbidden. They were valid for three years and initially cost £20.

The regulations for the issue of production licences, which confer an exclusive right 'to search and bore for and get petroleum', were more exacting. First, they were issued only at set times (1964, 1965, 1969, 1971, 1976) and only to selected applicants; the latter provision enabled the Minister to exclude companies who appeared to have insufficient financial and technical resources to carry out satisfactory work programmes. The fee originally charged was £200, with an additional fee of £5 for every block after the first ten. The licence ran for only six years in the first instance. At the end of that time it could be renewed for a further 40 years, subject to the agreed work programme having been satisfactorily completed. However, the terms of renewal were onerous; at least half the licensed area (not half of each block) thus becoming available for relicensing must be surrendered. This proviso, which makes it possible to raise the rent for developing a proved property, had previously been practised by the Alberta Government in Canada. Additionally, a royalty of $12\frac{1}{2}$ per cent was payable on the value of all oil or gas produced, though from this the annual licence fee could be deducted.

In October 1964, a Labour government, under Mr Harold Wilson, succeeded the Conservative administration that had established the basic rules for the exploitation of North Sea gas and oil. The new Minister of Power, Mr Fred Lee, in effect reiterated the existing criteria for the issue of production licences, but made one significant change. He made it clear that the participation of nationalised British industries would be encouraged:

I shall also take into account any proposals which may be made for facilitating participation of public enterprise in the development and exploitation of the resources of the Continental Shelf.

Notwithstanding differences of opinion on the correctness of government policy on the allocation of licences, it is a matter for record that when the second round of allocations was advertised in the London, Edinburgh, and Belfast Gazettes of 6 August 1965 by the new Labour government, there was strong competition for new blocks.

As far as the industry was concerned, the modified policy had important consequences. In the first round of allocations the Gas Council had a 31 per cent share in a group also including Amoco UK Petroleum Ltd, Amerada Exploration Ltd, and Texas Eastern (UK) Ltd. As the Gas Council is careful to point out in its Annual Report 1965/66, these are all British corporations—although it goes on to add they are offspring of 'American parent companies [which] have world-wide experience and success in exploration and pipe-lining'. In the second round, the Gas Council's participation in this group increased to 50 per cent.

No further allocation of licences was made until 1969, and the interval provided an opportunity for the government to reconsider its policy. In doing so, it had to take note of strong political pressures. Within the Labour Party there was antipathy towards private enterprise and a continuing belief that nationalisation was a remedy for all economic and social ills. In 1967, the National Executive Committee put forward a proposal that would in effect have created a nationalised North Sea oil industry—the National Hydrocarbons Corporation. How this was to be financed was obscure. Overall, the North Sea oil-fields are the most expensive to develop in the world. Estimates of the capital required are exceedingly difficult to make but Mackay and Mackay [14] produced forecasts based on the facts then known (1975). They concluded that by 1980 the UK sector would have demanded an investment of over £5000 million and that a further £10 000 million would be required thereafter, the rate of expenditure depending on the rate of extraction agreed. Additionally, expenditure of £1500 million would have been incurred by 1980 on development, and £1800 million on exploration. Thus they were thinking in terms of an overall expenditure of rather over £8000 million by 1980, by which time, as we have noted, Britain would probably only just have begun to be a net exporter.

That such a sum would be forthcoming was implicit in the whole project, but its source needs to be examined. It could certainly not have been raised in its entirety on the UK market, nor even within the European Community. In 1967 the possibility of massive foreign investment by the now suddenly wealthy OPEC countries had not arisen, and it was clear that the greater part would have to come from American banks and financial institutions. These had long experience of dealing with the oil majors and there was no reason to suppose that they would not underwrite the development of North Sea oil and gas which in any case, in the global context, was to them not an overwhelming proposition. But they would naturally prefer to entrust their investment to established companies with a proven record of success; a nationalised British industry, with no background of experience would be a different proposition. With the weak balance of payments situation then pertaining, Britain could not afford to discourage the inflow of foreign capital.

Practicable or not, these political rumblings could not be ignored. By that time interest was beginning to extend to the west of Britain, in what oilmen call the Celtic Sea. When the fourth-round allocations were made it was announced that in these western areas the issue of licences would be dependent on participation of the Gas Council (or the National Coal Board) 'so that the gas industry can gain the practical experience necessary to equip them to play an even more active role in the further development of the U K Continental Shelf'. Hitherto all the Gas Council's exploration and development activities for natural gas in the U K, and in the U K Continental Shelf, had been conducted by a wholly owned subsidiary, Gas Council (Exploration) Ltd. Up to the end of 1969 this company had received interest-free advances totalling £15.8 million from the Gas Council, to be repaid out of expected trading profits. This included exploration (£3.5 million); development wells (£4.5 million); production facilities (£3.3 million); and transmission facilities and terminals (£5.0 million) [14]. Further developments in the Irish Sea and Cardigan Bay were to be promoted by a specially formed subsidiary, Hydrocarbons Great Britain Ltd. Thus, although a nationalised oil industry was not set up, government participation through the existing nationalised industries was enhanced. Further, these industries were to be allowed considerable latitude in their relationships with their partners. The Minister decreed [15] that these might take the form of 'direct partnership or options or other acceptable arrangements which the parties may agree between them'.

NORTH SEA SURVEYS

Such, in brief, were the legal constraints within which North Sea operators had to work. We must now turn our attention to the methods used for locating and extracting petroleum and subsequently bringing it ashore for distribution. Although our principal interest is in gas, it must be emphasised that in the initial stages of exploration the methods used for oil and gas are identical. The prospectors' first objective is to locate geological structures in which oil and gas may be trapped by an overlaying dome of impervious rock. Having located such structures it is possible to determine their contents only by physically probing into them with a drill. This is tedious and very expensive and it seems probable that in the fullness of time new geophysical techniques may make this rather crude approach unnecessary. For the moment, however, it must be accepted as a fact of life that drilling alone can provide the essential information. It is a wasteful and frustrating procedure. On average something like nine wells out of ten are completely negative: if the structures ever contained hydrocarbons they have leaked away long ago. Of the remainder, many may prove to be too limited in extent to warrant exploitation. Worse still, some may prove to contain an abundance of some useless accumulation: the first German bore-hole struck gas, but it consisted largely of nitrogen and was therefore valueless. This was, in fact, rather fortunate, for on this occasion the gas-flow could not be fully contained and it flooded out round the rig. Had it consisted of hydrocarbons a dangerous explosion might have occurred. Other boreholes have struck nothing more valuable than salt water.

In seeking the most promising areas for exploratory drillings, the North Sea prospectors had three established techniques at their disposal. These were respectively magnetic surveying, gravity surveying, and seismic methods: of these the last is the most informative.

Although magnetic surveying indicates little except the variation in the depth of the sedimentary rocks, it has the advantage that it is relatively quick and cheap, since it can be conducted from an aeroplane making a series of spaced traverses of the areas to be studied. Large areas can therefore be quickly mapped. It is a useful means of obtaining a quick overall picture.

Gravity surveys depend on the fact that the attractive force of dense rocks is relatively more than that of lighter ones, such as the salt domes beneath which petroleum may accumulate. Unfortunately, the resulting differences in the earth's total gravitational field are extremely small and not easily measured at sea, the constant movement of which is not conducive to the use of delicate scientific instruments, even when modern stabilised platforms are used. Submarines, which can go below the area of turbulence, have been used but their scope is obviously limited. Nevertheless, a gravity map of the North Sea has been compiled and revealed some low-gravity areas of interest to oilmen, including one on the Dogger Bank in the UK sector.

The greatest amount of information, however, comes from seismic methods (see Plate 23). The term derives from the Greek word *seismos*, meaning an earthquake. In effect, the operator creates, by means of an explosion or sound generator, a shock-wave that travels down through the earth's crust and is partially reflected back at the boundaries between the various strata it traverses. To an expert, the nature of these reflected waves reveals a great deal of detailed information about the nature of the underlying rock structures and their shape. Seismic surveys are more easily carried out at sea than on land, because the explosions can be fired at the surface: on land, a 100-ft borehole has to be drilled first. In practice, the ship sails on a fixed course at a steady speed, trailing a cable behind it carrying detectors set at fixed intervals. At the moment of detonation the detectors are made stationary by paying out cable at the same speed as the ship moves. On land five or ten shots a day is counted good going for one team, but at sea well over 200 shots a day is quite possible in favourable weather. Thus very large areas can quickly be surveyed. In the 1960s other methods of creating shock waves were introduced, such as release of a jet of superheated steam.

Although simple in principle, such surveys demand considerable knowledge, judgment, and specialised equipment. The oil companies carry out such work themselves, but much of it is done by independent contractors, in some of whom the oil companies may, however, have an interest. The first magnetic survey, covering 144 000 square miles of the southern North Sea, was carried out in 1962 by Aero Service, a subsidiary of Litton Industries: it was supported by Shell, Esso, and B P. The Gas Council group's first survey started in 1963. In the mid-1960s more than a score of crews were carrying out seismic surveys in the area. About half of them belonged to Geophysical Service, a subsidiary of Texas Instruments founded in 1931. Other firms included Prakla, owned by the Federal German government, and Compagnie Générale de Géophysie, owned by the French government and the Compagnie Française des Pétroles. Fees were generally calculated on the basis of miles surveyed: £100 per mile would have been an average rate at that time [16]. Some companies invested up to £1 million in seismic surveys alone before making their applications for concession areas. The process tended to be a wasteful one, in that it involved much duplication, some of the survey teams carrying out similar programmes for different clients. However, some discreet exchanges were made: the first Report of the British Gas Corporation (1972/3) refers to 'further data acquired by trade and purchase'.

These surveys provided the basis for licence applications and expressions of preference for drilling locations. By the time the first production licences were issued in 1964 a pretty clear picture of the geology of the land beneath the North Sea had begun to emerge, even though no one party could see it clearly as a whole. In the first round 53 licences were issued to 23 licensees; they covered 348 blocks. The 23 licensees included all the major international oil companies as well as some fifty associated concerns [17, 18]. By this stage a great deal of money had been spent and a great deal more committed. Understandably, all parties were anxious to put their investment to the test, and one concern had started drilling its first deep well before 1964. This was Amoseas, owned jointly by the British subsidiaries of Standard Oil of California and Texaco. This boring was destined, however, to be one of the many unproductive dry holes. Before continuing this story, however, we must briefly indicate what drilling for petroleum entails, especially when it has to be conducted far out in a stormy sea.

EARLY DRILLING TECHNIQUES

Two methods are available for drilling deep holes in the ground. One is the percussion (cable-tool) method, in which a heavy iron (or, later, steel) bar, suspended at the end of a cable, is repeatedly raised and allowed to fall, each operation shattering some rock and driving it a little deeper. Originally done by hand, the advent of the steam engine made it possible to mechanise and speed up the process. By this means it is easily possible to drill holes to a depth of several hundred feet, and by 1900 the Chinese had reached depths of 3000 ft. It was a method very popular in mining and quarrying. The alternative, rotary drilling, was in use at least as early as the Middle Ages for drilling artesian wells. In this method a bit, mounted at the end of a rod, is rotated and virtually screwed into the ground; as it descends other rods are added. In this simple form, the method presents difficulties in extracting the displaced rock. In 1846 a French engineer, Fauvelle, introduced the use of pipes instead of rods to carry the bit; water could be pumped down the drill pipes to flush out the waste material. By this means he drilled wells to a depth of 550 ft at Perpignan. However, the use of the method was limited by the materials available; when E. L. Drake developed his original oil well in Pennsylvania in 1859 he had to rely on wrought iron bits with steel cutting edges. These soon became blunt and had to be renewed. Then, in 1864, Rudolf Leschof, a French engineer invented the diamond drill. In Germany a state mining engineer, Kobrich, pioneered its use in exploratory drilling for salt, coal, and other minerals. By 1909, depths of over 7000 feet had been recorded. At that time such depths were not of interest to the petroleum industry. Drake had struck oil at a mere $69\frac{1}{2}$ feet, and early operations in all parts of the world required only quite shallow bores. In 1901 the Spindletop well, the most productive drilled up to that time, blew out as a gusher at 1100 feet. This situation changed, however, as demand grew and the more easily accessible fields became exhausted. Up to about 1930, drilling rigs normally had a capacity of about 2000 feet, though a cable-tool well drilled in Pennsylvania in 1925 reached 7759 feet. By the 1930s, however, all-steel rigs capable of reaching 8000 feet were appearing.

At the same time, new areas began to be explored. At the turn of the century California oilmen, working from wooden piers, began to exploit the Summerland field close inshore. Between that time and 1930 drilling from piling-supported platforms was carried out on lakes in Louisiana and Venezuela. The first well in open water was drilled in the Caspian Sea, off Baku, in 1925. At about the same time, off the Gulf Coast of America, experimental drillings were attempted not from fixed structures but from floating barges. In 1932 the Texas Company designed a drilling barge designed to rest on the bottom in some 15 feet of water. This concept was developed into the Hayward–Barnsdale drilling barge of 1948; in effect this was an operational platform supported on columns above a floating barge. It could be towed into position and then the barge was sunk to the seabed, leaving the drilling platform well above the sea-level. By the middle of the century, therefore, sophisticated methods of drilling in the open sea were well established and had been used in many parts of the world, though in none as cold and stormy as the North Sea.

OFFSHORE DRILLING RIGS

Such briefly, was the development of offshore drilling up to the eve of the North Sea venture. Three main types of rigs were then in use:

(1) *Jack-up platforms.* These consist essentially of a floating hull, around the periphery of which there are a number of legs which can be jacked up or down. The rig is towed into position (occasionally it is self-propelled) with the legs extended upwards. To allow for the depth of water and finally to raise the hull some 50/60 feet above the waves, the legs may extend upwards as much as 250 feet in the towing position. These rigs have been extensively used in the southern North Sea. A preliminary survey of the seabed is essential to ensure that it will bear the load evenly; otherwise, the rig is likely to capsize.

(2) *Drilling ships.* These are vessels carrying a drilling platform either centrally or over the side. Their successful use depends upon their being maintained precisely in position by anchors or auxiliary propellers, and the drilling equipment must be able to absorb the up and down motion as the ship moves with the waves. They are, therefore, most suitable for relatively calm water.

(3) *The semi-submersible.* This may be likened to the submarine. Buoyancy tanks keep the hull stationary at a level in the water well below the surface turbulence. The working platform is well above sea-level and is much steadier than that of a drill ship.

As with surveys, drilling may be done by contractors; holders of production licences do not necessarily own the rigs they use. Rates are high: jacking platforms are generally the cheapest and the semi-submersible the most expensive. Prices quoted for the mid-1970s [19] were around $10 000 per day for jack-up units and drilling ships and $15–25 000 per day for semi-submersibles.

At the time when the North Sea development began, there were in the world only some 200 mobile offshore rigs that could be used for the task and most of these were unavailable. Such as could be spared were brought to the area, often from great distances. They amounted to some 16 in all: for details see [20]. Thus Shell/Esso's *Orient Explorer* was towed from Borneo in 1965. Unfortunately it was damaged in transit and had to be taken to Rotterdam for repairs and modification. Its place was taken by *Mr Cap*, built in 1957 for the Barnwell Offshore Company; it had been used in the Gulf of Mexico, off the Dutch coast, and had drilled the very first Amoseas well in the UK sector. The *Glomar IV*, a self-propelled drill-ship was brought from Galveston, Texas. By the end of 1965, both *Mr Cap* and *Glomar IV* had moved off again, this time to Nigeria. In the case of *Mr Cap* the reason was that its feet, shaped like inverted saucers, were more suitable for soft mud than for the hard bed of the North Sea.

These resources proved quite insufficient and a massive new building programme was launched. Some forty new units were put in hand in various countries, at a total cost of around £75 million. Eight were commissioned with British shipyards, at a cost of £20 million, a welcome boost to an ailing industry. Among them was the *Ocean Prince* launched only seven months after work commenced. It was built at Smith's Dock, Middlesbrough, for Odeco (UK) Limited, a consortium involving Ocean Drilling and Exploration Company of America, Burmah Oil, Murphy Petroleum, and Imperial Chemical Industries. The cost was £2½ million. This was the same price as the *Orion* ordered by International Drilling from John Brown. It was contracted to drill for Gas Council/Amoco for three years, at the end of which the group had the option to purchase: in the event this option was not taken up.

These costly rigs entail many incidental expenses. Working day and night, they require a crew of around 60. Shore bases are necessary to store supplies, and transport to carry men and material to and from the rigs. Men are often taken to and fro by helicopters, but materials must largely be taken by sea, in vessels that may cost more than £250 000 each. Again, these necessary services are usually supplied by contractors, working from bases on the east coast of Britain such as Great Yarmouth, Lowestoft, Middlesbrough, and Aberdeen. For a list of those operating by 1966, see [21]. The establishment of these has brought new prosperity and employment opportunities to the areas concerned, though it is understandable that the speed of events has also created social problems.

MODERN DRILLING TECHNIQUES

Finally, in this survey of what is involved in bringing gas and oil to the surface from their ancient reservoirs thousands of feet beneath the seabed, we must consider the drilling operation itself. Typically, this involves first driving a steel pipe, two to three feet in diameter, some 100 feet into the ocean floor and cementing it in position. Its top extends well above sea-level, and its purpose is to exclude seawater from the bore-hole. Only then can drilling proper commence. For the first few hundred feet of drilling, a drill-bit some 2-feet in diameter, and turning at about 120 revolutions per minute, would be used. With increasing depth, successively smaller bits are employed. As the bit descends, new sections of pipe, in 30-foot lengths, are added and the bore-hole is lined with more steel casing, so that a continuous steel-tube links the drill platform on the rig to the bottom of the hole, which may be some 14 000 deep. This process has been likened to a dentist operating his drill with his patient the length of a football pitch distant. The task is laborious: in soft rock progress may be made at a rate of 50 or 100 feet per hour, but when hard rock is encountered this may slow to only a few feet per hour. Further, hard rock rapidly blunts the bit and this means that the entire length of pipe to which it is attached has to be hauled up through the bore-hole and dismantled section by section. When the new bit has been attached the whole process has to be repeated in reverse. Drill pipe normally comes in 25/30 foot lengths. To save time and labour, however, it is dismantled in units of three sections, about 90 foot long. It is this procedure that makes necessary the tall derricks that are so characteristic a feature of oil rigs on land or off shore.

In the very early days of drilling artesian wells it was noticed that drilling was easier when muddy, rather than clear, water began to emerge. Quite soon it became regular practice deliberately to pump mud down the borehole. Today, this technique has become highly sophisticated and special chemical muds are prepared for the purpose and trained operators are required to apply them. These, too, have to be transported out to the rigs.

Generally speaking, the operator's aim is to drill a straight vertical hole, and, to ensure this, it is common practice to attach a heavy collar just above the bit. This adds to the weight of the whole assembly, which may exceed 100 tons in a deep bore. To stop the drill-tube buckling, most of the weight must be taken by a block and tackle at the surface. There are occasions, however, when an oblique bore is desired. On land, for example, this may be necessary when the target is situated beneath an urban area and drilling can be done only from the periphery. At sea it may be helpful to explore a considerable underground area from a fixed rig. A deviated bore-hole can be obtained by deflecting the drill-tube with a series of wedges, or whipstocks. By this means the bottom of a deep well may be displaced sideways by as much as a mile. This technique was used to develop the Wytch Farm oil field in Dorset, which when fully developed will be the largest onshore producing field.

As wells are drilled they must be 'logged': that is to say, a record must be kept of all the rock formations traversed. This alone may cost more than £10 000 per well. Logging, too, is often carried out by independent contractors. Today, much logging is done by lowering electric probes down the bore-holes to measure the electrical properties of successive layers of rock [22].

From the above, it is apparent that a great deal of money must be spent and committed before any return whatever can be expected. Depending on circumstances, a single 10 000-foot well in the North Sea may cost £1 million and take three months to complete. At the end of that time the chance of commercial success is no more than one in ten. It has been estimated that before any oil or gas whatever had been struck in the U K sector well over £100 million had been spent. In the other sectors half as much again had been spent.

THE FIRST NORTH SEA GAS

However, if the stakes are high, so too are the rewards for success. We may, therefore, appropriately conclude this catalogue of the practical difficulties with an account of the first success. In the autumn of 1965, on Friday, 17 September, the *Sea Gem*, operated by British Petroleum, was drilling some forty miles off Grimsby, and had been doing so for 104 monotonous days. Hard rock had been encountered at 8500 feet and drilling had slowed to a mere two feet per hour. Then, suddenly, the monotony was broken: the drill fluid coming up from the bottom of the well was frothy, a sign of gas. In itself this was not of special significance, for small pockets of trapped gas are not uncommon. However, it was thought sufficient to warrant a coded message to BP headquarters in London. By Sunday, 19 September, it was clear that this was no mere flash in the pan, and on the following day preliminary measurements of the flow and pressure of the gas were made. These were passed on to BP in London and after discussion it was decided to make a press release in the following cautious terms:

A test in BP's North Sea well now being drilled by the *Sea Gem* forty-two miles east of the Humber has produced gas, but not in sufficient volume to be commercially significant. The well is being drilled deeper in the hope that commercial production may yet be encountered.

Despite these very guarded terms, the press hailed the statement with great excitement and some extravagant predictions were made. On 1 October it was announced that more gas had been found at a deeper level, and the find was described as encouraging. Finally, on Wednesday, 9 December there was an outward and visible sign of success when a 50-foot gas flare was ignited at the top of the rig. This was, in fact, part of a test to measure roughly how much gas was available. If gas is allowed to escape freely, at a measured rate, the resulting drop in pressure indicates how much gas, in all, is available. Shortly afterwards, the Minister of Power informed the House of Commons that the well was yielding 10 million cubic feet of gas a day, a quantity sufficient (if maintained) to justify the laying of a pipeline to bring it ashore, and the drilling of further wells in the immediate vicinity. (See Plate 25.)

North Sea gas was no longer speculation but reality, though the road from this initial find to the creation of a new British gas industry was long and hard. Unhappily, success turned to tragedy before the year was out. On 27 December, as the *Sea Gem* was being prepared for movement to a new site, two of the legs collapsed and the whole rig capsized and sank, with a loss of thirteen of the crew of thirty-two on board; fortunately the number was less than usual because of the Christmas holiday and the impending move.

It has been emphasised that up to the point of actually striking hydrocarbons, the procedure is the same for oil as for gas. From this point onwards, however, the two products must be treated differently. If oil is encountered it can be loaded into tankers at the well-head for transport to refineries on land. If seabed conditions are favourable it can alternatively be pumped ashore through an underwater pipeline. In the case of gas there is, in practice, no alternative to a pipeline. In theory, of course, the gas could be liquefied at source and carried away in tankers, but as we noted earlier, in the context of Sahara gas, the necessary plant is so massive that it is difficult to imagine it being installed anywhere except on land. Nevertheless, this possibility should not be entirely discounted for the future.

UNDERSEA PIPELINES

Before anything at all can be done, the flow of oil or gas must be brought under control by capping the well with an appropriate system of valves and controls, the so-called Christmas Tree. A very important feature of the well-head equipment is the anti-blowout device designed to seal the exit should there be a sudden build-up of pressure. Capping in itself is no easy task.

If the depth of water did not exceed about 150 feet, the laying of a pipeline presented no great difficulties to companies with experience and the necessary specialised equipment. Such pipes had already been laid in many parts of the world, but especially in the Gulf of Mexico. Three different types of pipe laying are employed, namely the bottom-tow method, the lay-barge method, and the spool method. In the bottom-tow method the pipe is assembled on dry land by welding sections together. It is then weighted at intervals, given a suitable protective coating, and drawn by winch or boat across the stretch of water to be spanned. It is normally used for relatively short spans, as in crossing rivers, but much longer spans have been success-fully accomplished. The method was used, for example, to span fifteen miles of the Arabian Gulf between a new deep-water berth for large tankers and the Fao base of the Basrah Petroleum Company. In such cases the pipe is not prefabricated as a whole, but new sections are welded on as the tow proceeds. Generally, an underwater trench is dredged out to contain the pipeline.

In the lay-barge method, sections of pre-coated pipe—usually about 25-feet in length—are welded together successively on a specially equipped ship. As the barge works slowly forward the pipe hangs in the water in the form of a catenary—the shape assumed by a rope anchored at either end. If the water is no more than 200-feet deep the pipe is strong enough to hang without support: in deep water it must be supported by a submerged 'stinger'. Once laid, a trench is dug to contain and protect the pipe, and it is weighted down sufficiently to avoid risk of displacement by bottom currents. The route of the pipeline must be carefully surveyed to avoid unsupported stretches that might be liable to fracture. The lay-barge method is relatively straightforward in good weather, but impossible in bad. (See Plate 24.)

Finally, we must mention the more recent spool method, in which the welded pipeline is carried out to sea on a huge horizontal spool, from which it is unwound as the boat progresses. Before being consigned to the sea it is given a protective coating. In effect, this is similar to the lay-barge method but avoids the necessity of carrying out welding at sea.

The original B P find was in what is now known as the West Sole Field. The task of laying the 16-inch pipeline to bring the gas ashore was contracted out to what was generally regarded as the leading firm in this business; namely Brown and Root, a subsidiary of the Halliburton Company. Predictably, they elected to use the lay-barge method. Originally it was planned to bring it ashore near Cleethorpes, but the Silver Pitt trench lay in the way. To avoid this the line was diverted to Easington on the N. Humberside coast just north of the Humber. The cost has been stated to have been between £200 000 and £300 000 per mile. From that point onwards the transmission of the gas became the responsibility of the Gas Council, who concurrently started to plan and construct a 24-inch main, crossing the Humber and linking up at Totley, near Sheffield, with the existing high-pressure main distributing Algerian natural gas from Canvey Island to Leeds. The Easington terminal became operational early in 1967. Events had moved quickly, and not without risk. Two major questions had to be faced. Firstly, how much gas was available? Secondly, at what price should it be sold? While there were high hopes that more gas would be found there was, at this early stage, no guarantee of it.

THE FIRST CONTRACT

It was unusual, and possibly unique, for the potential of a field to be judged largely on the evidence of a single borehole. Nevertheless, this is what B P did in the case of West Sole. After protracted negotiations with the Gas Council—to whose Regional Boards all gas intended for use as fuel had first to be offered—the Company contracted to deliver gas at the rate of not less than 50 million cubic feet daily for fifteen years. Clearly, if against expectations this rate of production could not be maintained B P would be in difficulties. The same would apply to the Gas Council, for such supplies of natural gas could not be absorbed without substantial reorganisation of the industry. If it was for any reason not forthcoming their difficulties would be very great.

Even when this risk was acceptable to both parties they found themselves wide apart as regards prices. The Gas Council, anxious to keep their costs low, offered $2\frac{1}{2}d$. to $4d$. per therm, while B P, anxious to maximise their profits, thought in terms of $6d$. to $7d$. In the event a compromise price of $5d$. was agreed, after some intervention by the Minister of Power, who stressed that this first agreement (for three years in the first instance) should not be regarded as setting a precedent. This was, of course, wishful thinking: it was clear that future negotiations could not be conducted as though the B P/Gas Council agreement did not exist.

SHORE TERMINALS

However, before pursuing these commercial considerations in detail, we may conveniently conclude this chapter by describing other new technological factors. BP's responsibility ended when it delivered the gas at Easington, but it could not do so in the crude form in which it escaped from the seabed. It is at that stage saturated with water vapour which may combine in the pipeline with methane to form solid hydrates in quantities sufficient to block the system. There may also be a similarly troublesome accumulation of solid hydrocarbons. Existing 'slugs' of liquid impurities had to be extracted, and remaining water vapour removed by refrigeration, before the gas was acceptable to the Gas Council as the purchaser.

On the Gas Council's side of the Easington terminal a complex system of control equipment was necessary to take account on the one hand of variations in the rate of supply from the North Sea, and on the other of the fluctuating demands of the various regions concerned. Provision had to be made for metering the gas as regards both volume and quality; for controlling flow; for injecting methanol to avoid further formation of solid hydrates; for adding an odorant to the gas so that consumers could readily detect any leaks; for blending gas from different sources, if necessary; and so on. Only when all this had been done could the gas pass on to the feeder mains supplying the UK gas grid.

The laying of the submarine pipeline, the construction of the considerable shore terminal at Easington, and the linking-up with the high-pressure grid was a considerable undertaking. It was a remarkable achievement to complete it all so quickly that within less than 18 months of the proving of West Sole this field was supplying some 10 per cent of all Britain's gas. For the moment, however, this had to be reformed to make it compatible with existing manufactured gas. The full utilisation of North Sea gas, as such, still lay in the future.

NEW FIELDS

It was not a distant future, however. Between the summers of 1966 and 1967 three further large fields—Hewett, Leman Bank, and Indefatigable—were discovered off the Norfolk coast. The producers included a small Gas Council interest. The Gas Council thus became a producer as well as a customer. However, it was not the Council's policy to become a major producer; its chief concern was to gain sufficient experience and status to strengthen its negotiating position. The gas from these new fields comes ashore at a new terminal occupying some 180 acres of land on the low cliffs at Bacton, near Norwich (see Plate 26). Direct access was not possible because of the shifting Haisborough Sands which intervene. The Leman Field, the largest then discovered, became operative in August 1968. Indefatigable delivered its first gas ashore in September 1971.

Concurrently, the National Coal Board had achieved success with Conoco by the discovery of the Viking Field, with a shore terminus at Theddlethorpe on the Lincolnshire coast. This came into operation in the summer of 1972. The small Rough Field, discovered in 1968 by Gulf Oil, was not developed until after 1973, when it was transferred, with the approval of the Minister, to the Gas Council/Amoco group, which held an adjacent block. Its gas first came ashore, at Easington, in 1975.

All the above fields are alike in that their gas comes from the Rotliegendes sandstone, like Slochteren. Events took a new course with the discovery of an onshore field near Lockton, in Yorkshire. The producers were the Gas Council and Home Oil, the latter representing Canadian interests, including the Canadian Pacific Railway. This field, which was operational by the summer of 1971, derived its gas from a shallower formation, the Middle Magnesian Limestone, encountered at about 6000 feet. The gas was of slightly inferior quality in that it contained some sulphur, which must be removed: Rotliegendes gas is sulphur-free. As it was inappropriate to process the gas at Lockton, which is in the North Yorkshire Moors National Park, the terminal was established outside the Park, at Pickering. The field was, however, closed in 1974, owing to a steady decline in yield.

Finally, brief mention must be made of an important later development. This is the Frigg Field, located some 200 miles off the Aberdeen coast. It straddles the Norwegian–British demarcation line and although the same companies were working on both sides, separate contracts had to be made for each. Prompted no doubt by the physical barrier presented by the Norwegian Deep, which precluded the laying of a pipeline, the Norwegian government in 1973 approved an agreement for British gas to purchase the output, then expected to reach 1500 million cubic feet daily. To cope with this, Total Marine Oil contracted to lay a 240-mile undersea pipeline, via an intermediary offshore platform, to St Fergus near Peterhead. Depths of 400 feet had to be traversed and the pipeline was the longest of its kind in the world until the implementation of the Brent line. Crimond had been the producers' first choice for a shore base but the government refused to make it available. From St Fergus a land-line takes the gas south to link up with the existing high-pressure network.

The location of these fields is important. With the exception of Frigg, all are relatively close inshore: most of the major centres of population are within 150 miles of the terminals. American experience had shown that costs rise sharply with distance from source. Thus in 1966 Texas Eastern had a system of zone prices which varied by a factor of 2.5 between local (100 mile radius) customers, and those in the New York area (1500 miles).

The combined capacity of Easington, Bacton, Theddlethorpe, and Pickering was over 7000 million cubic feet per day, of which over half was represented by Bacton. This must, of course, be distinguished from actual throughput: in 1967 Britain's gas consumption amounted to no more than about 1000 million cubic feet equivalent natural gas daily. The vitally important thing was that supplies were sufficiently assured for the Gas Council to base its future policy on natural gas alone. The Gas Council's Annual Report for 1971/2 announced that facilities at both Bacton and Easington had been substantially increased.

INLAND TRANSMISSION AND STORAGE

To put this policy into effect the Gas Council had to have not only an absolutely reliable supply of natural gas but the means of transmitting it nationwide. Until this was done, it would be necessary to continue to manufacture some gas. A start had been made with the Canvey Island/Leeds high-pressure main and this had been extended to Easington, but far more was necessary. Four new 36-inch feeders brought Bacton into the system. They ran respectively to Churchover, near Rugby; Whitwell, near Stevenage; and Horndon-on-the-Hill, Essex. They were completed between 1968 and 1971. Pickering and Theddlethorpe were connected with the system in 1971 and 1972 respectively. Additionally, a ring main was laid round the Greater London area from Whitwell, through Slough and Mogador, and then on to connect with the original Canvey Island/Leeds main at Horndon. Compressor stations were necessary at intervals of about 40 miles.

The construction of this system required easements from many landowners. The negotiation of these was much facilitated by an agreement reached in 1966 with the National Farmers' Union and the Country Landowners' Association.

This, however, sufficed only to improve the supply to the eight Regions already receiving imported natural gas. It was, therefore, necessary to extend the whole system to bring in the other four Regions—Scottish, Wales, Northern, and South Western. The new pipelines extended to Glenmavis (near Glasgow), Wrexham, Runcorn, and Exeter. With the completion of these all the Regions had access to North Sea gas, its onward distribution within these areas being their own responsibility. The completed national trunk network totalled some 2000 miles.

From its earliest days, the gas industry has had problems arising from the daily and seasonal fluctuations in demand. This could be met partly by keeping reserves of gas in gasholders. The advent of North Sea gas did not solve this problem, though the cushioning effect of the large quantity of gas stored at high pressure in the transmission system itself was helpful. It was still necessary to provide stored reserves of gas at strategic points, and in doing this the liquefaction process, impossible with coal gas, was utilised. Above-ground storage tanks for liquid gas, with a total capacity of 5000 tons (equivalent to 250 million cubic feet of gas), were built at Ambergate, Derbyshire, and supplied by road tankers from Canvey Island. Further storage was required at Glenmavis, but this was beyond the effective range of road tankers from Canvey. It was decided, therefore, to liquefy gas on the spot and the necessary plant was completed there in 1972. It had a capacity of 20 000 tons, and could supply gas at the rate of 250 million cubic feet per day. It was designed primarily to accumulate liquid gas in the slack summer months, to be available in winter. Above-ground storage became standard; the frozen ground technique used at Canvey Island proved to present considerable technical problems and was not adopted elsewhere.

In many parts of the world surplus gas is stored in natural underground reservoirs known as aquifers. In these, water is trapped beneath an impervious rock dome, just as gas may be. If surplus gas is pumped into such a formation the water is displaced and we create, in effect, an artificial gas field which can be tapped at will. Unfortunately, such geological formations are rare in Britain, though an apparently suitable one has been located at Chilcomb in Hampshire. This is not ideal, as a shallow aquifer such as this is capable of storing gas at only relatively low pressure (300 lb per square inch). The gas would, therefore, have to be recompressed before return to the grid. However, the site is near the Southampton/Portsmouth conurbations where there is an industrial market for low-pressure gas. There was also a proposal to use the short-lived natural gas reservoir at Lockton.

By the early 1970s Britain's gas industry had effected a technological revolution. Fully adequate supplies of natural gas had been secured from North Sea fields; means had been provided for bringing it ashore and distributing it throughout the country by a high-pressure network of mains; and storage facilities had been created to solve the problems of peak loads. The properties of the new gas were, however, not the same as those of the manufactured gas it replaced and in the next chapter the implications of this must be considered.

REFERENCES

[1] 692 HC Deb. (5th Ser.) 897 (1964).
[2] DAM, Kenneth W. Oil and Gas Licensing and the North Sea, *Journal of Law and Economics*, **8**, 51 (1968).
   Idem. The Pricing of North Sea Gas in Britain, *Journal of Law and Economics*, **11**, 31 (1970).
[3] VAN MEURS, A. P. H. *Petroleum Economics and Offshore Mining Legislation: a Geological Evaluation*, pp. 64–85, Elsevier, Amsterdam (1971).
[4] VAN MEURS, A. P. H. op. cit., pp. 104–49.
[5] ERROL, F. J. Ministry of Power Release No. 4327, 17 September 1964.
[6] BUNYAN, Richard. *Ireland and Natural Gas*, p. 70, United Dominions Trust (Ireland) Ltd., Dublin (1974).
[7] VAN MEURS, A. P. H. op. cit., p. 173.
[8] DAM, Kenneth W. *Oil Resources: Who Gets What How?* University of Chicago Press, Chicago (1976).
[9] ROBINSON, C. *Competition for Fuel*, Institute for Economic Affairs, London (1971).
[10] MACKAY, D. I. and MACKAY, G. A. *The Political Economy of the North Sea*, p. 29, Martin Robertson, London (1975).

[11] COOPER, Bryan and GASKELL, T. F. *North Sea Oil—The Great Gamble*, pp. 58–9, Heinemann, London (1966).
[12] MACKAY, D. I. and MACKAY, G. A. op. cit., p. 95.
[13] 716 HC Deb. (5th Ser.) 1579 (1965).
[14] GAS COUNCIL. *Annual Reports and Accounts 1968/69*, pp. 27–8, HMSO, London (1969).
[15] 761 HC Deb. (5th Ser.) 1734 (1969).
[16] COOPER, Bryan and GASKELL, T. F. op. cit., pp. 74–5.
[17] Idem. Appendix A, pp. 151–63.
[18] HINDE, Peter. *Fortune in the North Sea*, Appendix I, pp. 191–220, Foulis, London (1966).
[19] HINDE, Peter. Exploration for Petroleum with Particular Reference to N.W. Europe. Paper presented to Institute of Petroleum Symposium, Aberdeen, 1972 (Revised March 1975).
[20] Idem. *Fortune in the North Sea*, Appendix II, pp. 221–38, Foulis, London (1966).
[21] COOPER, Bryan and GASKELL, T. F. op. cit., Appendix B, pp. 165–72.
[22] HINDE, Peter. *Exploration for Petroleum with Particular Reference to N. W. Europe*, p. 7.

BIBLIOGRAPHY

ALLCOCK, J. F. *Natural Gas Purchasing*, Institution of Gas Engineers, Communication No 1062, London (1978).

BRANTLY, J. E. *History of Oil Well Drilling*, Gulf Publishing Co., Houston (1971).

CALLOW, C. *Power from the Sea—The Search for North Sea Oil and Gas*. Gollancz, London (1973).

COMMISSION OF THE EUROPEAN COMMUNITIES. *New Technologies for Exploration and Exploitation of Oil and Gas Resources*, Symposium: Luxembourg, April 1979, Graham and Trotman, London (1979).

COOPER, Bryan and GASKELL, T. F. *North Sea Oil—The Great Gamble*, Heinemann, London (1966).

DAM, Kenneth. *Oil Reserves: Who Gets What How?*, University of Chicago Press, Chicago (1976).

THE GAS COUNCIL. *A Progress Report on North Sea Gas Contract Negotiations*, The Gas Council, London (1967).

HINDE, Peter. *Fortune in the North Sea*, Foulis, London (1966).

History of Petroleum Engineering, American Petroleum Institute, New York (1961).

KATZ, D. *et al. Handbook of Natural Gas Engineering*. McGraw–Hill, New York (1959).

MACKAY, D. I. and MACKAY, G. A. *The Political Economy of the North Sea*, Martin Robertson, London (1975).

PIRSON, S. J. *Elements of Oil Reservoir Engineering*, McGraw–Hill, New York (1950).

TAINSH, S. R. and CHURCHFIELD, S. E. 'Production of Petroleum and Natural Gas', in *A History of Technology*, WILLIAMS, Trevor I. (ed.), Vol. VI, pp. 376–409, Oxford University Press, Oxford (1978).

VAN MEURS, A. P. H. *Petroleum Economics and Offshore Mining Legislation: a Geological Evaluation*, Elsevier, Amsterdam (1971).

17

Conversion

It had been said, with a good deal of truth, that science owed more to the steam engine than the steam engine did to science. Much the same may be said of the gas industry for, as we have seen in earlier chapters, most of the pioneers were not trained scientists but practical men of affairs with a bent for mechanics or financial organisation. In the early years of the nineteenth century, when the foundations of the gas industry were being laid, the very nature of gases was only just being realised. Only gradually did it become clear that they were not just ill-defined 'humours' or 'airs', but specific substances as sharply defined as silver and lead or water and alcohol. Moreover, they have properties, such as weight and density, that can be measured precisely. However, these important distinctions emerged only slowly and were fully appreciated only by those with some technical training. Even in the middle of the twentieth century the ordinary citizen had somewhat hazy ideas about gases. Where there are marked differences there are no great problems: everybody recognises chlorine by its smell as the agent used to sterilise drinking water and swimming baths: carbon dioxide as the gas used to make fizzy drinks; neon as the one used in some street lamps; acetylene as a gas used for welding; and so on.

DIFFERENCES BETWEEN NATURAL AND MANUFACTURED GAS

From the point of view of application, manufactured and natural gas have none of the obvious differences that distinguish chlorine from neon or carbon dioxide from acetylene. To the ordinary citizen both were—and are—simply 'gas': they can come into his home through the same supply pipes, and they can both be burned in the same sort of appliances. Even if natural gas proved cheaper it would not be so much so as to cause general excitement: if gas were in future to be supplied in unlimited quantities for a small fixed price, like water, that would have been a very different story. Insofar as they thought about it at all, most people supposed that in the fullness of time North Sea gas would gradually take over from ordinary gas, and the change would be no more noticeable than when the first atomic electricity was fed into the national grid from the Calder Hall nuclear power station in 1956.

The reality was very different. As we have already noted, the chemical composition of North Sea gas is so different from that of manufactured gas (whether made from coal or oil) that it simply would not burn satisfactorily in existing appliances, nor would any simple adjustment of them overcome the difficulty. Having committed itself in the summer of 1966 to the direct supply of North Sea gas, the Gas Council had automatically committed itself also to the costly operation of modifying virtually every gas appliance in Britain. As part of the capital development programme this required government sanction. The full extent of the task could not at that stage be determined. Although the total number of consumers could, of course, be discovered through the Area Boards, there were no records to show how many separate appliances each one had. In the domestic field, for example, there would be households which had only a simple gas-cooker, and lodging houses with a multiplicity of gas-rings. With some 12 million domestic consumers on their books, the Area Boards would clearly have to be thinking in terms of around 30 million home appliance conversions, even if the average number of appliances per household was not more than three. Whatever the number, it was mounting rapidly. In 1964/5 the sale of new appliances, designed for manufactured gas, was running at the rate of over two million per annum [1], though some of these, of course, were replacements of old ones. While the number of commercial [about 500 000] and industrial [about 60 000] consumers was much less, each could be expected to have a higher average number of appliances. It must be remembered, too, that one appliance might contain several burners: a cooker, for example, would normally have 3/4 top burners, a grill, and an oven. Apart from the formidable total, there was a great variety of appliances to be considered. There were known to be thousands of different models in use, some long obsolete. In the event, there proved to be 35 million appliances distributed among $13\frac{1}{2}$ million premises: there were 8000 different domestic appliance models to convert, containing in all about 200 million burners.

From these figures alone it was obvious that the task of conversion would be an immense and lengthy one, fraught not only with purely technical difficulties but others connected with marketing, public relations, and so on. To co-ordinate this complex ten-year programme a Conversion Executive was set up at the end of 1966 as successor to a Conversion Committee which had established general policy. W. D. Ellis, formerly Deputy Manager of Watson House, was appointed Conversion Manager. His task was to organise the national programme; determine the national need for conversion kits; and provide a channel of communication between Area Boards and the Gas Council. For a few months in 1966 he had the benefit of the advice of C. V. Kroeger of Esso, who had had considerable American and European experience of conversions, but otherwise the Gas Council relied entirely on their own resources. In April 1968 the Conversion Executive was embodied in the newly created Marketing Division. The related organisational problems we will leave for later consideration, and concentrate for the moment on the strictly practical aspects. As a preliminary, we may usefully remind ourselves of the salient differences between manufactured and natural gas.

Natural gas has roughly twice the calorific value of normal town gas made by carbonising coal (roughly 1000 Btu per cubic foot compared with 500). It requires roughly twice as much air to burn it completely (about 9 cubic feet per cubic foot of gas, compared with 4). If it does not get this supply of air, only partial combustion occurs and a flickering, smoky flame is all that will be achieved.

The traditional burner was designed to draw in air at the correct rate as the gas issued at high speed from an orifice. It was then burned at the port, where a little secondary air was drawn in. This mixture gave the characteristic blue smokeless flame denoting complete combustion. To achieve the same result with natural gas the size of the orifice must be reduced and the pressure of the gas increased (from $2\frac{1}{2}$ inches of water for town gas to about 8 inches for natural gas). By this means the gas jet automatically draws in the right amount of air to achieve complete combustion. So far so good, but a further complication arises because of differences in the flame-speed factor (page 58): after ignition, a flame travels roughly three times as quickly through manufactured as through natural gas. If the flame cannot, as it were, keep pace with the gas issuing from the ports it will 'lift off': that is to say, instead of the flame being stabilized at the burner it may burn a little above it. Apart from the inconvenience of this, such a flame can very easily be blown out by draughts. For this problem there were two possible solutions. The first was to fit a small retention flame below the main flame so that the latter would be immediately re-ignited should it lift. The second was to reduce the speed at which gas issued from the ports by making them larger, but this was less easy than it sounds. Larger ports usually meant a larger burner and this could not necessarily be accommodated in an existing appliance: further, lower gas speed at the orifice meant that less secondary air was drawn in, to the detriment of the flame.

While the basic principles were perfectly well understood, thanks in substantial measure to work done over the years at Watson House, their application was a tricky matter. Flames, especially those associated with gas issuing from small apertures at high speed, are very sensitive. To make new appliances designed to burn natural gas efficiently was a great deal easier than to modify, as a field operation, some tens of millions of existing ones. We may perhaps compare it to modifying the carburettor of a motor-car to utilise a very different grade of fuel: every practical motorist knows the difficulty of getting jet sizes and air mixtures exactly right to suit new conditions.

THE CANVEY ISLAND CONVERSION

In 1965, the Gas Council, through the North Thames Gas Board, embarked on a pilot conversion scheme [2]. The site chosen was Canvey Island, which had been the UK terminal for imported liquefied natural gas since the first shipment from the USA by the *Methane Pioneer* in February 1959. The choice was a logical one, in that there was an assured supply of natural gas on the spot, and the possibility of conversion had already been considered as early as 1963. Being on an island, the community supplied could very easily be isolated from the rest of the Board's system. A further consideration was that by 1965 the local increase in demand was such that the Board faced difficulty in meeting its future commitments without some substantial increase in capacity. With the increase in gas central heating, and wider use of gas fires, the Board faced a possible doubling of peak day-demand within three years. To meet this new demand and avoid heavy capital expenditure on new manufacturing plant, a crash programme of conversion was embarked upon. The decision to go ahead was taken in the autumn of 1965, with a view to carrying out the whole scheme in June and July of the following year. By any standard it was an ambitious project; to attempt it in Britain, with no previous experience, might have been judged foolhardy. Nevertheless, it all turned out reasonably satisfactorily. In the gas industry's published account of the exercise [2] it is recorded (1966):

The exercise has proved to be a success. . . . Technically, it has been nothing like so fearsome as had been expected . . . The customers at Canvey are well satisfied and relations between them and the Board are very good indeed.

Even if it is noted later in the same account that 'complaint work will be reduced as the standard of conversions improves'—and that some independent commentators (p. 188) were less than kind—we may agree that this exercise was indeed a success, bearing in mind that it was the first of its kind in Britain. It deserves to be studied in some detail, for it was in many, but certainly not all, respects a model for the national programme that followed.

Canvey Island lies in the Thames about 30 miles from London and has an area of some six square miles. In 1931 it was linked to the mainland by a bridge at South Benfleet. In 1965 the Board had some 7850 customers there. Until some years previously it had been primarily a place to which people retired or where they maintained holiday homes, and it had a large proportion of old-age pensioners. It was, therefore, not representative of the North Thames area as a whole. Latterly, however, it had attracted a growing number of permanent residents, mainly as a result of the local growth of light industry and the establishment of petroleum refineries. In 1953 it had suffered a disastrous flood and following this a large number of gas mains and services were relaid: the conversion programme was, therefore, unlikely to be complicated by the discovery of defects in the distribution system. The earlier (1963/4) proposal to convert the island to natural gas had got as far as a survey of existing appliances, the result of which was as follows:

APPLIANCES IN USE ON CANVEY
ISLAND IN 1964
[Figures in parentheses indicate results of a
later survey, January–April 1966]

Meters	6600	[7885]
Cookers	6126	[6959]
Water-heaters	3750	[4505]
Refrigerators	1513	[1927]
Fires	1042	[2696]
Portable heaters	485	[717]
Radiators	179	[392]
Central heating boilers	143	[545]
Solid-fuel grates	1088	[911]
Wash-boilers	1270	[1203]
Washing machines	144	[133]
Boiling rings	346	[446]
Drying units	201	[239]
Pokers	425	[597]
Pistols	548	[581]
Light fittings	684	
Gas irons	12	
Towel rails	10	
Incinerators	8	[760]
Grills	6	
Bunsen burners	63	
Blow torches	2	

More detailed analysis of the results of this preliminary survey showed a considerable
variation in the age of appliances in use.

AGE CATEGORY OF APPLIANCES FOUND ON CANVEY [%]

Appliance	Under 5 yrs	5–10 yrs	10–15 yrs	Over 15 yrs
Cookers	30	17	12	22
Room heaters	48	14	3	35
Sink water-heaters	14	40	1	45
Bath and multi-point water-heaters	42	25	21	12
Refrigerators	31	42	24	3
Washing machines and wash-boilers	34	22	7	37

On the basis of this information each appliance manufacturer (in so far as he
was still in business) was visited to discuss the nature of the conversion kits
required. For current and recent models the assembly of these presented
mainly technical problems which could be solved without too much difficulty
. on the basis of the combined knowledge and experience of the manufac-

turers (who already had experience of supplying to overseas markets appliances designed to burn natural gas), the Board, and—above all—Watson House. The biggest difficulty was the speed with which they were required, but the great majority were in fact available within six months, together with instruction leaflets for the fitters. Such complaints as there were largely emanated, understandably and justifiably, from the small residue of customers whose kits were not available on time. The use of such kits, unique to this country, proved highly successful in the main programme starting at Burton on Trent in the summer of 1967.

The older and obsolete appliances naturally presented greater problems, and it was decided as a matter of general policy not to seek conversion kits for appliances of which ten or less were identified on the island. The orders to manufacturers were subsequently modified on the basis of a further complete survey of all premises carried out in the first four months of 1966: these amended figures are shown in parenthesis in the accompanying table recording the results of the 1964 survey. The biggest change, in accordance with the national trend, was the increase in the number of gas fires found to be in use.

This second survey produced a complete written record of every gas appliance on the island. Each customer visited was asked to sign the survey form as a true record of all the items in his possession. The citizens of Canvey Island are no doubt as honest as those in the rest of Britain, but the Board thought it prudent to protect itself against the possibility of customers subsequently buying-in antiquated appliances, at a trifling price, and claiming free replacement by modern ones. As it was, the Board had to provide over 800 free appliances to replace old ones, the conversion of which proved impracticable. Generally speaking, these were not new models but reconditioned ones, which the great majority of customers were only too glad to accept.

At the same time, the opportunity was taken to draw consumers' attention to the advantages of purchasing new appliances, purpose-built for natural gas, instead of having their old ones converted. As an inducement, prospective customers were offered allowances equivalent to what the Board would save by not having to effect the conversion: this was in addition to the usual trade-in allowance then current. As an example, the owner of a current-model cooker might claim up to £16; at that time, this would have made a substantial contribution towards the cost of a new natural-gas cooker. Under this scheme 1652 replacement appliances were sold, mostly cookers and water-heaters (1195 and 252 respectively).

A few diehards stood by their strict legal right to have their appliances, however old, converted. This was a workshop job, inevitably difficult and expensive. On the other hand, some Islanders were so impressed by the visiting evangelists preaching conversion that they bought additional new appliances.

While these urgent matters of supply were being put in hand, the Board launched a considerable public-relations campaign. It would have been naive to have supposed that there would be much spontaneous public enthusiasm for conversion. For the domestic consumer, who predominated, it seemed to promise at best the inconvenience of form-filling, of visiting officials, of having supply interrupted, of having fitters working in the house and—at the end of the day—no evident difference in performance or much lowering of cost. For the minority of industrial and commercial consumers much the same arguments applied, except that the consequences of supply interruption were likely to be more serious, often requiring that conversion work be done at night or weekends. Clearly, as much as possible had to be made of the advantages. In the main, these were that every appliance had free servicing and was brought up to a high standard of performance and safety; owners were made aware of appliances that were dangerous because of defects or because they were not properly installed; and the opportunity to buy new appliances on favourable terms. Wisely, the Board amended the gas tariff to allow 1d. off the commodity rates for gas for all customers. This, it is recorded, 'proved to be an undoubted advantage in determining the many minor problems that arose between the Board and customers during the various phases of conversion work'.

The campaign was pressed at two levels: first, with the various relevant organisations on the Island and, secondly, with the individual consumers. The first move, before any public announcement was made, was to inform the Urban District Council of the proposals: old-age pensioners, of whom there was a rather high proportion, were informed through their organisations. A special display was mounted in the Board's local showroom and Home Service Advisers gave special demonstrations of natural gas in use. Particular care was taken to establish liaison with the police, whose co-operation would be essential in coping with traffic problems resulting from road works, parked vehicles, and the like.

As soon as the press had been informed, all customers were informed of the Board's intentions and this was followed up by a personal visit. Subsequently, as a firm programme emerged, a further letter was sent and a card giving the exact date on which conversion would be effected.

With the supply of conversion kits in train and customers conditioned as far as possible for the change, there remained the formidable task of organising the work, which would have to be done with military precision. If the scheme was badly carried out, and there was much public dissatisfaction, the repercussions would spread far beyond Canvey Island and be damaging to the industry as a whole. As a general basis, it was agreed that every domestic consumer should have at least the cooker available for use by the evening of the first day; all other appliances should be converted by the second or third day. This requirement to a considerable extent dictated the logistics of the whole exercise. Initially a three-day cycle twice a week was adopted, but later this was improved to a two-day cycle three times a week. This was a very great improvement on some conversion programmes overseas, which had been studied by Gas Council staff, who had visited Belgium, France, and Germany. In some cases abroad, supply had been interrupted for as long as 3–4 weeks, but it was not thought that UK customers would accept this.

The necessary fitters were derived from the Board's own staff, drawing on Canvey Island itself and the two adjacent divisions. In all, 250 were thus made available, the more easily so because conversion was scheduled for the relatively slack months of June and July. This number of fitters was judged rather more than sufficient, rightly as it proved, to deal with 24 sectors, each containing around 350 houses: the over-provision arose from the Board's understandable anxiety that this preliminary exercise should go well. In later conversions the size of sector tended to be based on the expected number of appliances rather than number of premises. The fitters worked in teams of twelve, each of which was drawn from the same depot so that they were already used to working together. Smooth working was further facilitated by keeping in close touch with the trade unions and shop stewards concerned.

In the course of conversion, town gas must be flushed out of the system and completely replaced by natural gas before the supply is re-connected to the consumer. It was, therefore, necessary to isolate the sector being converted at any given time. Fortunately the Canvey area was already served by a high-pressure mains system well supplied with valves, and only 27 additional valves had to be installed. Great care had then to be taken to make absolutely certain that the valves did in fact isolate the sector in question, to ensure that there was no leak into or from it. As in other areas, the Canvey Island system had grown up more haphazardly than would be tolerated today and it was not unknown for premises outside the sector to be supplied from mains within it. Most of these anomalies were cleared up by patient survey work beforehand.

Despite this careful preparation a few surprises occurred, but none beyond the capacity of the local organisation. A few householders telephoned to say that there was 'something wrong with the gas': these proved to be strays living outside a converted sector but supplied from it. All such complaints were remedied by effecting conversion the same day. Rather more serious was the discovery, at five o'clock one evening, that a school canteen, supplying 1200 meals a day, fell into this category; it was supplied with gas from a sector due to be converted the following day. This emergency was met by working on the conversion all night so that natural gas was available in the morning. On one occasion a sector-isolating valve proved defective, allowing town gas to seep back, and the area had to be re-purged. On the whole, however, it is fair to say that such incidents were remarkably few and were effectively dealt with.

On Canvey Island prepayment meters predominated. Since these measure the volume of gas passing through them, whereas gas is now sold according to its thermal value, they had all to be reset to take account of the fact that the new natural gas had roughly twice the calorific value of the town gas it replaced. Like other appliances, a number of meters did not lend themselves to conversion and had to be replaced: this was usually done before conversion day.

By comparison with private houses, industrial and commercial conversions were simple because the number involved was small. There were only 40 industrial appliances on the Island and the work necessary for their conversion was all carried out in the industrial laboratory of the Bromley-by-Bow works. Commercial conversions were carried out at night: in those cases, particularly cafés, where even brief interruption of supply was unacceptable, Calor gas cylinders and hotplates were made available.

Bearing in mind the total lack of previous experience, and the speed with which the Canvey Island conversion was carried out, the North Thames Gas Board was justified in claiming it as a success. The judgment of the Consumers' Association 'that this pilot operation can be thought of as a success only if in future conversions the Gas Boards are able to eliminate the many problems that arose' [3] seems, in retrospect, unduly harsh. The account [2] on which this history of conversion at Canvey has largely been based states that a 100 per cent complaint load was recorded in the first three months after conversion, but adds that this had been expected on the basis of experience of Continental operators. It is clear, however, that while some of these were quite legitimate complaints—arising mainly from excessive delay in delivery of certain conversion kits—others were trivial. For example, there were over 2000 complaints of leaks. While some of these were justifiable, the primary cause was over-odorisation of the new gas: the inevitable minor leaks just made themselves too apparent. Again, many customers were slow to realise that with natural gas the flame is much more sensitive to the control tap on cookers and rings, making it necessary to take greater care when simmering. A further reason was that the very process of conversion gave people a sudden new interest in gas:

Customers largely accept indifferent performances of their appliances without comment, because the deterioration takes place over a long period. Conversion, however, excites their interest in gas and the performance of their appliances. Inevitably, this leads to their demanding a higher standard of performance from these appliances than they were experiencing before.

The whole Canvey Island exercise was carefully monitored, and an encouraging improvement in the use of fitters' time was recorded as the work went on. Working time rose from 46 to 54 per cent and waiting time diminished from 29 to 22 per cent. The work was carefully costed and

worked out at approximately £32 per dwelling, of which about £25 represented actual conversion and the balance was made up by distribution
costs (£4) and general administration (£3).

As we have noted, Canvey Island was not a typical community, but the
conversion there was a valuable proving ground for the national scheme that
was to follow. There were, however, certain special circumstances to be
noted:

(1) Canvey was essentially a crash programme for a small community, so
there was little time to learn by experience as the work proceeded. By
contrast, the national scheme was spread over some ten years.

(2) The Canvey conversion was not to North Sea Gas but to imported
liquid gas from Algeria which is very similar, but not identical, in composition. The differences were sufficient to call for further slight modifications in
appliances in some Regions, particularly in the early stages of the national
programme when the quality of the kits left something to be desired and they
only just conformed to acceptable tolerance limits.

No history of the gas industry in Britain would be complete without an
account of the conversion of Canvey Island, which is historically doubly
significant, as being also the site of the first natural-gas terminal in Britain. It
would, however, be laborious to record the story of conversion in the rest of
the country in the same detail and we will restrict ourselves to the overall
picture, exemplifying the development of the programme generally by
reference to a few specific Regions.

THE NATIONAL CONVERSION PROGRAMME

The bare facts are recorded in the Gas Council's Annual Reports and
Accounts from 1967/8 onwards. They record that, following Canvey, the
Board first in the field was the East Midlands, which began its conversion
programme at Burton-on-Trent in the summer of 1967. In September of the
same year the North Eastern Region began work at Withernsea, on the east
coast of Yorkshire. By the end of March 1968, 50 000 consumers were being
supplied directly with natural gas. Three more Boards (West Midlands,
Eastern, and Southern) started in 1968/9: by the end of March 1968 close on
half a million conversions had been effected and progress was being made at
the rate of 12 500 per week. Three more Boards started in 1969/70 and the
last two (South Western and Scottish) in April and June 1970. By then the
conversion rate had more than doubled to 29 000 domestic conversions per
week. The Annual Report and Accounts for 1969/70 records that over a
million domestic conversions had been made in that year alone, bringing the
total to $1\frac{1}{2}$ million, plus 52 000 commercial and 8000 industrial. The same

Report announced plans for two million conversions in 1970/71; these were duly achieved, thereby completing roughly one quarter of the total programme, with the expectation that the halfway point would be reached by April 1973. Finally, at a ceremony in Scotland on 1 September 1977, Sir Denis Rooke, Chairman of the British Gas Corporation, announced [4] completion of the entire programme—on sectors at Muirkirk, Ayrshire, and Stockbridge, Edinburgh—almost exactly ten years from its start. It had cost around £600 million which, allowing for inflation, was under the £400 million estimate made in 1966. However, the total cost was in reality, as he pointed out, nearer £1000 million because of the need to write off gas manufacturing plant that had been made prematurely obsolete. Nevertheless, the whole of that sum would have been written off against revenue by the end of that financial year. The British programme compared well with others undertaken abroad. Apart from being self-financing, it had been relatively much quicker both overall and, as we have noted, in the duration of supply interruption to individual consumers. The Dutch took $4\frac{1}{2}$ years to convert their 2 million customers; the Japanese had allowed themselves 12 years for their 5 million users; and Hungary expected to take 15 years to convert Budapest alone.

Such, in brief outline, were the salient facts (summarised in the accompanying table) but they do less than justice to what Sir Denis Rooke described as 'perhaps the greatest peacetime operation in this nation's history'. Although a highly technical operation, requiring most detailed organisation, it was still one of a highly personal nature. Indeed, it could scarcely have been otherwise when representatives of the gas industry descended on some 12 million homes, encountering their inmates under all sorts of conditions. Something of this personal element shows through even the technical and statistical language of the various official reports. We have already noted, for example, the wariness of the North Thames Board towards slippery customers who might acquire obsolete appliances, for little or nothing, in the hope of eventually trading them in for new ones. An account of the conversion of Central London by the same Board provides other examples [5]. By that time the Board had come a long way from Canvey, and there were 1 650 000 conversions behind them. Central London was different however; indeed, it could fairly be called unique in the whole country. Apart from the remarkable variety and congestion of buildings, and the problems of carrying out roadworks amidst some of the busiest traffic in Britain, there was a very mixed population:

The type of premises vary from the Royal Palaces, town houses and luxury flats to council estates and tenement blocks, from the major hospitals and University to the Law Courts and business premises of the City of London. Some areas, such as Whitehall and Soho, retain neighbourhood characteristics but very often the sector will contain representatives from each end of the social scale occupying adjoining buildings.

Although all the Board's customers had properly to be regarded as equal, some were clearly more equal than others. It was impossible to ignore the fact that they included many 'influential opinion formers'—such as 296 members of the House of Lords and 180 members of the House of Com-

HISTORY OF THE NATURAL GAS CONVERSION PROGRAMME

| Region | Start | Finish | Customers converted (£000) | | | Ratio domestic to commercial/ industrial |
			Domestic	Commercial	Industrial	
Scottish	Coldstream, Berwicks June, 1970	Comely Bank Edinburgh Sept., 1977	806.2*	20.4*	3.0*	34.5
Northern	Penrith, Cumberland April, 1969	Newcastle upon Tyne July, 1975	702.8	21.8	1.0	30.8
North West	Saddleworth, Yorks March, 1968	Stockport, Cheshire Feb., 1976	1770.5	65.9	12.4	22.9
North Eastern	Withernsea, Yorks Sept., 1967	Ossett, Yorks Jan., 1976	840.4	35.6	5.9	20.2
East Midlands	Alrewas, Staffs. May, 1967	Ulcehy, Lincs. Aug., 1974	1320.7	24.3	5.0	29.3
West Midlands	Tipton/ Coleshill, Staffs. July, 1968	Bromford, Birmingham Aug., 1976	1233.9	35.8	6.3	29.3
Wales	Colwyn Bay, Denbigh April, 1969	Nanthmoed, Glam. June, 1974	510.8	27.3	0.7	18.2
Eastern	Hitchin, Herts. April, 1968	Harpenden, Herts. Nov., 1974	896.2	19.7	4.0	37.8
North Thames	Corringham, Essex April, 1968	Beckton, London Aug., 1976	1845.6	49.8	11.5	30.1
South Eastern	Cranleigh, Surrey June, 1969	Biggin Hill, Kent June, 1976	1735.0	34.4	4.1	45.1
Southern	Bletchley, Bucks June, 1968	Reading, Berks. Feb., 1975	756.4	21.3	2.0	33.9
South West	Wickhamford, Worcs. April, 1970	Fishponds, Bristol Nov., 1975	565.4	30.4	1.4	17.8
Total			12983.9	385.7	57.3	29.3

* Estimated figures

mons. Again, the luxury flats of Dolphin Square, bounded by tenement buildings on one side and a local authority estate on the other, constituted half a conversion sector. In the case of the luxury flat dwellers 'intrusion is resented and highly articulate and well-directed complaint follows every lapse'. Nevertheless, the Board assures us, the poor and inarticulate were not neglected:

In a 'high income' section of that [local authority] estate, are housed civic dignitaries, television personalities and the like. Although the details of such customers are noted, in order that they may be extended the niceties demanded by their standing, the aim must be to produce an overall standard of conversion acceptable to all classes of customer. The aged and infirm, however, are categorized for priority attention wherever practicable.

Central London has, too, more than its share of shifting population. The 1966 census showed that 15 per cent of Londoners moved house in that year, compared with 11 per cent for the whole of England and Wales, and the figure for the central area was higher still. There were, for example, 200 000 students and 13 000 squatters. In many areas apathy rather than touchiness was the main problem:

the blunt fact is that it is becoming more difficult to get customers even remotely interested let alone concerned about conversion. The result is that public relations may well find itself spending more time in post-conversion public relations problems rather than pre-conversion.

In bedsitter-land the problem was often to find the occupant and even then he might not know, or care, who was ultimately responsible for a substandard installation.

Yet another complication was the fact that the conversion of central London coincided with an outbreak of terrorist activity and small parcels left lying unattended were viewed with suspicion. Very often, therefore, the conversion teams had to bring the kits with them instead of delivering them beforehand.

Commercial conversions in this area provided problems almost as diverse as domestic ones. The Houses of Parliament represented 'an interesting exercise rather than a major operational problem'. There were still 2000 gas street lamps, including the splendidly ornate ones in Friary Court, St James's Palace: their conversion presented special problems because of their sensitivity to changes in gas pressure. A little unexpectedly, the Region still maintained lamp-lighters to attend to the 109 gas lamps remaining within the precincts of the Inner and Middle Temple. Sector 637 covered the heart of theatre land and the southern part of Soho. It included 14 theatres and cinemas, 11 clubs, 16 public houses, 84 restaurants, 3 schools, a church, an hotel, and a hospital. The account goes on to tell us that:

These statistics do not take account of the many other rather unusual establishments which, although classified as domestic, operate as clubs.

This terse comment prompts speculation: perhaps some of these 'rather unusual establishments' were later featuring 'What the Fitter Saw'.

Within the scope of industrial conversion lay Hatton Garden, centre of the precious metal and jewellery trade. Here conversion was not particularly difficult, but the special security arrangements presented a considerable problem. Security of a different kind presented problems in government offices, including 10 Downing Street. The half square mile around Fleet Street which houses the national newspaper industry was also an area with special problems. Where newspapers were printed at night it was not too difficult to carry out conversion during the day, but sometimes a major evening newspaper used the same equipment as a daily, so that it had to be kept in operation almost continuously. When this account [4] of Central London's conversion was written, this area was still to be tackled: it was scheduled for the autumn of 1975. Those responsible were conscious, however, that failure here would bring on their heads wrath far in excess of that mustered even by the articulate residents of Dolphin Square, the television stars of Pimlico, or even the Lords of Westminster:

If there is one area in this country where a conversion failure would most certainly result in instant and stunning condemnation, it is Fleet Street. It follows that this part of the exercise will not take place without due care and attention.

Other Regional Boards had their own special problems, over and above those inherent in the conversion programme generally. In certain areas there were language problems among the immigrant population. Interpreters had to be engaged and explanatory leaflets were issued in Urdu, Bengali, Punjabi, and Gujerati. The special status of women in these communities created access difficulties. The North Eastern, the East Midland, the North Western, and the North Thames Boards all had to contend with this problem.

Rather disappointingly, the gas industry's concern for the safety of its customers often generated a measure of ill-will. For the first, and probably the last, time the conversion programme provided an opportunity for literally every appliance in the country to be inspected. Inevitably, this brought to light a fair number which were not merely defective but actually dangerous, either because of deterioration in use or because of faulty installation in the first place. Over the years, too, views on safety had changed and, even if carefully maintained, some older appliances which had conformed with regulations in force at the time of installation no longer did so. Nevertheless, the owners took it very much amiss if they were not converted. The appliances had served them well for many years and no doubt would have

continued to do so had not the inspectors arrived. They needed the equipment, and thought themselves harshly treated if conversion was refused. In
many cases the cost of replacement and re-installation was a serious question, for the more antiquated appliances naturally tended to be found in
poorer homes. The local Boards exercised their discretion in dealing with
such cases, but they would have shirked their responsibility had they left any
customer with an appliance which, by current standards, was unsafe. From
September 1969 only balanced-flue, multi-point, water-heaters were acceptable in bathrooms; a year later the sale of portable radiant-heaters was
stopped and the conversion of existing models discontinued.

This concern for safety was both commendable and commercially sound
from the Gas Council's point of view: gas disasters might be rare, but they
always attracted much press comment. From the point of view of the
appliance manufacturers, however, it imposed restrictions which some
found it difficult to understand, since they did not apply either to paraffin
heaters or to powerful heaters run on bottled gas. From the consumer's
point of view, too, they created problems and expense. In the absence of a
chimney, which many modern dwellings do not possess, gas fires could be
situated only on outside walls through which a hole had to be broken to
provide the necessary vent. The expense of installation, coupled with the
fact that gas appliances—unlike electric ones—need regular servicing if they
are to function satisfactorily, took away some of the advantage's conferred
by the basic cheapness of the fuel and its efficiency of utilisation. Indeed,
efficiency was diminished by the extent to which hot exhaust gases were lost
through the vent.

These decisions, taken by the industry on its own initiative, were incorporated in the Gas Safety Regulations (1972). This owed much to the results of
an inquiry into the safety of natural gas conducted by Professor Frank
Morton, FRS of Manchester University in 1970 [6]. This was set up by Mr
Harold Lever, then Paymaster General, in response to public concern,
which had developed into something of a political issue, over a number of
gas explosions. The terms of reference specifically included 'conversions of
domestic appliances to burn natural gas' and Professor Morton, a very
distinguished chemical engineer, paid particular attention to the whole of
the conversion programme. He visited Watson House to investigate the
approvals procedure; he watched conversion in the field; he studied the
training given to the conversion teams (a particular subject of criticism); and
so on. At the end of the day he concluded that 'natural gas can be stored,
distributed and used with safety in correctly designed and properly maintained equipment'. He particularly stressed the contribution to safety that
the conversion programme itself was effecting:

There are certain major advantages arising from the conversion to natural gas which
lead to greater safety of the whole system. These arise from the review and checking

of all distribution systems. . . . These benefits, independent of any national economic benefit arising from the use of natural gas, are positive contributions to the safe use of gas, and will result in the safer fuel system being available to the public.

While conversion was steadily going on, so also, though to a very much lesser extent, was re-conversion. Britain's population is a restless one and every year there are tens of thousands of moves from one part of the country to another. Very often householders take their gas appliances (except hot water boilers) with them: if they were moving from an area supplied with natural gas to one still utilising town gas all their appliances naturally had to be converted back again. When natural gas finally reached their new area, a third conversion was necessary.

In central London, one of the areas we chose to exemplify the national programme, the special problems were a high density of population, congested properties of widely differing nature, exceptionally busy traffic, and a rather anonymous and indifferent floating population. By contrast, we may briefly turn our attention to South Western Region, where special problems arose in some relatively sparsely inhabited areas. Cornwall, in particular, presented a difficulty because it was supplied by a single trunk main, which obviously could carry only town gas or natural gas and not both at once. One possibility for getting over the resulting difficulties was to lay a new temporary main to supply natural gas to newly converted sectors, but this would have been very expensive. Because of the distance, it was judged impracticable to bring liquid gas from Canvey Island. The solution finally adopted was to provide a temporary supply of substitute natural gas—a mixture of propane (obtained from an oil refinery) and air. It was not ideal, but was adequate to cover the period of some fourteen weeks required to complete the operation. As the problem had been encountered on a smaller scale in such towns as Minehead, Bideford, and Brixham, the Board had gained a fair measure of experience and confidence before embarking on the much larger Cornish exercise. Two large depots, with compressors, were established at Penzance and Truro; these were supplied with propane in rail-tank cars which took it from the refinery as far as Penzance, where it was transferred to road tankers. Smaller mobile plants were set up successively at St Ives, Falmouth, and Newquay. The peak of the operation was in July 1973, when for one week all Cornwall's 29 000 customers were receiving substitute natural gas. The trunk main was then purged of town gas and the regular supply of natural gas permanently established. There was the usual post-conversion tidying-up operation, complicated in this case by the fact that two local authorities (Redruth, Camborne) chose the week after conversion to re-number certain streets.

Although the Regional Boards operated their own programmes—determined by such factors as the actual availability of natural gas to them; long-term contracts for purchase of coke-oven gas; availability of fitters;

desire to phase out obsolete gas-manufacturing plant or avoid building new—the conversion executive provided a means by which one could gain from the experience of another. This is reflected in the statistics for call-back in the weeks following conversion; during the first eight weeks all defects were put right free of charge. The national rate was reduced from 25 per cent in the winter of 1969/70 to a little over 12 per cent in the summer of 1971. The industry was unlucky in that the higher rate coincided with, and perhaps contributed to, the public disquiet that led to the Morton inquiry.

THE ROLE OF APPLIANCE MANUFACTURERS

Up to this point we have, for convenience, considered the national conversion programme in terms simply of the gas industry, but we must now look at the other side of the coin and consider the outside help it had to enlist. First and foremost, it had to ensure the co-operation of the appliance manufacturers. The gas industry could carry out a national census of all existing appliances; it could catalogue these in detail in terms of manufacturer (not all still in business) and model; with the resources of Watson House it could specify the essential contents of conversion kits for models known to exist in large numbers; and in its own workshops it could carry out a great deal of adaptation of appliances too rarely encountered for it to be practicable to prefabricate kits. But the gas industry, as we have noted earlier, was not an appliance manufacturing industry, even though it provided the major sales outlets. Thus, the success of the programme was dependent upon the close co-operation of the independent manufacturers.

Secondly, the actual work of converting every serviceable appliance in the country in so short a time was beyond the labour resources of the industry. All but two of the twelve Boards had to enlist the help of outside contractors. The organisation of this in terms acceptable to both parties was a major operation in itself.

The manufacturers, of whom there were nine major concerns plus many relatively small ones, were naturally anxious to be co-operative, but not to the extent of ignoring the very real problems that conversion presented. They could clearly discern the overall expansion of business that the conversion programme would bring. Commercially, they were to some extent at a disadvantage: in the old days they had over a thousand separate gas undertakings providing retail outlets; now there were, apart from a few authorised dealers, only the twelve Area Boards, and while these were largely autonomous so far as the sale of appliances was concerned, the existence of the Gas Council as a unifying influence could not be ignored. They were further put on the defensive by the fact that if conversion was unsatisfactory they would have to share the blame with the gas industry. They therefore had strong reasons for falling in with the gas industry's wishes, but the practical difficulties would not simply go away as a result. One of the biggest of these difficulties was the speed with which the Gas Council wished to move; this, as we have seen, was imposed on them by the speed with which natural gas was going to become available. To produce the great variety of conversion kits at the required rate put a considerable strain on the industry, so much so that research and development work on new models had to be restricted. It proved hard also to reconcile the speed of the programme with the need to have all standard sets approved by Watson House. It was difficult initially even to get a supply of North Sea gas for test purposes. A further problem was the finite length of the programme. At the start of conversion both parties knew that some ten years hence they would arrive at the edge of a precipice; quite suddenly the work of conversion would stop and so would the demand for conversion kits. The appliance manufacturers had to plan to phase out their new commitments as well as to phase them in. They had also to phase in production of new appliances designed from the outset to burn North Sea gas. It was agreed that from February 1967 new appliances submitted to Watson House for approval should be capable of conversion at nominal cost: in April 1968, this provision was extended to models in production.

For the conversion sets there was in fact only a single buyer, for the gas industry recognised that area requirements would have to be channelled through a central purchasing unit if all the vast number of separate items were to be available in the right number at the right time. Such advantage as the gas industry gained from this monopoly of purchase was to some extent set off by the fact that it was early decided, as a matter of policy, that each manufacturer should be asked to produce the conversion kits for his own appliances. Many appliances, of course, had been made by firms no longer in business, and these had to be treated on an *ad hoc* basis. This effectively made competitive tendering impossible and a great deal of effort had to be expended within the gas industry to determine, as a basis for negotiation, the fair price of any particular item. This then became the basis for agreeing the price with the manufacturers, who collaborated with each other through the Society of British Gas Industries, which comprised some fifty appliance manufacturers in all. One complication was that initially only tentative orders could be placed. The full national census of appliances inevitably took a great deal of time and initial estimates had to be based on random samples by the gas industry, and manufacturers' analyses of their own past sales. At first, inevitably, the manufacturers viewed the Gas Council's proposals with some suspicion, but as the conversion programme developed a satisfactory *modus vivendi* developed. This survived even such unforeseen setbacks as unexpectedly severe inflation, a price freeze, and the three-day week.

Bearing in mind the over-riding demand for speed, it is fair to say that the manufacturers of appliances put up a very creditable performance in the supply of conversion kits. One impressive measure of success was the fact that throughout the conversion programme there were relatively few delays due to lack of availability of the necessary parts. Total success was certainly not achieved, however, as is evidenced by the number of post-conversion complaints and the fact that certain kits proved so unsatisfactory in practice that they had to be modified and re-submitted to Watson House; in some cases there even had to be third generation kits. Against this, it must be remembered that the number of items required was enormous. The Radiation Group, for example, provided conversion sets for three million cookers, two million water-heaters, over one and a half million fires, and 52 000 central heating units. Overall, the national census revealed, in the domestic field alone, the existence in use of 7976 different models of appliance, for which 3957 conversion sets were devised and 1406 conversion procedures. The fact that 2324 model types were not convertible is a little misleading: many of these turned up in very small numbers indeed and in the aggregate they represented only about one per cent of the total. The 3957 types of appliance for which kits were devised represented over 90 per cent of the total number of appliances involved. (See Plate 29.)

CONVERSION SUB-CONTRACTOR'S

Finally, in this context, we must turn our attention to the third leg of the conversion tripod, namely the teams who carried out the necessary work on the district. In all but two areas (Southern and North Eastern) the Boards relied heavily on outside contractors. In either case the recruitment and organisation of the labour force presented considerable difficulties: as with other aspects of conversion the running-down of the operation had to be planned as carefully as its initiation.

From the nature of the work the men engaged had to meet quite demanding requirements: there was no question of simply recruiting casual labour as it presented itself. They had to be adaptable men willing to undergo training and be prepared to live a nomadic life for lengthy periods. No less important, they had to be trustworthy and presentable, for they were to be the gas industry's representatives in the homes and premises of millions of customers throughout the country. It is interesting to note that in a postal survey of 5000 converted domestic customers, carried out in September 1967, only one per cent made any complaint about the conversion teams.

To provide the necessary training thirteen schools were eventually set up in various parts of the country, providing basic courses of four to six weeks' duration. In addition they organised special courses for teams engaged in commercial or industrial conversion; refresher courses; and courses designed to enable fitters to qualify for promotion. The training syllabus was agreed jointly by the Gas Council and the Training Boards of the Gas and Construction Industries, in consultation with the General and Municipal Workers Union. Knowledge and understanding of the conversion programme was, of course, necessary not merely for those actually engaged in the work. Salesmen, public-relations staff, home service advisers, and many others had to be fully aware of the implications of what was going on.

Taking the country as a whole, by far the greater part of the conversion work was done by contractors, who had to face the fact that although very substantial contracts were to be had, the conversion programme was a strictly limited one. Once Britain was converted, after a period initially estimated at between ten and twelve years, there would be no more conversion work to be done. While the expanding and demonstrably ambitious gas industry might then well offer useful contracts of a different kind, it was clearly important to realise that much substantial investment in tools, equipment, and specialised transport would have to be written off (unless supplied by the gas industry) in the course of a few years. The contractors had, therefore, to negotiate terms that made provision for this. This point was the more important because the Boards did not offer contracts for the whole of their conversion programmes but only for two or three years in the first instance. It can be argued that the Boards might have got better terms by making agreements for longer periods, but it was tacitly understood that if the original contracts were satisfactorily fulfilled they would be renewed. The contractors, therefore, had some incentive to keep their estimates low, in the hope of more to come, and the Boards were not irrevocably committed if things turned out unsatisfactorily.

Where contractors were involved there were two main types of contract. One was based on a fee but with reimbursement of costs on an agreed basis: these included management and supervision, supply of tools and equipment, labour costs, and so on. The other was on the basis of a lump sum payment, usually including escalation clauses: it was based on an estimate of the number and type of appliances to be converted and the average number per customer. In either case there would, naturally, be allowances, according to whether the contract covered a densely populated urban area or a relatively diffuse rural one.

The satisfactory winding-up of the conversion programme needed careful planning on both sides. The men involved had received special training which qualified them for alternative employment and it was understandable that with the end in sight they would tend to drift away to take other jobs with longer-term prospects if these offered themselves. With an inescapable commitment to complete the conversion programme, it might therefore have been necessary to put men through expensive training courses even though there was the prospect of only a few weeks' work for them afterwards. Moreover, it would be difficult to recruit men of the necessary calibre on a short-term basis. To avoid all this, it was agreed with the contractors that a substantial terminal bonus should be paid to all employees who stayed on until their services were no longer required. This proved an effective incentive and seems to have fully justified its considerable cost. Financial incentives were a feature of the programme as a whole. Bonuses were paid to teams who improved on the average time allocated for a particular type of conversion: to avoid the risk of careless work that this might entail, bonuses were also commonly paid for a low 'call-back' rate after the job was done.

The unusual nature of the work, involving as it did a great deal of overtime, unsocial hours, constant movement, unpredictable holidays, and so on naturally demanded close contact with the trade unions involved. At an early stage in the conversion programme the main contractors had formed themselves into a special group—the Gas Conversion Group of the Society of British Gas Industries. The constitution of this Society, however, was such as to preclude discussion of wages, conditions of service, and other matters falling within the province of the trade unions. In 1968, therefore, eight of the main contracting companies formed and registered their own trade association, the Gas Conversion Association. In 1969 a general agreement was concluded with the General and Municipal Workers Union with which other interested parties—notably the Constructional Engineers and the Transport and General Workers—concurred. The agreement was examined annually, and amended as seemed appropriate, throughout the ten years of the conversion programme.

PUBLIC RELATIONS

We have now outlined the way in which, through the Conversion Executive, the conversion programme was planned by the Area Boards and carried out in close collaboration with the manufacturers of appliances and contractors responsible for carrying out the work in the field. No comparable operation had ever before been carried out in Britain, and certainly not one in which so many numbers of the public had been directly involved. That it went so well is due primarily to the careful design of the machinery set up to effect it, but the smooth running of this machinery owed much to its careful lubrication by the gas industry's public-relations staff, at both national and local level.

Immediately following the Canvey Island conversion in 1965, William Camp, head of the Gas Council's public-relations department, set up a small working party to consider the whole question of public-relations in the context of the national programme looming ahead. It consisted of representatives of his own headquarters department and the Conversion Executive, and of the public-relations department of four Area Boards, under the chairmanship of his Chief Press Officer, Charles Elliott. One of its most valuable products was a Conversion Handbook, designed as a source of information and a guide to procedure for all concerned with the conversion programme. In its field it earned high praise. Norman Rogers, of the Institute of Public Relations, described it as 'one of the most remarkable, if not *the* most remarkable text-book on an industry's public relations work I have ever seen.'

Abraham Lincoln's famous dictum of 1858—that 'you can fool all the people some of the time, and some of the people all the time, but you can not fool all of the people all of the time'—might have been designed as a maxim for modern public-relations men. Certainly the gas industry in Britain realised that strict objectivity was their best policy. They could stress all the virtues of natural gas, the drama of exploration and production in the North Sea, its competitive position in relation to alternative fuels, and the highly sophisticated technology of the industry. But they were well aware that it would be futile to try to persuade their customers that the change to North Sea gas would happen by magic, that there would not be—for every one of them—an intermediate period of disturbance and inconvenience. What they could do, however, was condition them to the change by telling them through all the available channels exactly what they were to expect.

Some aspects of the way in which the gospel of conversion was preached have already been alluded to. Not least was the direct personal contact made with virtually every consumer shortly before work began and the follow-up after it was completed. Allied with this, at the local level, were background stories in the press, talks to organisations representative of particular sectors of the population, and displays and demonstrations in local showrooms. At a national level, appropriate information was steered in the direction of the newspapers, radio and television, the leading women's journals, the technical press, and so on. Journalists were encouraged to visit North Sea rigs, on-shore terminals, and major pipeline constructions to see at first hand what was going on. Close contact was maintained with the Information Department of the Ministry of Power, particularly to provide the Minister with the facts necessary to answer Parliamentary questions, a major occupational hazard of all the nationalised industries.

Such measures may in the main be described as putting carefully prepared information in the way of those likely to use it. The gas industry had, however, no means of ensuring that it was in fact used, or of influencing any gloss put upon it. In addition, therefore, there was a massive advertising campaign in which what was said, how it was said, and where it was said was strictly under control.

Inevitably, the gas industry suffered two disadvantages that affect the whole world of public-relations. The first is the general indifference of the public:

Lady Middleton . . . exerted herself to ask Mr Palmer if there was any news in the paper. "No, none at all", he replied, and read on (Jane Austen, *Sense and Sensibility*).

The second is that there is vastly more news value in things that go wrong than in things that go right. A disaster at sea, in the air, or on the railways is headline news: the countless millions of journeys safely accomplished are no news at all. An error of judgment, a mistaken policy, an ill-considered comment are of far more public interest than quiet achievement. This is all quite understandable and is indeed a reason why a free press is both more influential and more interesting than that in countries where it is subject to strict control by the State. It is to be hoped, however, that the media will be responsible and report the facts accurately and comment on them without malice. On the whole, these hopes are fulfilled, especially considering the conditions under which news stories have to be contrived. When news is received in, say, the late afternoon—possibly incomplete and garbled—it is not easy for an editor, however well intentioned, to form a balanced judgment on it before going to press later in the evening.

Bearing in mind the magnitude of the operation, the gas industry had good reason to feel that its carefully planned public-relations work earned a fair reward. Even if only one conversion in ten thousand had been unsatisfactory, there would have been well over a thousand dissatisfied customers up and down the country and it was inevitable—and in no sense unreasonable—that some of these would air their complaints in public and that the press might use this as a peg for editorial criticism. This was quite different from a 'knocking' campaign in which a small number of complaints was magnified to discredit an exceedingly complex programme, which, in fact, was proceeding normally and satisfactorily. One of the few such campaigns was that conducted in the *Evening Standard* towards the end of 1972, and directed against the North Thames Board. It was suspected that this arose from some influential member of the newspaper staff having had an unsatisfactory conversion despite the special efforts made for the Fleet Street area. However, this was short-lived and at the end of the day the *Standard* conceded that 'there is no doubt that the majority of consumers have been satisfied with the service they received.'

Earlier, in the context of the Canvey Island conversion, it was stated—with no claim to originality—that the conversion programme was organised 'with military precision'. As a final comment on it, we may perhaps reflect that, when carefully scrutinised, even the most successful military campaigns in history were not won without setbacks. Certainly the gas conversion programme was not an unqualified success, nor did the industry claim it as such. To the end, automatic ignition systems presented problems and so did simmering hot plates. Not every customer was finally a fully satisfied customer. Nevertheless, it was as well-planned and executed as could reasonably be expected.

The programme must be judged, too, on grounds other than its direct public consequences. It was a major step on the long road to corporate identity that, in the long run, was implicit in a single source of gas, of a new kind, and a national system of distribution. This evolution had begun hesitantly with the local mergers of the latter part of the nineteenth century, had been greatly advanced by nationalisation in 1948, when twelve Area

Boards arose from the ashes of some 1200 separate undertakings, and culminated in the setting up of the British Gas Corporation under the Gas Act 1972. The Area Boards, still autonomous under the general umbrella of the Gas Council, had been obliged both to establish closer internal co-operation between their different departments, and, through the Conversion Executive, to operate in close collaboration with each other. National policies were evolved for execution at the local level. The fruits of experience were widely shared, and common codes of practice were adopted. In retrospect it is clear that conversion to natural gas would have been beyond the capacity not only of the fragmented pre-war industry but of the original nationalised one based on coal. The intermediate phase of manufacture from petroleum, eliminating solid by-products and allowing adoption of the sophisticated technology of the chemical industry, was an essential stage on the road to unity.

REFERENCES

[1] *The Growing Gas Industry: the Development Plan of the Gas Industry to 1970*, p. 5, The Gas Council, London (1965).
[2] RHODES, R. P. *Conversion of Canvey*, Institution of Gas Engineers, Communication 730 (1966).
[3] *'Which?'*, May (1967).
[4] BRITISH GAS CORPORATION. Press Release 8405, 1 September 1977.
[5] RHODES, R. P., COLLINS, F. A., and GREENE, J. D. *The Conversion of Central London*, Communication 935, Institution of Gas Engineers, London (1974).
[6] MORTON, F. *Report of an Inquiry into the Safety of Natural Gas as a Fuel* (Ministry of Technology), HMSO, London (1970).

BIBLIOGRAPHY

BARNES, N. and HENSHILWOOD, C. P. *Effect of Natural Gas on Domestic Appliance Design*, Institution of Gas Engineers, Communication No. 740, London (1967).

BRITISH GAS CORPORATION. *Watson House 1926–1976*, London (1976).

DENSHAM, A. B. and GIBBONS, R. M. *Properties of British Natural Gas*, Research Communication GC 187, Gas Council, London (1971).

ELLIOTT, Charles. *The History of Natural Gas Conversion in Great Britain*, Cambridge Information and Research Services Ltd, Royston (1980).

ELLIS, W. D. and ASPINALL, P. M. J. *National Aspects of Conversion to Natural Gas*, Institution of Gas Engineers, Communication No. 767, London (1968).

HARRIS, J. A. and PRIGG, J. A. Domestic Aerated Burners for Methane, *Journal of the Institution of Gas Engineers*, 5, 203 (1966).

HENSHILWOOD, C. P. and PRIGG, J. S. Modification of Domestic Appliances for Gases of High Calorific Value, *Journal of the Institution of Gas Engineers*, **6**, 106 (1966).

HUTCHISON, K. 'Natural Gas and Clean Air'. Address to London and Home Counties Clean Air Advisory Council. 29 July 1966.

JONES, Robert, J. and PEEBLE, John G. *Customer Service Management and Training*, Institution of Gas Engineers, Communication No. 934, London (1974).

KENWARD, E. J. *London is Different*, North Thames Region Internal Report CPD 73/13. London (1973).

PROBERT, W. R. *Experience of the East Midlands Gas Board in Conversion to Natural Gas*, Public Works and Municipal Services Congress, Final Report (1968).

SMITH, B. C. and HEALY, H. B. *Converting Customer Service*, Institution of Gas Engineers, Communication No. 874, London (1972).

TAYLOR, B. (Ed.) *Le Fevre's Domestic Utilization of Gas*, 3rd ed. Benn, London (1973).

VAN DER LINDEN, A. 'Some Fundamental Viewpoints Concerning Gas Quality, Conversion of Appliances and the Design of Multi-Gas Appliances, *Journal of the Institution of Gas Engineers*, **7**, 195 (1967).

WILSON, A. *Horses for Courses—A Short History of the Technical Aspects of Negas Conversion*, Institution of Gas Engineers, Communication No. 987, London (1976).

WILSON, D. Scott. *The Modern Gas Industry*, Edward Arnold, London (1969).

18

Marketing North Sea Gas

IN the context of industry generally, marketing is by no means synonymous with selling, for it covers a very broad field of activities. These are not always very clearly defined but the meaning of marketing to the Gas Council was very precisely spelled out by B. G. H. Clegg, then Deputy Director of Marketing, to an international audience in the autumn of 1972 [1]:

Marketing covers the whole range of product strategy, resource allocation, market selection, advertising, sales, service and conversion, together with the planning, monitoring and control of achievement, productivity and profitability. This we consider to be Total Marketing.

In considering these facets of marketing we must keep in mind one major constraint which the new industry had to accept. This was that demand had to be matched to supply rather than vice versa: while there was fair expectation that new commercially viable gas-fields would be found, there was no absolute guarantee of this and new wells certainly could not be produced to order. Those responsible for marketing had, therefore, to be constantly on their guard against overselling. It is a slight exaggeration to call this a 'unique position', as F. J. Johnson [2] has done, for it is encountered, for example, in industries that depend on the annual vagaries of such crops as rubber, cocoa, and coffee; nevertheless, it does indicate a real difficulty in marketing natural gas. We must remember, too, that the advent of North Sea gas did not free the industry from various measures of price control of the sort to which it had been subject throughout its long history. Sir Arthur Hetherington, Chairman of the then newly formed British Gas Corporation, complained forcefully about government interference when announcing a loss of over £41 million in 1974. This was attributed to government action in forbidding increases in the price of gas; although compensation was to be paid the Chairman did not regard this as a satisfactory solution:

Whilst appreciating the problem of H.M. Government in trying to limit inflation, the Corporation dislike the whole concept of compensation and are firmly of the view that they should be allowed to operate commercially. Given reasonable freedom, the Corporation could earn a proper return on their assets and meet their financial obligations under the Gas Act 1972, namely, to ensure that revenues are sufficient to meet outgoings and to make such allocations to reserve as they consider adequate. [3]

Only two years later the new Chairman, Sir Denis Rooke, had to report that the wind was blowing in the opposite direction. Following a relaxation of earlier restrictions, the Corporation had increased the price of gas by 12.3 per cent from 1 October 1976, and had announced that 'subject to the Government's management of the economy' no further increase would take place for 12 months. The government's management at that time, however, was being rather conspicuously unsuccessful and on 15 December, the Chancellor, seeking a massive IMF loan, announced that the Government was asking British Gas to raise prices to increase the rate at which the Corporation repaid capital to the National Loans Fund, to the extent of £100 million in 1977/78 [4].

Generally speaking it was the domestic consumer—charged in accordance with published tariffs—who was affected. Sometimes he lost and sometimes he gained, though generally speaking nobody is the gainer from artificial rigging of the economy in response to political expediency. Industrial consumers, working within the terms of long-term contracts negotiated on an *ad hoc* basis, were generally immune. However, it is worth noting that even industrial consumers cannot count on long-term contracts as being absolutely binding. The first big industrial contract ever signed by the Gas Council was with ICI in 1969 and it was of a size to attract widespread attention: it provided for the supply of 1000 million therms of gas annually for fifteen years at an initial price reported to be $1.7p$ per therm: in the next eight years various escalation clauses raised this to $2.7p$. However, this was not politically acceptable and Mr Wedgwood Benn, the Energy Secretary, criticised the contract as being too favourable to ICI even though it had been negotiated against a background of falling oil prices which experts expected to fall still lower. ICI, with direct stakes of their own in the North Sea—and the right to acquire gas as feedstock without offering it to the Gas Council—were ultimately obliged to re-negotiate a much higher price, despite a favourable decision when the dispute went to arbitration. The consequence was that ICI sought an immediate increase in the price of fertilisers [5]. This was, indeed, what the dispute was all about. Other fertiliser manufacturers, particularly Fisons, who had been less astute in assuring for themselves supplies of cheap North Sea gas, found themselves unable to compete with ICI.

The freezing of prices to domestic consumers in 1973, the increase in price to the same class of consumers in 1976, and the enforced re-negotiation of the ICI contract before it had run half its course, may perhaps be regarded as perturbations of an otherwise relatively smooth system. Nevertheless, they are a reminder that when we are talking about marketing, and particularly when we are trying to make comparisons with other fuels equally subject to arbitrary political decisions, our figures may contain elements which have no direct economic relationship to charges made and prices paid. Any concept of Total Marketing must recognise this.

17. Even at the end of the conversion programme a few small coal carbonisation plants remained in operation, like this one at Muirkirk (1977).

18. The Catalytic Rich Gas (CRG) plant at the Bromley-by-Bow works of the North Thames Gas Board. It was the first in Britain and had a capacity of 4 million cubic feet a day. Although they were to become redundant in Britain with the advent of natural gas, such plants were profitably licensed abroad.

19. On nationalisation, the Area Boards inherited a mixed bag of assets—including many small undertakings such as this one at St Just, Cornwall (1946).

20. Local gas showroom in Frome 1946, typical of small undertakings.

21. Canvey Island Terminal, Essex, showing unloading facilities and insulated storage tanks for liquefied natural gas.

22. The *Methane Pioneer*, the vessel which brought to Canvey Island the first load of liquefied natural gas ever to be transported by sea to Britain, on arrival, 20 February 1959.

23. Geophysical exploration of the sea bed by seismic techniques charts the underlying strata by analysis of the sound reflected.

24. Underwater pipeline being laid by the pipe-laying barge *Hugh Gordon* to link the Gas Council-AMOCO Group's Leman Bank Field to the Bacton terminal. This barge also laid the first 18-inch pipeline from the BP West Sole Field.

25. After drilling more than 40 wells in the Gulf of Mexico, this drilling rig *Mr Louie* operated off the German coast before working for the Gas Council-AMOCO Group. *Mr Louie* was the rig which first struck gas for this Group, and is of similar construction to the rig *Sea Gem* which had located Britain's first supplies of offshore gas for BP in October 1965, which later capsized.

26. Aerial view of the Bacton Terminal which gathers gas from the Hewett, Leman, and Indefatigable fields off the Norfolk Coast.

27. An essential stage in the conversion of an area to natural gas was to flush out the existing town gas. The latter was flared off, and the change in the character of the flame showed when the process was complete. This scene at Westminster was typical.

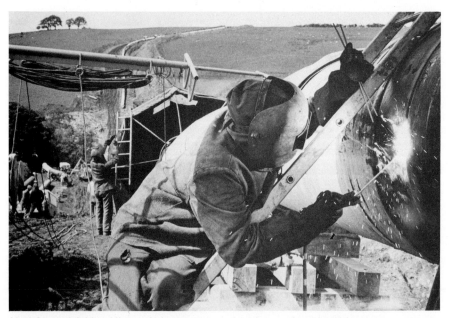

28. Advanced field welding techniques were employed to produce the high-pressure national transmission system.

29. The national conversion programme demanded the setting up of enormous stores at strategic points to make the necessary conversion kits readily available.

30. For a century and a half, gas mains were made of iron or steel joined with lead and yarn or later with mechanical glands. From 1970 heat-welded polyethylene (PE) pipe began to be used, as shown here. In the first years approximately 100 kilometres were laid. Subsequently PE accounted for the great majority of new and replacement mains.

31. From 1967 the gas industry's policy was rapidly to expand the premium industrial market. Here gas is being used for the manufacture of electric lamp bulbs—for which it is uniquely suitable.

32. Steel ingot heated in gas-fired furnace.

For political reasons the nationalised industries have been made to serve social ends, by being required from time to time to supply their goods or services on terms that are not commercially justifiable. These ends may be quite unexceptional. It may well be desirable, for example, that some sections of the community should travel at unrealistic fares; pay less for electricity or gas; have extended credit when they have difficulty in paying; and so on. But it is questionable whether these ends are best attained by imposing artificial constraints on the public corporations rather than by direct assistance to the individuals or groups concerned. If direct political control is desired, then it would clearly be better for the industries to be constituted as departments of state rather than public corporations, the whole purpose of which was to provide a high degree of independence and freedom from interference.

THE STRUCTURE OF THE MARKET

Just as marketing requires some definition, so too does the market, namely the customers to whom the efforts of marketing men are directed. The breakdown of these as at 1972—that is, about half-way through the conversion programme—was as follows [6]

Domestic customers	12 800 000
Commercial and public administration	522 000
Industrial	68 000

The domestic and industrial customers were further analysed according to their average annual consumption (expressed in therms):

Therms	Domestic	Industrial	
Less than 200	6 800 000	Less than 1000	54.4(%)
200/400	2 700 100	1000/10 000	30.3
400/1000	2 500 000	10 000/50 000	9.0
Over 1000	800 000	50 000/10 000	4.8
		0.1 m/0.5 m	0.6
		0.5 m/1.0 m	0.3
		1/2 m	0.3
		2/5 m	0.2
		5.10 m	0.1
		Over 10 m	0.1

The commercial market was not analysed in the same detail, but it ranged from hospitals taking around one million therms to small retail shops comparable with an average home. In between are such establishments as schools, offices, and banks: a substantial number of such premises used no gas at all.

The total size of these three markets (million therms per annum) were stated in the Annual Report and Accounts 1972/3 to be as follows:

Domestic	4603
Industrial	4530
Commercial	1046
Total (including 58 m therms used by British Gas)	10 237

The same report indicates that the total gas then available was 11 171 million therms (3000 manufactured gas and 8151 natural). There was, therefore, already a sufficiency of gas, and with increasing flow from the North Sea imminent the gap between supply and demand was clearly likely to widen rapidly. A big and rapid increase in sales was, therefore, essential and the lesson of these figures was that this was likely to be found largely in the industrial field. The dilemma was that this market had to be built up in step with the inflow of gas. If the market did not in fact develop, or did not develop as quickly as expected, the Gas Council would be obliged to pay for gas for which it had no use. On the other hand, it could very easily over-sell and find itself in the position of being unable to supply customers with whom it had binding long-term contracts. In the event, as we shall see, the industry's managerial skills matched its technological ones, and in the first decade of natural gas its performance matched its intentions with remarkable precision.

CONTRACTS FOR PURCHASE OF GAS

The assault on the North Sea achieved quick results. BP met with early success and other fields were opened up as rapidly as the most optimistic could have hoped for. Negotiations between the Gas Council and the producers had to move with corresponding speed, and in 1965, the Council set up a Special Projects Department which included this among its responsibilities. Leaving aside for the moment details of the price to be paid, contracts were usually subject to the following general provisions [7]:

(1) An annual contract quantity (ACQ) was agreed. This was the amount of gas the industry agreed to pay for each year whether or not it was actually taken.

(2) Up to an agreed limit the industry may purchase further gas (called 'valley' gas, after the summer dip in the load curve) at a lower price.

(3) The producers undertake to supply relatively more gas in the high-demand winter months. This would commonly be about 167 per cent of the ACQ expressed as an average daily quantity (ADQ) over the year.

We have noted that the first contract concluded was that with B P in 1967. It ran for three years in the first instance and provided for the purchase of 360 million therms per annum at a rate of 5*d*. (2.083*p*) per therm. This was generally regarded within the gas industry as too high and thought to have resulted from Ministerial pressure. This contract was announced in the Gas Council's Annual Report and Accounts for 1965/6, but the Report for the following year merely records that, while discussions had proceeded with the other producers who had been successful meanwhile, 'at 31st March, 1967, no agreement had been reached'. Clearly, all parties were taking their time. The Report for 1967/8 notes that a 25-year contract had been agreed with the Phillips Group, on 2 March 1968, for the supply of its share (probably a little more than half) of gas from the Hewett Field. Delivery was to commence in the summer of 1969 at an initial rate of about 600 million cubic feet per day. The price agreed was 2.870*d*. (1.2*p*) per therm for the A C Q gas, and 2.052*d*. (0.84*p*) for valley gas. It was recorded that negotiations were proceeding with other groups and the Report and Accounts for 1968/9 noted that these had been concluded. It was stated that the contract with the Arpet Group for its share of the Hewett Field was identical with that concluded with the Phillips Group in the previous year. This was scarcely surprising: with the Phillips contract signed, Arpet was not in a strong bargaining position. It also states:

In December 1968, the Council signed contracts with the Shell/Esso Group and with the Gas Council/Amoco Group for their respective shares in the Leman Bank Field and Indefatigable area. All of these contracts are for a period of 25 years.

The price negotiated was not stated in the Report of the Gas Council, but the basic facts were given by the Ministry of Power [8]. Shell/Esso were to get 2.87*d*. (1.2*p*) per therm for the first 600 million cubic feet, for Leman Bank gas. A slightly higher price (2.90*d*.) was agreed for Indefatigable which was somewhat further offshore: we have already remarked that the laying of pipeline, and transmission through it, was an important element of cost in development. A contract in similar terms was quickly reached with Gas Council/Amoco. For Lockton, the short-lived onshore field with smaller distribution costs, a price of 1.0575*d*. was agreed. In all contracts there was provision for automatic price changes linked to relevant price indices recognised in the petroleum industry; for periodic re-negotiation; and for arbitration as a last resort.

At first sight, it may seem a little surprising that such protracted argument was necessary over a mere fraction of a penny. To do so is to ignore the enormous quantities of gas involved. On the basis that the Gas Council was to receive some 4000 million cubic feet of gas daily an additional tenth of a penny per therm could cost them well over £100 million over a twenty-year period. A further cause for delay was the interpretation of the 'reasonable price'—a term having no legal validity in Britain—at which the producers were obliged to offer gas (for use as fuel) to the Gas Council. At the outset the two sides were putting different interpretations on what was reasonable. The Gas Council, with the Ministry of Power in the background, considered that the price should be determined on cost-plus basis. Any other arrangement might enable the producers (of whom, incidentally, the Gas Council itself was a minor one through its association with Amoco) to make undue profits—a thought very unfashionable in the political climate of the day. The companies, on the other hand, argued for a market price figure which would take account of the considerable element of risk involved. The fact that they had been unexpectedly successful in their early exploration was, they claimed, no guarantee for the future: a higher price was necessary if further exploration was to be encouraged. While this attitude was understandable, the producers were not arguing from a position of great strength. As far as gas for use as fuel was concerned, they were bound to offer to the Gas Council all brought ashore in Britain. The alternatives open to them were more apparent than real. In theory, they might export it, but the proximity of the British coast to the gas-fields and the relative distance of the coast of Europe made this an unattractive possibility. Moreover, the British people were by then coming round to the thought that in North Sea gas and oil lay their hope of economic salvation, and to see it carried away by foreign companies and sold to other foreigners would be bound to create political uproar. Again, if deadlock ensued, and the producers found the Gas Council's best offer 'unreasonable', they might seek a court order obliging the Minister to let them sell direct to industry. But the outcome of such litigation would have been uncertain and delay inevitable. Delay was something both parties were anxious to avoid at that stage and this favoured a compromise. Even then, however, an unexpected development clouded the issue once again. In November 1967 a price of around 2.85d. (1.2p) per therm seemed to satisfy the aspirations of both parties, subject to minor adjustments to take account of special circumstances peculiar to each field. Then Britain announced a devaluation of the pound and the producers immediately proposed that their price should be increased in strict proportion. Against this, the Gas Council and the Ministry argued that a substantial part of the cost of exploration and development was a sterling charge. It was at this stage that Phillips—supposedly anxious to generate cash—agreed to settle at a post-devaluation price of 2.87d. and led other producers to follow suit [9].

MARKETING STRATEGY

While future supplies of gas at an acceptable price were thus being secured, the Gas Council was engaged in formulating its strategy for selling it on economically viable terms to its many millions of customers. In doing this it had to take account not only of its own internal requirements, but of general government policy with regard to fuel. The latter was set out in a White Paper in 1967 [10]. This reminded its readers that Britain was undergoing a transition from a two-fuel economy (coal, oil) to a four-fuel one (coal, oil, natural gas, nuclear power). In 1956 coal supplied 84.9 per cent of Britain's energy and oil 14.5 per cent. Ten years later coal's share had diminished to 58.7 per cent and oil's had risen to 37.5 per cent; natural gas made a minute contribution of 0.4 per cent. Nevertheless, the government was confident of the long-term potential of North Sea gas and looked forward to production at the rate of 4000 million cubic feet daily in 1975; this was four times the then current consumption of manufactured gas. The long-term national objectives were clearly stated:

The Government's immediate objective has been that North Sea gas should be brought rapidly into use to enable the country to benefit as soon as possible from the advantages of this new indigenous primary fuel. Speedy use of the gas will also be an incentive to the exploration needed to extend our information about the size of the North Sea reserves.

The White Paper proceeds to argue the pros and cons of slow or rapid depletion of the North Sea gas fields:

The Government's studies have suggested that the saving in resources from introducing natural gas is likely to be the highest where it commands the greatest price premium. Hence resource savings are in general likely to be highest where natural gas is replacing manufactured gas, intermediate where it commands a moderate premium in price over oil, and lowest in the bulk industrial market. This is a conclusion of major significance in the development of a rational strategy for gas absorption. However, the price to the gas industry depends on the economics of natural gas production which favour a rapid build-up in supplies and a depletion period which is too long. To confine supplies of the gas to premium markets means both a slower build-up and a longer depletion period, and the price to the gas industry is likely to be higher. In order to build up supplies quickly to the chosen depletion rate some gas would have to go to the bulk industrial market where, as stated above, the resource savings are likely to be lower. To some extent, therefore, these considerations pull in opposite directions.

However, the White Paper, having considered these conflicting factors, reaches the conclusion that:

the greatest gain to the economy will be obtained by a policy of rapid absorption, with most of the gas going to premium markets (where it would largely be displacing oil) and some bulk sales to make possible a rapid build-up of supplies to the most economical depletion rate. This will mean some displacement of coal by natural gas in the bulk energy markets but the coal markets that will be lost in this way would in all probability, fall to oil if natural gas were not available.

In the event, Gas Council policy closely followed the proposals of the White

Paper, except that rather less natural gas than expected was used for the generation of electricity. As this is a rather wasteful use for gas, this was just as well.

While the role of government was to formulate a broad national fuel strategy, it was the task of the Gas Council to give effect to it so far as natural gas was concerned. It was an immense and highly complex task, carried out with commendable speed and efficiency. Less than ten years after the White Paper appeared the whole of England, Scotland, and Wales had been converted to natural gas. Phoenix-like, a new industry with a highly advanced technology had risen from the ashes of the old retorts.

Once the fundamental policy decision had been taken to supply natural gas direct to all consumers the immediate need was to tackle all the practical problems that flowed from it. Some of the purely practical ones, such as conversion of appliances and enlargement of the gas grid, we have already discussed and in the present context we will restrict ourselves to marketing strategy.

In 1966, a year before the White Paper appeared, Sir Kenneth Hutchison, Deputy Chairman of the Gas Council, gave a clear indication of the Council's intentions over the next decade [11]. He began by tracing the changing fortunes of the industry in recent years and remarked that North Sea Gas came at an opportune moment:

It is fortunate that the gas industry was in a buoyant and confident mood and, therefore, well able to cater for expansion on a scale that would have seemed highly improbable a few years ago.

As evidence of this buoyancy, he pointed out the steadily increasing sales that had been achieved in the preceding five years:

Year	Forecast of increase in annual sales for following five years (%)	Actual increase in year of forecast compared with previous year (%)
1962	1.7	1
1963	3.0	3
1964	5.0	5
1965	7.5	8
1966	8.2	10

At that time, the extent of the North Sea reserves was far from clear, but it was assumed that an output of at least 1500 million cubic feet per day could be sustained for 20 years. On this basis, the Gas Council carried out two case studies. The first assumed that 1000 million cubic feet of gas per day would be available from the North Sea and a further 100 million imported as natural gas; any balance required would be manufactured. The second assumed that 4000 million cubic feet per day would come from the North Sea. After making some reasonable assumptions about the cost of natural gas (the B P contract had not then been completed) detailed analysis led to the following estimate of tariffs and revenue.

Case 1	£ million
Domestic: 4800 million therms @ 20*d*.	400
Commercial: 1000 million therms @ 16*d*.	67
Industrial: 1800 million therms @ 10*d*.	75
Total revenue	£542

Case 2	
Domestic: 8700 million therms @ 14*d*.	507
Commercial: 4000 million therms @ 12*d*.	200
Industrial: 5300 million therms @ 6*d*.	133
	£839

These case studies, however tentative, clearly showed that substantial reductions could be made in the price to the consumers as the scale of operation increased. At the same time, falling prices would encourage new customers or larger consumption by existing ones. They also showed a great variation, nearly three-fold for Case 2, in the winter and summer requirements. It was considered that, apart from drilling more wells, these seasonal differences could be evened out by substantially increased storage facilities either as liquefied gas or, if they could be found, underground acquifers (p. 178). A further, and novel, solution to this problem was the concept of interruptible supply for industry, according to which the consumer is not guaranteed a continuous supply of gas but one which may be cut-off in pre-agreed circumstances. By way of compensation, such gas is offered at an attractively low rate. Such arrangements were common in the USA, with its long dependence on natural gas, but then unknown in Britain. In the event, interruptible-gas contracts were to form an important part of the Gas Council's marketing strategy and we will consider them in more detail later (p. 217).

The summary of Sir Kenneth Hutchison's paper lists the nature of the conversion programme as the most important single decision to be made: when it was to start and at what rate it was to proceed. Tentatively, it was thought that 600 000 dwellings would have to be converted in the first year, rising to twice this in the following year if the results of drilling continued favourable. It was recognised that 'the machinery to carry out this operation will have to be on a very much larger scale than the facilities available at the Council's research and development centre at Watson House.' Consideration was given to the possibly serious effects on the appliance manufacturing industry. As the public became aware of the imminence of large-scale conversion there might be a general reluctance to buy new appliances for fear that they would become obsolete. The whole question of public-relations would need very careful handling:

The preparation of public opinion as to the consequences of natural gas will have to be carefully worked out. There may be strong objections from coal interests and the oil industry must view with mixed feelings a development equivalent to 45 million tons of oil a year, even though this can be accommodated within the natural growth of the economy.

There was speculation about the way in which the very high cost of conversion might be funded. Case Study 1 had indicated that a price reduction might be effected once conversion was in full-swing and the output of gas had doubled. This reduction might not be possible in the early stages and the following suggestions were put forward to overcome the difficulty:

(1) That the cost of conversion ought to be outside the target of profit (over and above interest on capital) which the industry undertakes to reach.

(2) That the Gas Council should subsidise the cost of conversion on a per-consumer basis out of the surplus on 'own gas' and a possible levy on all North Sea gas.

(3) That the period of conversion be extended.

(4) That the producers should be persuaded to sell at a low initial rate with a built-in escalation for some years so as, in effect, to bear part of the conversion cost in the early stages.

In a footnote to this lucid and prescient paper [11] Sir Kenneth Hutchison was at pains to state that it was a personal compilation and that he alone was responsible for the methods used in calculation, the conclusions reached, and for any errors in the working-out. Nevertheless, we may take it as clear evidence that the Gas Council had lost no time in formulating its general strategy to cope with the advent of North Sea gas.

In the five or six years before North Sea gas, sales had been rising steadily and the industry had been carrying out regular market surveys to monitor and promote this increase [2]. This enabled the Council to build up a fairly clear classification of their customers, the kinds of appliance they wanted, and where the principal growing points lay. From this, it became clear that in the early 1960s the main reason for the steady increase in gas sales was the rapid improvement in gas-fire sales. The efficiency of the fires had been increased from around 40 per cent to about 65 per cent and, no less to the point, their appearance had been greatly improved by more imaginative design, in tune with contemporary taste. Central heating, too, was becoming much more widely demanded. It was clear that the domestic market was capable of further rapid expansion, but that on any realistic view this alone could not possibly take up gas in the sort of quantity that was confidently expected to be available in the fairly near future.

The commercial market, too, had great potential for development, especially for space heating, but again it was clear that this was limited and even spectacular success by salesmen could not produce the sort of overall expansion that was essential. As with the domestic market, the load factor—by which is meant average daily use in a normal year divided by maximum daily use in a severe winter—was not favourable. The industrial load factor was much better.

The question of maintaining supplies under exceptional conditions was one that had always greatly exercised all the fuel industries. Customers naturally expected to have all their demands met whatever the weather; if not, they grumbled and the supply industry was subject to severe public criticism. On the other hand, it was clearly uneconomic—whether one was supplying gas, coal, electricity, or oil—to have manufacturing capacity that might be needed only once in a decade or even less frequently. In 1965 when the first serious estimates of the demand for North Sea gas were being made, this thought was very much in the minds of the planners. Only two years before (1962/63) Britain had suffered a winter almost unparalleled in living memory, and considerable hardship had been suffered. It is not altogether surprising, therefore, to see the Council involved [12] in a complex statistical analysis of weather records, going back to 1853, in an attempt to find 'a measure of winter severity of interest in the planning of capital investment in the gas industry.' These were very interesting and important studies but had something in common with North Sea gas itself: analysis of past events gave a useful guide to future trends but could give no more than an indication of probability. Another exceptional winter could occur as unexpectedly as a major new discovery of gas.

THE INDUSTRIAL MARKET

By 1967, it had become clear that the only effective means of selling North Sea gas in the quantities that were becoming available was to bring about a large and rapid expansion of the industrial market. It was also clear that the gas industry was not as fully informed about the nature of this market as it needed to be. To make good this deficiency major research surveys were made in 1967 and 1968 [2]. They were designed to answer the following questions:

(1) In which industries were fuels used, what types of fuel, and in what quantities?

(2) What was the geographical pattern of industrial fuel usage?

(3) For what processes in the various industries were the different fuels used?

(4) What prices were paid for the various fuels?

(5) Were there any advantages of some fuels over others in various processes: could these be cost-evaluated and did industry act upon cost evaluations?

These inquiries were pursued with great thoroughness. To answer the first two questions a census was completed of all firms with more than 50 employees: one or two of the Area Boards went even below this level, but in retrospect this was thought probably not to have been worth while. In all, 29 500 questionnaires were sent out and 19 000 were returned: a satisfactorily high response. On the basis of this original response a much more intensive investigation was made of about 100 industrial customers in each Area, i.e. about 1200 in all. These were individually approached and interviewed in order to find answers to questions (3), (4), and (5), and to identify the main competitive fuel in each case. The market thus revealed was classified into three main groups—upper premium, lower premium, and non-premium—roughly in accordance with the price of their principal fuel. These grades of fuel were as follows:

High premium Electricity, gas, gas-oil, light fuel-oil, light petroleum gas (from refineries).
Lower premium Medium fuel-oil.
Non-premium Heavy fuel-oil and solid fuel used for crude heating.

In the final analysis it was shown that the total annual industrial demand for fuel at that time was 21 500 million therms, made up as follows.

	Therms (millions)
Upper premium fuels	2700
Lower premium	1200
Non-premium	17 600
Total:	21 500

Sales of gas to industry were then 908 million therms annually, only about 4 per cent of its total usage. Clearly, therefore, there was great scope for expanding sales, even if only upper and lower premium users (18 per cent of the total) were taken into account. The opportunity open was all the greater because the total demand was expected to rise steadily. The White Paper on Fuel Policy [10] assumed the total inland demand for energy (expressed as million tons of coal equivalent) as 298 in 1966, rising to 310 in 1970, and 350 in 1975. These were overall estimates, but included an upward trend in industrial consumption.

While the surveys had revealed the size of the industrial market they provided no clue as to how it might be penetrated. Three main situations had to be considered:

(1) Installation of new plant. The customer has to be persuaded that gas is suited to his needs, that no unduly expensive equipment is necessary to use it, and that it is cheaper than the alternative fuels open to him.

(2) A change-over situation. If a potential customer has in mind discontinuing with his present fuel and changing to gas he has to write-off existing equipment, buy new, and pay the installation cost.

(3) The gas industry could not be complacent and assume that all existing users of gas would remain loyal. They, too, would be subject to the temptation of rival offers.

No traditional tariff system, based simply on a steady reduction in price as consumption rose, could satisfy all these possibilities. It was therefore decided to adopt a market-related pricing policy for consumers requiring more than about 100 000 therms annually. Expressed in everyday language, this means no more than that the particular circumstances of any new customer were carefully assessed and he was offered gas on terms made as attractive to him as was consistent with a satisfactory return to the Area Board concerned. The latter, it may be noted, competed on equal terms as far as the price they themselves paid for gas was concerned. At the outset, the Gas Council considered the possibility of charging slightly differing prices, on the grounds that there would be differences in the transmission costs from the East Coast terminals. However, it was argued, among other considerations, that this might not always be true: in the future, discoveries might well be made off the West Coast. To facilitate calculations of the prices to be charged a 'building bricks' system was devised to take account of the various factors involved in the new business, changeover, and load retention situations [2]. The implementation of this policy was not without its difficulties. The Gas Act 1948 provided that Area Boards might enter into special agreements but it also insisted that they should 'not show undue preference to any person, or class of person'. The satisfactory interpretation of 'undue preference' involved long and complex legal arguments. The relevant section of the Gas Act 1972 was reworded to take account of this.

It was as part of this market-related pricing policy that the interruptible supply contract was introduced. This, as North American natural gas undertakings were well aware, was a very convenient means of resolving the problem of seasonal variations in demand. Under this system the industrial consumer is not guaranteed a continuous supply, day and night, as the domestic or tariff customer is. As a result he must have alternative stand-by fuels (usually oil) to tide him over the period of interruption. While the actual terms of business were very flexible, two main types of contract were introduced. One was the storage interruptible, by which the customer has say, 3/4 weeks' oil storage—which he can stock up in the summer months— and the interruption of supply is guaranteed not to exceed that period. Customers accepting the alternative strategic interruptible must be prepared to be without supply for longer periods; in a severe winter this might be a couple of months. Such customers must have considerable storage capacity or a reliable alternative fuel supply. Among other variations introduced were seller's option gas (a minimum quantity guaranteed during the course of the year but the time of supply being at the seller's option). The price agreed naturally depended on the inconvenience suffered by the consumer, usually measured in strictly economic terms covering the difference in cost of the alternative fuel and the cost of installing and maintaining storage tanks, alternative burners, etc. Although a new concept for British industry, the interruptible supply system proved widely acceptable to users requiring not less than one or two million therms annually.

An important new market for gas was developed for the on-site generation of electricity, for which special terms were quoted. Ordinary contracts excluded this use. For this purpose interruptible supply contracts were acceptable, as gas turbines can be converted to gas-oil in less than a minute. As already noted, sales of natural gas to the Central Electricity Generating Board were less than expected, but among the contracts secured was one to supply Hams Hall 'C', near Coleshill, on a seller's option basis. This was close to the natural gas grid, and its existing coal-fired boilers, installed when the station was commissioned in 1958, were particularly suitable for conversion, at a cost of about £1 million. It was estimated that this capital cost would be recovered in less than three years. A station at West Thurrock was converted in 1972.

At the outset, some very large industrial contracts were secured. These included the 15-year ICI deal already mentioned (p. 206), and a similarly substantial one for five years with Shell shortly afterwards. In the early years, however, most industrial contracts were on a three-year basis. In four years from 1969 gas sales to industry increased roughly four-fold: some 600 000 customers were getting gas at a price around 3p per therm. In 1970/71 no less than 580 contracts for 1500 million therms annually were negotiated [13], and industrial sales were by then roughly on a par with domestic ones.

THE COMMERCIAL MARKET

A similarly thorough analysis of the commercial market was made, but by methods different from those used to analyse the industrial potential. The large number of relatively small establishments precluded a postal survey and recourse was had to representative sampling: nationwide, some 3600 interviews were conducted. These established [2] that six market sectors accounted for 64 per cent of market sales of all fuels.

SURVEY OF COMMERCIAL FUEL MARKET

Type of establishment	Total thermal usage (%)	Establishments in commercial markets (%)
Hospitals	15	1
Schools	15	3
Retail distribution	14	40
Hotels and residential establishments	8	4
Local government	6	1
Public houses	5	5
Others (entertainment, transport, churches, garages etc.)	45	46

The market was further analysed according to the kind of fuel used and the use to which it was put. This led to the following breakdown:

PERCENTAGE OF ALL COMMERCIAL FUEL USAGE ACCOUNTED FOR BY:

Gas	14	Catering	9
Electricity	16	Water heating	17
Solid fuel	19	Space heating	51
Oil	51	Other	23

Finally, the existing gas market share of the four processes identified above was found to be as follows

PROCESS	GAS MARKET SHARE
Catering	66
Water heating	11
Space heating	9
Other	4

In addition, special surveys were made, by independent market surveyors, of the needs of hotels and shops, collectively representing an important sector of the commercial market.

Thus statistically armed, the industry was able to formulate a logical strategy for expansion in the commercial market embodying the following general principles:

(1) To concentrate effort in the top six market sectors.

(2) To sell gas for space heating to major customers, if possible on a tariff basis, but otherwise by special contract.

(3) To maintain its already large hold of the catering market.

Where individual contracts were offered, these were devised on a 'building brick' system similar to that used for industrial sales. As in that field, the most important brick is the price of the competitive fuel. It was therefore necessary systematically to keep track of competitors' going rates. In general, institutions are reluctant to reveal their detailed costs beyond the limit of their statutory obligations. To obtain the desired information the Gas Council had, therefore, to offer some kind of inducement. In effect, they set up a monitoring panel to review the market monthly and prepare a full-depth analysis twice a year [2]. This panel obtained its information by giving the competitive fuel users concerned the benefit of the results of these surveys: the user could, therefore, judge how far his own supplier was giving him a fair crack of the whip. If he was not, the user had the evidence on which to seek more favourable terms, even if he did not transfer his allegiance to gas.

The gas industry had long been conscious that their interest—and, in-deed, their responsibility—did not end with securing a new customer. To retain the business, it was necessary to provide a service appropriate to the demands of different kinds of customers. As the conversion to natural gas proceeded, research into consumer attitudes received more emphasis and in 1970 Mass Observation carried out an opinion poll among some 5000 representative groups. The results of this provided a useful guide to de-veloping service policy. A second survey, in 1973, showed that performance was judged to have improved, but at the same time customers had become more exacting in their demand. Marketing is not an activity that ever reaches finality.

To summarise, market strategy for North Sea gas was based on the following principles:

(1) Thorough knowledge of the fuel market generally and the way in which it was changing, in order to see where effort could most usefully be deployed.

(2) A readiness to replace the traditional system of reducing prices step-by-step as consumption rose, by much more sophisticated contracts, keenly judged to make it worthwhile for users to switch from rival fuels to gas and yet leave the gas industry an adequate margin of profit.

(3) Systematic monitoring of customers' attitudes to gas.

(4) An efficient sales service designed to keep customers satisfied.

In a laboratory experiment it is possible to judge the results of altering various factors in a situation by carrying out control experiments in which these factors are varied one by one. In marketing, and in real life generally, such control experiments are not feasible and the success of the strategy adopted must be judged by results. In the case of North Sea gas considerable success was achieved if we take the forecasts in the White Paper on fuel policy [10] as a yardstick. As the figures below indicate [13], the gas industry was overall a little ahead (about 1 per cent) of target by 1975/6:

GAS SALES—MILLIONS OF THERMS PER ANNUM

	1967/8	1971/72	1975/76	White Paper forecast 1975
Domestic	2652.1	4045.1	5940.8	5100
Industrial	914.5	3069.7	6072.2	7200
Commercial and public administration	632.5	876.8	1440.5	1000
Total	4199.1	7991.6	13 453.5	13 300

The pattern did, however, differ slightly from that forecast in the White Paper [10]. Commercial and domestic sales were substantially higher than predicted but industrial sales were lower, mainly because sales to power stations had not been actively pursued. This, however, was an area in which political rather than market-related factors were dominant, and in any event the gas industry would have regarded this as a rather wasteful use of gas.

In retrospect, the marketing strategy of concentrating—though not exclusively—on the upper section of the industrial premium market appears to have been substantially correct. Certainly Britain has been notably more successful than Holland, even though the latter was first in the field and had far simpler extraction problems, being possessed of a huge onshore field. It is now generally conceded that the Dutch sold too much gas too quickly and too cheaply, thereby actively encouraging its use in areas where lower-premium, or even non-premium, fuels would suffice. The consequences of this have come to be known as 'the Dutch disease'. There will be general agreement with the post-OPEC conclusion of D. I. and G. A. Mackay [15]:

The North Sea oil and gas reserves are a gift to be nurtured, not squandered in an attempt to avoid harsh realities.

In big corporations much depends on the work of teams and it can be invidious to single out individuals for special mention. Nevertheless, it would be less than fair to omit mention of the fact that the success of the marketing strategy has been closely linked with the name of James Buckley. He ended a long career in the industry as member for Marketing in the British Gas Corporation to which he had, in effect, been appointed by Sir Henry Jones in 1968 [16].

REFERENCES

[1] CLEGG, B. G. H. 'Total Marketing Strategy', Paper III–6 delivered to an International Colloquium about Gas Marketing, The Hague, September 1972.

[2] JOHNSON, F. J. *Marketing Research Used in Strategic and Tactical Decision Making*, p. 7, British Gas Corporation (1974).

[3] BRITISH GAS CORPORATION. *Annual Report and Accounts 1973–74*, p. 8.

[4] Idem. *Annual Report and Accounts 1976/77*, p. 8.

[5] *Daily Telegraph*, 29 October 1977.

[6] BUCKLEY, J. A. 'The Customer and the Industry', Lecture delivered to a meeting of the Institution of Gas Engineers at Pembroke College, Oxford, 18 September 1972.

[7] HETHERINGTON, A. F. 'The Gas Industry in the United Kingdom', Lecture delivered in Melbourne, 11 October 1971.

[8] MINISTRY OF POWER, Press Release 5721 (1968).

[9] DAM, Kenneth W. *Oil Resources: Who Gets What How?*, pp. 73–86, University of Chicago (1976).

[10] *Fuel Policy*, Cmnd. 3438, HMSO, London (1967).

[11] HUTCHISON, W. K. 'The Future of the Gas Industry in Great Britain', Address delivered to the Canadian Gas Association, 24 June 1966.

[12] LYNESS F. K. and BADGER, E. H. M. A Measure of Winter Severity, *Journal of the Royal Statistical Society, Series C (Applied Statistics)*, **19**, 119 (1970).

[13] BUNYAN, Richard. *Ireland and Natural Gas*, p. 75, United Dominions Trust (Ireland), Dublin (1974).

[14] BRITISH GAS CORPORATION. *Annual Report and Accounts 1975–6*, pp. 60–1.

[15] MACKAY, D. I. and MACKAY, G. A. *The Political Economy of North Sea Oil*, p. 16, Robertson, London (1975).

[16] BATTISON, Geoffrey. James Buckley—an Appreciation, *Gas World*, October 1976, p. 560.

BIBLIOGRAPHY

ADELMAN, M. A. The Supply and Price of Natural Gas, Supplement to the *Journal of Industrial Economics*, Basil Blackwell, Oxford (1962).

BUCKLEY, J. A. 'Marketing Natural Gas', Address to London and Southern Section, Institution of Gas Engineers, 15 February 1972.

BUCKLEY, J. A. 'The Customer and the Industry', Lecture delivered to a course organised by the Institution of Gas Engineers, Pembroke College, Oxford, 18 September 1972.

CLEGG, B. G. H. 'Natural Gas Marketing in the UK', EEC Symposium on Problems Relevant to Natural Gas Markets in Europe, Barcelona, October 1970.

Costs and Efficiency in the Gas Industry. Cmnd. 4458, HMSO, London (1970).

DAM, Kenneth W. *Oil Resources: Who Gets What How?* University of Chicago Press, Chicago (1976).

DE MELVERDA, H. A. A. *Marketing Patterns*, Institution of Gas Engineers, Communication 933, London (1974).

DORAN, J. F. *Marketing—Southern Style*, Institution of Gas Engineers, Communication 933, London (1974).

Second Report from the Select Committee on Nationalised Industries, Session 1967–68, *Exploitation of North Sea Gas*, HMSO, London (1968).

Fuel Policy, Cmnd. 3438, HMSO, London (1967).

Gas Prices (First Report). Cmnd. 3567, HMSO, London (1968).

HETHERINGTON, A. F. 'The Gas Industry in the United Kingdom', Lecture delivered in Melbourne, Australia, 11 October 1971.

HUTCHISON, W. K. 'The Future of the Gas Industry in Britain', Address delivered to Canadian Gas Association, 24 June 1966. (Published in *Journal of the Institution of Gas Engineers*, Communication 717, 1966.)

JOHNSON, F. J. *Marketing Research Used in Tactical Decision Making*, British Gas Corporation (1974).

JONES, Robert J. and KEEBLE, John G. *Customer Service Management and Training*, Institution of Gas Engineers, Communication 934, London (1974).

JENSEN, W. G. *Energy in Europe 1945–80*, Foulis, London (1967).

LITTLE, I. M. D. *The Price of Fuel*, Clarendon Press, Oxford (1953).

MACKAY, D. I. and MACKAY, G. A. *The Political Economy of North Sea Oil*, Robertson, London (1975).

POLANYI, George. *What Price North Sea Gas? A Study of Economic Issues of Fuel Policy*, Institute of Economic Affairs, London (1967).

PRITCHARD, R., GUY, J. J., and CONNOR, N. E. *Industrial Gas Utilisation*, Bowker, Epping (1977).

POSNER, Michael V. *Fuel Policy: a study in Applied Economics*, Macmillan, London (1973).

19

A New Structure for a New Industry

THE gas industry up to the time of nationalisation, and for some years beyond, had something in common with the older brewing industry. There the sales area of the individual brewery was largely determined by the daily range of the drays. Because of its bulk and low value, long-distance transportation was feasible only by water and even then only the stronger brews would survive the heat and motion of long overseas voyages. A pattern emerged, as early as the eighteenth century, by which a few great brewers supplied each of the great urban areas in Britain, while rural areas depended on much smaller concerns. By 1800 Whitbread, Barclay, and Truman were all brewing more than 100 000 barrels annually and a handful of big brewers supplied three-quarters of the London trade. So it was with the gas industry. Densely populated areas, with many consumers within a few miles radius of an undertaking, were served by very large companies such as the Gas Light and Coke Company: the needs of rural areas were satisfied by works with only a handful of employees. Even as late as the 1930s, economic considerations argued against anything like a national gas-grid in Britain; such a system was viable only in densely populated industrial areas.

We have seen, however, that by the 1950s this situation was changing. Not least of the consequences of the change from coal to oil as the raw material for gas-making was that the new processes generated gas at high pressure, altering the whole economic basis of long-distance transmission. As they also lent themselves to production of gas in large units, the development of integrated grid systems became feasible. Further encouragement for this development, and indeed a necessity for it, came with the advent of imported liquid gas. It was practicable to develop only one terminal for reception of this and although onward transportation by road or rail tanker was possible over relatively short distances, only trunk mains were feasible for distributing the gas in the country generally. We have already noted the building of the 18-inch pipeline from Canvey to Leeds, with its 150 miles of spurs, which enabled eight of the twelve Area Boards to be supplied with Algerian gas. We have noted, too, how this original system was rapidly extended to link up with the east-coast terminals for natural gas from the North Sea and to make it available for all the Area Boards. This development we must now consider in somewhat more detail not only because of its technological interest but because, as we shall see later in this chapter, it had profound effects on the structure of the industry. With growing dependence on natural gas, and the rapid decline of gas manufacture, the role of the

Area Boards inevitably changed considerably. They were no longer pre-occupied with ensuring, year in and year out, that they made enough gas to meet all needs. The marketing of by-products similarly diminished. Now, through the grid, they could depend upon being supplied with sufficient natural gas to meet their requirements and needed to give increased attention to developing sales and service. It was not to be expected that a form of organisation based on local manufacture and distribution would serve equally well in these new circumstances.

THE NATIONAL TRANSMISSION SYSTEM

The development of the national transmission system was in many ways as remarkable an achievement as the bringing ashore of North Sea gas and the conversion programme: certainly it was a no less necessary part of the whole enterprise. Not only was it a very big operation in itself, carried out with remarkable speed, but it had to be most carefully planned to phase in with the rest of the operation: it was no good acquiring the gas if it could not be distributed, nor would the transmission system have been any good with no gas to fill it.

High pressure pipelines are an effective means of transmitting energy. Thus a 36-inch main operating at 1000 lb per square inch pressure (about 70 times that of the atmosphere) can transmit 400 million therms of gas a year over distances of up to 100 miles without pumping. Such results are not easily achieved, however. The high working-pressures subject the pipes, and particularly the joints between sections, to severe strain. The welding must be carefully checked in the field by X-ray methods and special steel—not readily available—is required for the pipes themselves. Booster, or compressor, stations are in practice required at intervals of about 40 miles and at main branches in the network. The supply of gas must be very carefully controlled, in step with the demand, which is subject to wide and rapid fluctuation. This demands a system of central control kept informed by a nationwide telecommunications network. Some provision must be made to store a reserve of gas: this can often be effected in parts of the grid not being used at capacity, but this, too, is possible only with careful monitoring. Stored gas cannot be made instantly available to more distant parts of the network.

The trunk pipeline to Leeds from Canvey Island was completed in 1963, but long before this the mileage of mains in use had been increasing steadily. At nationalisation it totalled 74 400 miles. By 1965 it had risen to 105 600 miles, and by 1973 it had reached 127 000 miles. Over the same period (1948–73) the amount of gas sold rose from about 2300 million to 4603 million therms, an almost exact doubling. By far the greater part of this new mileage was, of course, ordinary low-pressure main. While some high-pressure main was laid to meet the needs of the new plants making gas from

Growth of the national gas high pressure transmission system 1966–1978/9

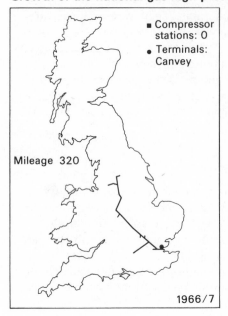

■ Compressor
stations: 0

● Terminals:
Canvey

Mileage 320

1966/7

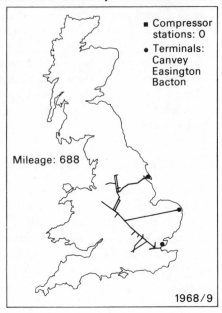

■ Compressor
stations: 0

● Terminals:
Canvey
Easington
Bacton

Mileage: 688

1968/9

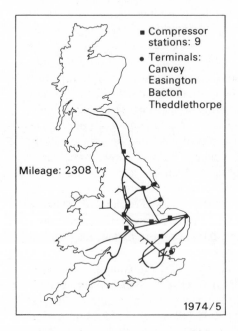

■ Compressor
stations: 9

● Terminals:
Canvey
Easington
Bacton
Theddlethorpe

Mileage: 2308

1974/5

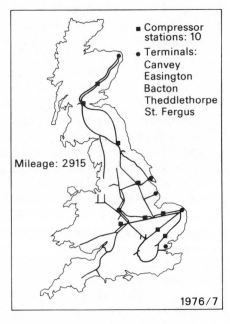

■ Compressor
stations: 10

● Terminals:
Canvey
Easington
Bacton
Theddlethorpe
St. Fergus

Mileage: 2915

1976/7

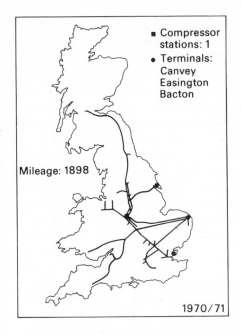

■ Compressor
stations: 1
● Terminals:
Canvey
Easington
Bacton

Mileage: 1898

1970/71

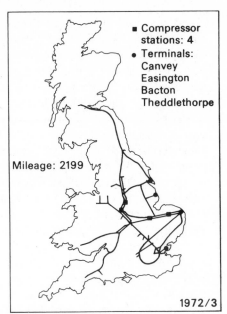

■ Compressor
stations: 4
● Terminals:
Canvey
Easington
Bacton
Theddlethorpe

Mileage: 2199

1972/3

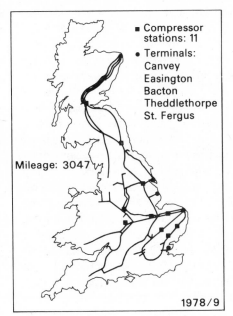

■ Compressor
stations: 11
● Terminals:
Canvey
Easington
Bacton
Theddlethorpe
St. Fergus

Mileage: 3047

1978/9

oil, we may usefully start the history of the high-pressure grid for North Sea gas with the 200-mile stretch from Canvey to Leeds. By 1965 the Gas Council had plans for a high-pressure grid totalling 1250 miles, based on the Canvey–Leeds–Easington spine, at an estimated cost of £110 million. The speed with which a start had to be made, primarily to allow some gas to be delivered into the Killingholme works of the East Midlands Board in the winter of 1966/67, made it necessary to buy some of the special steel-pipe abroad, and the Council gave warning in their Annual Report 1965–66 that some dependence on imported pipe was likely to be necessary in at least the early stages of the scheme [1]. As we shall see, this prediction proved correct, though every effort was made, in collaboration with the two main British suppliers, to purchase in this country. Naturally, this purchase abroad had political repercussions, but it may be remarked that even in the 1970s the US Government had a similar problem with the great 600-mile Alyeska Pipeline in Alaska. To its considerable embarrassment, all the special steel-piping had to be imported from Japan. With the granting, in June 1967, of permission to develop the natural gas terminal at Bacton, work was carried on to construct feeder mains to link it with the main gas system. The first to be laid was a 123-mile pipeline, of 36-inch diameter, joining the natural gas backbone near Rugby. It was filled with gas in May 1968. Insufficient pipe was available in Britain and importation from Europe continued to be necessary.

The Annual Report for 1967–8 announced that the programme of construction had been enlarged to provide for a system of 2500 miles, to be completed by 1972–73; it also gave a great deal of information on achievement to date, and future plans [2]. In the year then under review 250 more miles of pipeline had been laid, despite considerable delay occasioned by a serious outbreak of foot and mouth disease which restricted movement on agricultural land—one of the unexpected hazards which can upset the most careful plans. The 24-inch feeder from Easington to Totley became fully operational in July 1967. This had been planned in 1965 to link Easington with the Canvey–Leeds pipeline. The supply of pipe again caused problems and yet again importation from Europe was necessary. Hopes that the situation would improve were not fulfilled, for 80 000 tons of pipe had to be imported from Italy as late as May–August 1969. Apart from steel quality, part of the problem was the specification—based on recommendations of the Institution of Gas Engineers and the American Petroleum Institute—of a wall thickness up to 5/8th of an inch, which was greater than was then commonly used anywhere else in the world.

The same Annual Report (1967–68) records the Gas Council's decision to establish a new operational pipeline control centre at Hinckley, in Leicestershire, the existing centre at Canvey Island being inadequate. Work began at Hinckley in January 1969 and it became operational in the following year. Strategic control was to be exercised from the Council's London headquarters. The successful operation of the system demanded constant and reliable communications and a system of trunk communication by Post Office broad-band circuits was adopted, with a complementary private microwave system. This entailed siting about sixty 150-ft aerials at intervals along the routes of the pipelines. In the event, it proved possible to place the majority of these on masts already built or needed by other users and only about 10 new masts were required. An Argus 500 computer was chosen to provide maximum information on the state of the system—pictorially displayed on cathode-ray tubes—and to optimise its operation. Elaborate safety precautions were evolved in the event of a failure of communications and in December 1969 a code of practice was developed for dealing with possible emergencies.

The theory of networks—whether they convey gas, or water, or electric-ity—is very complex, and advanced mathematical treatment is necessary to predict how changes in one part of a system are reflected in others. If there is an unexpectedly heavy demand for gas at, say, Dunstable, how can the supply be maintained at Bletchley and Hitchin? What are the best sites for booster stations and what are their horse-power requirements? What is the cheapest method of delivering gas to any particular point when taking into consideration peak load demand figures and financial objectives? Questions of this kind were answered by advanced computer programmes developed by the London Research Station.

In 1968–69 a further 384 miles of the high-pressure grid was completed, bringing the total to 1072. Some rephrasing of the programme was done, however, and the date for completion of the full 2500 miles was put back from 1972–73 to 1975–76. The supply of pipe still presented problems and what was obtained was not fully satisfactory. There were variations in quality, and welding problems resulted. To cope with this, the Gas Council set up its own quality control and inspection service for pipes and high pressure equipment generally; within a year the service was extended to the Area Boards for certain specified components purchased by them. In December 1970 the Institution of Gas Engineers published revised recommendations on transmission and distribution practice.

In May 1970 the advancing pipeline system crossed the border into Scotland, the last of the areas to receive natural gas. This brought the total mileage to 1899 miles, rising to 2106 miles in the following year.

As the transmission pipeline network grew, so too did the number of compressor stations necessary to ensure that it worked at maximum efficiency. The design and construction of these involved more than purely technical problems. Compressors tend to be noisy and for environmental reasons noise must be suppressed. The stations, powered by very large gas turbines, had, therefore, to be sound-proofed. The first compressor stations were those at Ambergate, Alrewas, King's Lynn, and Peterborough (1970/71). A fifth, at Churchover, in Warwickshire, was added a year later and five more were then planned or actually under construction. In 1971 some transportable compressor units were introduced.

In contrast with the electricity industry with its overhead cables strung from long lines of pylons striding across the countryside and its power stations with their giant cooling towers, the installations of the natural gas industry are unobtrusive. The whole of the transmission and distribution system is decently buried underground and the surface vegetation is restored. The only installations above ground are the shore terminals, the compressor stations, and the liquefaction and storage plants. By 1973, when the British Gas Corporation was established, only 81 gasworks remained; their number was falling steadily and many of the traditional gas holders had been dismantled. The sites of many of the old works had been developed for housing, industrial, or commercial purposes. The industry on which a new structure was being imposed, was not only different—it looked different. To this new organisational structure, and its development, we must now turn our attention.

REORGANISATION

A measure of central control and co-ordination is implicit in the concept of nationalisation. If local interests are not to some extent to be subordinated to national ones the point of nationalisation is lost. The operative word, however, is subordinate; the retention of some degree of local management is necessary not merely to take note of differing outlooks and patterns of life in various parts of the country, but for administrative reasons. This has long been recognised in government; throughout the world an effective local government organisation is an essential instrument of successful central government. When it has interests on a national scale, private industry, too, has always recognised the importance of regional organisation, often combined with a product-based organisation. ICI, for example, has always been organised on a divisional basis [3]; insofar as there had been argument about this, it has largely concerned not the principle, but the proper balance of power between the centre and the local organisations. In any circumstances, the chief determinants must be assessment of the organisation appropriate for the particular industry; the creation of efficient machinery to make it work; and the establishment of strong central control to ensure that, within the agreed definition of policy, the balance of power is maintained. Whether political or industrial, all organisations are collections of individuals whose natural instinct is to increase rather than diminish their own power. If the central control is weak, the local organisations will assume greater authority; ambitious men at the centre will tend to take power, if they can, from the regions. To an extent, therefore, there is a constant process of attrition, and this in itself is no bad thing. Even in the unlikely event that at a particular moment an organisation is ideally constituted, it could not long remain so, for the milieu in which it operates is constantly changing. All successful organisations must have some in-built capacity to respond to changes outside themselves. Generally this will be gradual, but the natural process of evolution is likely to be punctuated by radical reorganisations when a marked disparity has developed between the existing set-up and the needs it has to fulfil.

All these general considerations apply to the structural evolution of the British gas industry after the Second World War. The Gas Act 1948 in itself brought no immediate material change. The industry for which the Gas Council assumed authority on 1 May 1949 was precisely the same as that which had supplied Britain's gas on the previous day. There were still over 1000 operating gasworks. What had changed radically were the principles on which it was in future to be run: for the first time there was some capacity for concerted action on a national basis. The vesting date marked no more than the start of a long process of organisational development for realising this capacity. We have already noted (Ch. 13) the form of organisation imposed on the gas industry by nationalisation. Our present concern is to consider how this evolved in the following quarter of a century, culminating in the new organisation, dictated by the Gas Act 1972, by which the present British Gas Corporation was established.

The original nationalisation Act gave great power to the twelve Area Boards and their functions were in fact stated in the Act before those of the Gas Council. The first prescribed role of the Gas Council was to advise the Minister and 'promote and assist' the Area Boards in the efficient exercise and performance of their functions. It might act on behalf of the Area Boards, but only 'if so authorised by all the Area Boards or a group of Area Boards.' It could demand that the Boards kept it informed as to what they were doing. It could borrow money, particularly to compensate dispossessed owners. But only two members of the Gas Council—the Chairman and Deputy Chairman, both appointed by the Minister—had a nominal degree of independence. The remaining twelve members were, *ex officio*, the chairmen of the Area Boards. Moreover, it was the Area Boards which generated both the gas and the revenue: the Council contributed nothing financially. It followed as a matter of course that the chairmen of the Area Boards were very powerful. In the circumstances of the day this was no bad thing. They were all experienced men, though none had governed enterprises as large as those for which they had overnight become responsible, whose immediate task was to rationalise the gas undertakings of which they had become the heads. This involved modernising and, if necessary, extending the larger and more efficient works and closing the small and inefficient ones, and introducing new and improved methods of manufacturing gas. A measure of their success is that by March 1960 only 428 gasworks were in operation, compared with 1050 on vesting day.

It was not to be expected, however, that such a form of organisation would be permanent, especially as with the advent of imported natural gas, and later North Sea gas, a central source of supply, distributed through a national network of pipelines, began to replace the multiplicity of local works and local systems of supply. Nevertheless, the nature of the business demanded the retention of close links with the local communities which it served.

Not until 1960 was any new statutory change proposed for the industry. The Gas Act 1960, in effect, did little more than increase the Council's borrowing power. Under the original Act the Council's borrowing power, except for the payment of compensation to dispossessed owners, was limited to £450 million and this limit was fast being approached. Under the new Act the limit was raised to £500 million (or £525 million if the Minister approved).

The Gas Act 1965, however, was much more far-reaching; its general effect was to put the Gas Council on the same footing as the Area Boards. It was given powers 'to manufacture gas, to get or acquire gas in or from Great Britain or elsewhere and to supply gas in bulk to any Area Board.' It might also 'manufacture, treat, render saleable, supply or sell solid fuels, by-products and products' in the same way as Area Boards. To strengthen it in fulfilling these new powers, the Act enabled the Minister to appoint up to three additional members to the Gas Council. These were full-time appointments, made from within the industry. The Minister's first appointment was that of Mr D. E. Rooke, then the Council's Director of Production and Supplies, who became Chairman of the British Gas Corporation in July 1976.

The magnitude of the Gas Council's new commitments was reflected in the Gas (Borrowing Powers) Act 1965. This set a new limit of £900 million, which the Minister was empowered to increase to £1200 million. This limit excluded stock issued as compensation and certain other commitments incurred prior to the vesting date. At that time the Gas Council expected that an extension of borrowing power to £1000 million would cover its requirements until 1970. The additional £200 million was sought as a means of meeting 'possible major fluctuations in investment in the later years': that is to say, it was to be a long-stop [4].

With this shift of the balance of power towards the centre, correspondingly more staff were required in London. In October 1964, final arrangements were concluded for the provision of new offices at 1 Grosvenor Place, London, on the same site as the original Murdoch House. Within a month, however, this plan was frustrated by the Government Statement on Office Building, which restricted the execution of major office building projects in central London. Formal application for a permit was made in April 1965 but this was rejected. In May 1968 the Council finally moved to large new offices at 59 Bryanston Street, Marble Arch.

The growing sense of corporate identity and the new importance of gas in the national economy was reflected also in the establishment, in May 1965, of the Gas Advisory Council. This was a central body through which employers and employees—through the trade unions involved—could discuss the development of the industry in relation to national objectives for economic growth. The Annual Report for 1966–67, for example, records it as having discussed the exploration programme and pipeline plans for the North Sea, as well as winter gas supplies, the commissioning of new plant, and the interlinking of the Area Boards' distribution systems.

At the beginning of 1966, three new divisions were established in London to facilitate existing activities of growing importance [5]. They were respectively:

(1) *Co-ordination and Planning.* Its responsibility was to co-ordinate the capital development programmes of the Council and the Area Boards; to review programmes generally with the Boards, and maintain liaison with the Ministry of Power with regard to the investment plans of the industry as a whole.

(2) *Production and Supply.* This was responsible for the production, transmission, and storage of gas. This included consideration of proposals for interlinking the supply systems of neighbouring Area Boards or the joint use of production facilities or sources of raw material. It also reviewed supplies of gas and gas-making materials and exercised general supervision of the Council's North Sea activities.

(3) *Special Projects.* This had a particular responsibility for negotiating arrangements for the importation of liquefied natural gas and natural gas offered for sale by the North Sea producers. It was also responsible for preparing and presenting the Council's case at any hearings that might be held under the Continental Shelf Act 1964.

NEW TECHNIQUES OF MANAGEMENT

These changes were a preliminary to a more radical reorganisation adumbrated in the Annual Report for 1967–68, in which it was stated that in the summer of 1967 the Council had sought the advice of leading independent consultants (McKinsey and Company) on organisation and management. The Company submitted a proposal for a detailed study at the end of July and estimated that it would take five months to complete [6]. Their advice quickly bore fruit [7]. The general effect was to enable the Gas Council to take a stronger lead in initiating and co-ordinating planning for the whole industry. The roles of the Chairman and Deputy Chairman were redefined. Sir Henry Jones, as Chairman, was left free to concentrate on policy and future development and his Deputy, Mr Arthur Hetherington, became chief executive of the Council with responsibility for all departments, and for settling all day-to-day issues. The new management structure embodied eight departments. These were respectively secretariat; legal; public-relations; production and supply; marketing; economic planning; personnel; and research and development. As the accompanying chart shows, the responsibilities of the various departments include not only many traditional functions but some which were either not contemplated at the time of nationalisation or were then of relatively minor importance. Among such we may mention conversion, metrication, and transmission planning. The introduction of members for marketing and for economic planning was an important step towards the achievement of integrated policy and performance.

While these changes were taking place at the centre, the various Regions were undertaking their own reorganisation projects to improve their business efficiency. The Annual Reports for these years make constant reference to major structural reorganisations. These were years in which British industry was becoming aware of the new techniques of management being developed in the USA. There, young graduates of the Business Schools attached to the leading universities were securing lucrative and influential posts in industry, commerce, and government service. In Britain, the Administrative Staff College had been founded at Henley-on-Thames in 1946, and the British Institute of Management was established in London in 1947. Academic developments came much later, however. The Manchester Business School, the London Graduate School of Business Studies, and the Oxford Centre for Management Studies, were not founded until 1965.

Once seized of the idea of management as a proper subject for independent study, however, British industry embraced it with enthusiasm. Indeed, some of those engaged in industry at that time felt that the zeal of the converts was excessive; so much time was devoted to studying and seeking to apply new techniques of management that, in the short term at least, actual production tended to be impaired. However, this is not to deny that managerial methods in Britain were outdated, nor that from the turmoil new styles of management evolved that were considerable improvements on the old ones. In its way, the managerial revolution proved as important as the scientific and technological revolutions that preceded it. The control of North Sea gas, the development of a national transmission grid, and the conversion programme could scarcely have been contemplated on the management basis prevalent in British industry in the 1940s.

The gas industry was quick to recognise the new trend. From 1952 onwards there were gas industry representatives at every session of the Administrative Staff College and six-week residential courses were organised in collaboration with the School of Management and Business Studies at Brooklands Technical College. For the latter, an average of 80 nominations were made every year up to 1967, drawn from Area Boards, the Council, and members of the Society of British Gas Industries. In addition, several Area Boards ran their own short management and executive development courses.

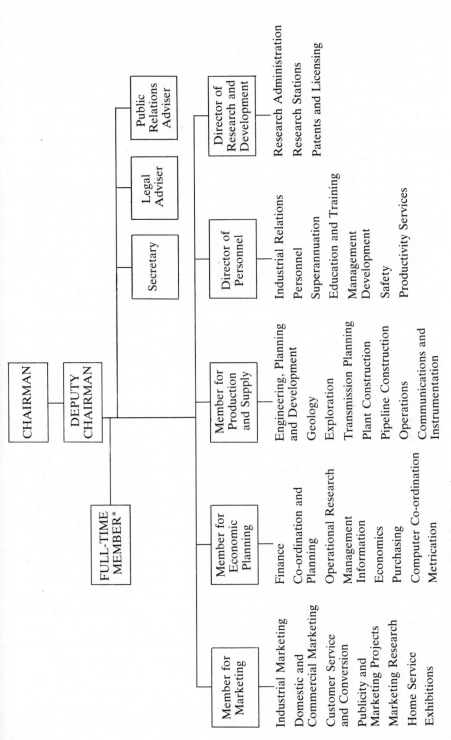

CHAIRMAN

DEPUTY CHAIRMAN

FULL-TIME MEMBER*

Member for Marketing

Industrial Marketing
Domestic and Commercial Marketing
Customer Service and Conversion
Publicity and Marketing Projects
Marketing Research
Home Service
Exhibitions

Member for Economic Planning

Finance
Co-ordination and Planning
Operational Research
Management Information
Economics
Purchasing
Computer Co-ordination
Metrication

Member for Production and Supply

Engineering, Planning and Development
Geology
Exploration
Transmission Planning
Plant Construction
Pipeline Construction
Operations
Communications and Instrumentation

Secretary

Legal Adviser

Public Relations Adviser

Director of Personnel

Industrial Relations
Personnel
Superannuation
Education and Training
Management Development
Safety
Productivity Services

Director of Research and Development

Research Administration
Research Stations
Patents and Licensing

* Also, Chairman, Gas Industry Training Board.

The Annual Report for 1967–68 shows how deeply the industry had become involved in the new methods. Area Boards had enlarged their sections devoted to Organisation and Methods and to Work Study; where appropriate, outside consultants had been brought in. A Work Study Officers' Committee had been established and was meeting regularly 'to keep under review the results of schemes already introduced and to examine proposed standards for future schemes' [8]. The new techniques were being applied in such diverse fields as plant maintenance; appliance installation; clerical procedures; design and layout of depots and stores; and transport and delivery of materials. The Area Boards established their own management service units embracing staff responsible for operational research, organisation and methods, and statistics. Their main object was to bring together the services which provide information for short-term and long-term planning decisions. Schemes were introduced for job evaluation, staff appraisal, and investigation of job satisfaction. In short, the gas industry climbed aboard the new band-wagon of management as eagerly as the rest of progressive British industry. At the end of the ride, when the more extravagant excursions had been discounted, the new methods were established, with advantage, within the structural organisation of the gas industry.

THE GAS ACT 1972

All these developments in organisation and management techniques, energetically and purposefully pursued, were paving the way to a general restructuring of the gas industry as a whole. The need for this was accentuated, as we have noted, by the change in the source of gas. In the days of manufactured gas, the main preoccupation of the Area Boards was to ensure that, whatever the vagaries of the fickle British climate, the supply of gas matched the demand. With increasing, and ultimately complete, dependence on natural gas this ceased to be an anxiety, for gas flowed into each region from outside instead of being manufactured within it.

While the gas industry had a considerable degree of freedom to organise itself as seemed most appropriate for the discharge of its obligations, it had to exercise this freedom within the constraints of the Gas Acts of 1948 and 1965. By 1969 the government had reached the conclusion that for the fullest possible reaping of the advantages of North Sea gas a more radical reorganisation, with increased transference of power to the centre, was called for. In November 1969 a Bill to this end was introduced in Parliament. It progressed to Committee stage but was then lost as a consequence of the dissolution of Parliament in May 1970. In the general election that followed, a Conservative government was returned. This had more immediate concerns than the organisational problems of the gas industry, to which it did not turn its attention formally until 1971. Probably the respite was a good thing and might even with advantage have been a little greater. The conversion programme was then just about at its peak. Just over six million customers had been dealt with, very nearly half the total, and no less than 18 per cent of all customers were converted in 1971–72. Both at headquarters and in the regions, there had already been, as we have noted, very considerable organisational changes and changes in management style. The imposition by statute of a further considerable reorganisation, however desirable it might be in the long run, was bound to present particularly great difficulties at that time. Nevertheless, the new government was anxious to take up the task that its predecessor had laid down, despite the fact that on the side of government, too, there had been major organisational changes which needed to be digested. The abortive Bill of 1970 had been introduced by Mr Roy Mason, as Minister of Power. The new Bill was introduced under the auspices of Mr John Davies, Minister for Trade and Industry; in between, the Gas Council had been responsible to Mr Davies as Minister of Technology.

The government's intention under the new Bill, introduced in January 1972, was to consolidate the new arrangements and to put full responsibility for the industry in the hands of a new statutory body, the British Gas Corporation. The Bill received Royal Assent on 9 August 1972 and the new Corporation formally came into being on 1 January 1973, the day on which Britain entered the Common Market. In introducing the new Bill, the Minister stressed that, with conversion more than half completed and likely to be finished within four or five years, it was not sensible to think in terms of an interim measure: the government had in mind legislation appropriate for the industry of the 1980s. He recognised, however, that even thinking ten years ahead brought the industry within the scope of many imponderables. The Bill did not, therefore, seek to impose a rigid organisation on the industry, which would be relatively free to take its own decisions—in the light of changing circumstances—as to how managerial functions should be distributed between the centre and the periphery. As the Minister put it, introducing the Bill:

It is more sensible to proceed gradually, by enabling moves away from the present structure and the present distribution of responsibilities to take place as and to the extent that they become, in management's eyes, necessary for the efficient conduct of the industry. But the industry must have direction and control, and never more so than at a time of rapid development and change. We have therefore decided to put full statutory control in the hands of a single body, the British Gas Corporation. The Statutory area boards will be abolished, and all the assets of the industry will vest in the corporation.

The dissolution of the Area Boards was the main feature in which the new government's policy differed from that of its predecessor. In a memorandum [9] submitted to the Select Committee on Nationalised Industries in May 1968, the then Minister of Power (Mr Ray Gunter) said that in respect of future legislation he had considered this possibility but had rejected it, partly in order to ensure that the industry's sales and service responsibilities were fully reflected in the Council's planning and strategy. Partly, he rejected it also:

> . . . because of the importance, at a time when the industry is already tackling immense tasks, of reducing to a minimum the inevitable disturbance caused by structural changes. In general, the gas industry has shown itself to be thoroughly efficient and morale is high.

In subsequent questioning by members of the Select Committee the Minister was asked to elaborate his views on the role of the Area Chairmen. The Committee had 'thought they were a very lively lot and a very intelligent lot,' but wondered whether they did not sometimes find themselves in an anomalous position, in that they would feel responsible to the Minister who nominated them, rather than to the Council. In a sense they had to wear two hats. When acting in his local capacity an Area Board Chairman was a retailer, but when sitting as a member of the Council he was a wholesaler. The Minister did not see this as a major problem. He believed that the Area Board Chairmen were strong individuals; that they did not tend to team up together; and that they were well able to stand up to the pressures imposed on them.

In expressing these views, the Minister must presumably have been depending largely on the advice of his permanent officials, for he had taken office only the previous month, and, as it turned out, he had gone again two months later. This raises a general problem of the nationalised industries which must be considered in more detail later, namely the incompatibility of the industrial and the political time-scales. For the realisation of major industrial enterprises an overall development time of around ten years is normal, and this applies over a surprisingly wide field [10]. The recent history of the gas industry admirably illustrates this general thesis: between the decision to embark on the conversion programme and its completion some dozen years elapsed. But in political life this may represent three or four governments—not necessarily all of the same political persuasion—and many more Ministers, each anxious to make his mark and be remembered for doing something different from his predecessors: politicians do not advance their careers by maintaining the status quo. The reconciliation of these opposing factors is a problem yet to be solved. To an extent, of course, it is not a problem peculiar to gas and the other nationalised industries; all sections of industry are influenced not only by specific legislation but by the prevailing political climate. The nationalised industries are particularly vulnerable, however, because of their direct responsibility to a minister and that minister's responsibility to Parliament. The question of the relationship between the industry and government is one to which we shall return later.

In general the 1972 Act resembled that of 1948 and much of the phraseo-logy remained unchanged, with the very important exception that where questions of responsibility arise the Corporation is substituted for the Area Boards. Thus the original Act states:

It shall be the duty of every Area Board [the Corporation] to develop and maintain an efficient, co-ordinated and economical system of gas supply for their area [Great Britain] and to satisfy, so far as it is economical to do so, all reasonable demands for gas within their area [in Great Britain].

The words in square brackets indicate the changes in the original basic remit embodied in the 1972 Act. Additionally, as might be expected, there is specific reference to natural gas and petroleum which did not feature as such in the Gas Act 1948 because it did not then seem a possibility. The Corpora-tion was empowered:

(1) To search and bore for and get natural gas.
(2) To bore for and get petroleum found in the form of crude oil as a result of its searching, boring and getting.

Like the old Area Boards, the Corporation was empowered—but on a national and not a regional basis—to manufacture gas from any source; to transmit and distribute gas; to manufacture plant required for its own purposes; and to manufacture, supply, and maintain gas fittings. The Cor-poration was, however, to restrict its activities to Great Britain in the widest sense, this including areas covered by the Continental Shelf Act 1964. It might neither export gas nor manufacture gas fittings for export.

The Gas Consultative Councils, established by the original Act, for each region, were to be replaced by Regional Gas Consumers' Councils (p. 280). Like their predecessors, these were to consist of nominees of local author-ities and representatives of local commerce, industry, and labour. Generally speaking, they were supposed to be watchdogs for consumers, acting as a go-between, but with limited powers. They had to consider representations made to them by consumers (or potential consumers), including those concerning variation of tariffs, and might, without such prompting, consider relevant local issues. They could then pass their conclusions on to the Corporation either directly or through the National Council. The Corpora-tion was under an obligation to consider their conclusions or reports, but was under no obligation to take any action as a result. With the transfer of power to the Corporation from the Area Boards a national counterpart to the Regional Councils became necessary, and a National Gas Consumers' Council was set up. This consisted of the chairmen of the Regional Councils and such other persons (including the chairman) as the Minister might think appropriate. The National Council was to consider the interests of consumers generally, and was normally to report to, and be consulted by, the Corporation. It might, however, also be consulted by and report to, the Secretary of State for Prices and Consumer Protection.

In the interest of continuity, the new Act provided that those appointed members of the Corporation should meet before it came formally into existence, to plan the future organisation and operation of the industry. In October 1972 Mr Arthur Hetherington, chairman designate of the new Corporation, and chairman of the existing Gas Council since January 1972, had used the occasion of the publication of the Annual Report to give some public indication of the future of the industry. He sought to allay anxiety that the new organisation would be so centralised and bureaucratic as to be unapproachable. He made it clear that the Corporation was to remain decentralised to the fullest possible extent compatible with efficiency. In particular, the existing organisation embodying twelve regions was to be maintained, and the chairman of each would be responsible to the Corporation. This message he reiterated in the first Annual Report (1972–73) published by the new Corporation:

The Corporation decided that a regional structure was right for an industry with such strong local roots. The supply of gas to customers, particularly to domestic customers, and the sale, installation and servicing of appliances are essentially matters which need local initiatives. Each region is a complete management unit on its own under the Regional Chairman and is given the necessary authority and the responsibility for dealing with these matters. Those aspects of the Corporation's activities which were already being dealt with on a national basis will continue to be dealt with in that way and it may be necessary or desirable to develop more uniform practices and standards throughout the country.

Arrangements for communication and the co-ordination of the wide range of activities that make up the total business are now well developed between Headquarters and Regions. These add strength to policy making and to effective action thus obtaining the advantages of both coherent overall progress and local initiative.

This was all sensible enough and in accordance with the Ministerial advocacy of *festina lente* indicated when he introduced the Bill. For most of the chairmen of the former twelve Area Boards, however, it must have been a disappointment, for they lost their automatic right to a seat at the centre and they were clearly destined for more uniformity of action.

The Act empowered the Minister to appoint as Members, the Chairman and not less than 10, nor more than 20 others, one or more of whom he might designate deputy chairman or chairmen. In making his appointments the Minister was enjoined to have regard to the desirability of having members who were familiar with the special requirements and circumstances of particular regions. Membership of the new corporation numbered fifteen of whom only five, in addition to the chairman and deputy chairman, were full-time. Of the eight part-time members only four were drawn from the twelve regional chairmen. The other four represented outside interests.

They were respectively, the Professor of Applied Economics in the University of Dundee; the General Secretary of the National Union of Textile and Allied Workers; the Chairman and Chief Executive of Reed International; and the Chairman of Unilever Limited. In effect, therefore, the universities, the trade-unions, and private industry were represented. Looking a little ahead from the proper end of this history, we may end by noting that by 1976/77 the number of part-time members had been increased to nine, of whom only four were original members, and only three were Regional Chairmen.

In the early 1960s the economic historian R. H. Tawney wrote:

The transfer of property in return for compensation which nationalization involves, is a means, not an end. Its purpose is to ensure that services, on which the general welfare depends, shall be conducted with a single eye to that objective, under authorities accountable for their proceedings to the public. Its success depends, therefore, not on the mere change of ownership, but on the degree to which advantage is taken of the opportunity offered by it to secure first-class management, to carry through measures of re-organisation which private enterprise was unable or unwilling to undertake, and to enlist the active co-operation of employees in increasing production [11].

With these general sentiments few would quarrel and certainly they are in accord with the structural reorganisation undergone by the nationalised gas industry during the first quarter century of its existence.

REFERENCES

[1] THE GAS COUNCIL. *Annual Report and Accounts 1965–66*, p. 9, HMSO, London (1966).

[2] THE GAS COUNCIL. *Annual Report and Accounts 1967–68*, pp. 12–13, HMSO, London (1968).

[3] READER, W. J. *Imperial Chemical Industries: a History*, Vol. II, pp. 25–31, Oxford University Press, London (1975).

[4] THE GAS COUNCIL. *The Growing Gas Industry: the Development Plan of the Gas Industry to 1970*, p. 16, London (May 1965).

[5] THE GAS COUNCIL. *Annual Report and Accounts 1965–66*, p. 2, HMSO, London (1966).

[6] McKINSEY and COMPANY. *Memorandum of Proposal to the Gas Council*, 31 July 1967.

[7] THE GAS COUNCIL. *Annual Reports and Accounts 1968–69*, p. 6, HMSO, London (1969).
   Idem. *Gas Council Reorganisation*, Press Release 7350, 4 April 1968.

[8] THE GAS COUNCIL. *Annual Report and Accounts 1967–68*, p. 40, HMSO, London (1968).

[9] Second Report from the Select Committee on Nationalised Industries. Session 1967–68, *Exploitation of North Sea Gas*, p. 136, HMSO, London (1968).

[10] ENOS, J. L. *The Rate and Direction of Inventive Activity*, Princeton University Press, New Jersey (1962).

[11] TAWNEY, R. H. (ed. R. HINDEN). *The Radical Tradition*, p. 160 (1964).

BIBLIOGRAPHY

Copp, D. L. *Gas Transmission and Distribution*, 2nd ed. King, London (1970).

The Gas Council. *The Growing Gas Industry: the Development Plan of the Gas Industry to 1970*, London (May 1965).

Pryke, Richard. *Public Enterprise in Practice*, MacGibbon & Kee, London (1971).

Report from the Select Committee on Nationalised Industries. *The Gas Industry*, HMSO, London (1961).

Robson, William A. *Nationalized Industry and Public Ownership*, 2nd edn., Allen and Unwin, London (1962).

Second Report from the Select Committee on Nationalized Industries. *Gas, Electricity, and Coal Industries*, HMSO, London (1966).

20

Relations with Government

IN Chapter 13 we considered the events that led up to the nationalisation of certain key British industries immediately after the last war, and to a limited extent before it, and the differing ways in which the government tackled the problems posed by the differences between industries concerned. In the chapter just concluded we considered the changing organisation of the nationalised gas industry, partly in response to the statutory requirements of the Gas Act 1948 and subsequent Acts; partly in response to technological change; and partly in response to new managerial techniques that were being widely introduced in British industry. No industry, least of all a great national corporation, can operate in isolation and we must now also examine the development of the gas industry in relation to the various sectors of the outside world—to government, to other nationalised industries, to the nation at large, and to its customers.

Our immediate subject is the relationship of the gas industry with government, but we must consider this in the context of the nationalised industries generally. At the outset it must be said that this is a difficult subject: it is often hard to establish the facts, let alone discern any consistent interpretation of them. When scrutinised, the records show many seeming contradictions. Possibly historians of the future, profiting from a lapse of time which makes it easier to distinguish the essential from the inessential, will find it possible to present a coherent and convincing picture of the relationship between nationalised industries and government in the 1950s and 1960s but for the moment this is not easy.

This is not to say that certain general relationships are not perfectly clear, for they are embodied in a succession of Acts of Parliament and accepted codes of practice. What has been going on in recent years is essentially a testing of the interpretation of the subtler provisions of these Acts, rather as the interpretation of ordinary legislation is tested in the courts and case law is established for future guidance. Hitherto, the interpretation of Acts governing the nationalised industries has not been tested in the calm and dispassionate atmosphere of the courts, nor is it likely to be. Instead, it has been argued in the politically charged atmosphere of Parliament and in the press, on radio, and on television. Moreover, this testing period has been one of great political, economic, and social change. While both Parliament and the media can, at their best, be both responsible and helpful, they often merely cloud the issues involved and, at worst, are uninformed, trivial, and destructive. Issues of real importance get swallowed up in attempts to score party political points, or to provide sensational news stories. Reality becomes obscured by ill-defined, emotive phrases such as 'accountability to Parliament', 'public responsibility', 'the will of the people', and so on.

In theory–and for much of the time in practice also—the management of all the nationalised industries is on similar lines, even though somewhat different patterns were adopted in individual cases. The government's general proposals for the industry would be introduced as a Bill which, after lengthy debate and going through the normal procedures, would finally emerge as an Act giving statutory effect to the will of a democratically elected Parliament. Thus far, at least, the will of the people may be said to have been recognised. The general effect of every such Act was to give ultimate authority in respect of policy to a Minister, himself responsible to Parliament, but leaving the industry free to manage its own affairs as seemed most appropriate to it. The Act would define certain general principles, of which one would be the administrative organisation; within this the Minister would himself be entitled to make certain key appointments and give certain directives. There would be important financial clauses, concerning such matters as borrowing powers and the need for Ministerial approval of major capital expenditure proposals, an outstanding example of which, in the case of the gas industry, was the conversion programme. There would be obligations to balance revenue and expenditure. There would be a requirement for the industry to render an annual account of its stewardship, in a prescribed form, to the Minister, for him to lay before Parliament. There would be a requirement for the industry to consult with statutory bodies representing its customers. The overall nature of these and other similar provisions, and the reasons for them, would be generally understood and accepted, and provided all went well there would be no great reason to question them.

But, of course, things did not always go well; nationalisation did not prove the panacea for all industrial ills that its more naive proponents had predicted. The nationalised industries could lose money, have dissatisfied customers, have labour disputes, come into conflict with the interests of other industries, both nationalised and private, and generally run into difficulties common to industry the world over. They might be nationalised but they were not internationalised; they could not escape the political and economic realities of the world at large. They might, in what seemed to be the best interests of the industry and its customers, wish to adopt a course of action for which their authority was questionable. When difficulties arose the interpretation of the various Acts was questioned and ambiguities often became apparent. Some might hold that difficulties had arisen because the industry had been secretive and failed to disclose its problems early enough for effective ministerial action to be taken: others would claim that these problems had arisen, or at least been aggravated, because the industry had had to conduct its affairs with a degree of publicity to which private firms were not subject. Words and phrases well understood in common parlance, were seen to lack precision within the framework of a Parliamentary Act. What constituted a 'reasonable' service or 'undue' preference? In the context of profitability what was meant by 'taking one year with another'? If parts of an industry were profitable, while others ran at a loss, was it sufficient that there was an overall surplus? Did the corporations have an obligation to make special concessions to poorer customers, or keep inefficient works open to provide employment in depressed areas, when this was demonstrably uneconomic for them? When the interests of one nationalised industry were clearly opposed to those of another, was the problem to be resolved by ordinary market forces or by politically imposed directions? This last point was very precisely made by Lord Robens, chairman of the National Coal Board, in giving evidence to the Select Committee on the Nationalised Industries in 1968:

Each nationalised industry today, of course, runs a completely separate company in absolute competition without fear or favour and no quarter—no holds are barred. My own conception of nationalised industries is that they should work virtually as a team and that the Ministry would be a holding company taking the advantages and disadvantages, drawing the bottom line and producing the balance sheet. This is not, however, Government policy. Therefore, we immerse ourselves into competitive battle.

Generalisations are always dangerous, but it is probably fair to say that the nationalised industries, especially those that serve the public directly, have never really been popular in Britain, and this through no fault of their own. The public do not read *in extenso* the reports of Parliamentary committees, of debates in the House, or the Acts to which they eventually give birth. Nor do they read the relatively easily digestible annual reports of the various industries. To them nationalisation means that they own the industry; and if they own it, it had better serve them well. If services decline and charges rise, even if this is in response to forces inescapably affecting industry generally, their industry has not lived up to their expectations. Superimposed on this are other difficulties, not least of which is that the British public do not merely look without much favour on nationalised industry; they are somewhat contemptuous of industry generally, especially large concerns. There is no doubt that a major factor in Britain's steady economic decline has been her failure to accord industrialists generally, and applied scientists and engineers in particular, the status they have gained among our most successful rivals abroad. There has been much public concern about the distribution of wealth and remarkably little about its creation.

Finally, there was the political factor. This was, of course, most evident among the very small minority who took an active part in the political life of Britain, but it extended also to the people generally. The nature of the British voting system is such that large Parliamentary majorities do not correspond with large differences in the numbers of votes cast. In all

post-war elections, regardless of outcome, something like half the electorate
voted Conservative and the Conservatives were in principle opposed to
nationalisation. In five general elections between 1955 and 1970 the Conservatives polled a minimum of 11 418 000 votes and a maximum of
13 751 000 out of a total of around 28 000 000 votes cast: there was, therefore, always a substantial body of public opinion that was disposed to be
critical of the nationalised industries on no grounds better than simple
prejudice, however hard they tried and whatever success they achieved.

On the other side of the political coin, the situation was not helped by
extravagant claims made by responsible Ministers in Parliament. For example, while the Transport Bill was being piloted through Parliament in
1946/7, quite unrealistic claims were made by the Transport Minister, Mr
Alfred Barnes (p. 111), and the Lord President of the Council, Mr Herbert
Morrison [1]. They well knew—everybody knew who travelled and kept his
eyes open—that the railways were in a desperate plight and that improvement would be long and painful. There was no possible course of action that
could effect the sort of rapid transformation they publicly promised. The
Chancellor of the Exchequer, Dr Hugh Dalton, took a much more realistic
view when he spoke of 'a poor bag of assets'. When, inevitably, the hopes of
the travelling public were dashed, they naturally became restive and wanted
to know what had gone wrong.

These general observations apply in full measure to the gas industry, the
more so because of its very large number of customers throughout the
country. Between nationalisation and 1972 the number rose from about 12
million to $13\frac{1}{2}$ million. Of these about 95 per cent were domestic consumers,
and many represented multiple users—families, occupants of lodgings, and
so on. Unlike electricity, which had become practically all-pervasive, there
were some considerable geographical gaps, but it is certainly true to say that
the great majority of people in Britain were to some extent dependent on
gas, and actively interested in the service they received. Almost everybody
was a potential critic. Further, it started with a poor public image. In the
immediate post-war years few would have given much for its future prospects: fewer still would have predicted that within two decades it would be a
thriving industry in the very front rank of technological progress. A cynic
might have argued, of course, that so far as public opinion was concerned
this depressed state was in the industry's favour: almost any change must be
for the better.

THE ROLE OF THE MINISTER

As we have noted, the direct relationship of the national corporations to
government is through the responsible Minister who, in Parliament, must
speak for it. The relevant Acts give no powers to Parliament as such, but its
influence is nonetheless very considerable. It alone can approve the form of

the initial Act of nationalisation and any subsequent amending ones. It can, if it so chooses, make the life of the Minister very uncomfortable and even put his office in peril. Individual members can draw public attention to legitimate complaints made by their constituents. They are collectively a force that cannot be ignored. We have already noted, for example, the special care devoted to the conversion programme in the Palace of Westminster: a care matched by that devoted to Fleet Street.

It is not practicable to consider the relationship between a nationalised industry and government in complete isolation, for it is a relationship to some extent influenced by extraneous pressures to which both parties are subject. As far as the Minister is concerned he himself has very considerable statutory powers, but he is also subject to a great deal of influence by the Treasury and, on major issues, the views of his Cabinet colleagues. Some would wish that he would rely wholly on such powers and that, if he found himself in dispute with a public corporation, he would give it a public direction if he believed that it ought to take a course of action contrary to its own judgment. This would at least have the advantage of indicating clearly where responsibility for subsequent events really lay. But this would put the Minister in a position of exercising both power and responsibility, a combination which not all relish. If exercised unduly, such powers would reduce the corporations to, effectively, the status of government departments, a state of affairs which nationalisation was never intended to bring about and, indeed, sought to avoid. Further, such authoritarian management is alien to British tradition, which has always been inclined towards control by persuasion or informal compromise rather than by strict legality. In the event it is this course that has generally been adopted, though not with entirely satisfactory results. An ambitious and aggressive Minister may be given to excessive interference. Mr Harold Watkinson, as Conservative Minister of Transport and Civil Aviation (1955–59), stated in May 1956 that one clear precedent that he intended to maintain was 'that BOAC policy is a matter between me and the chairman' [2]. Challenged in the House, he avowed that 'the chain of command is that I am responsible to the House and the chairman is responsible to me'. In the same year he maintained this attitude in respect of the British Transport Commission which, with a mounting deficit, proposed to increase both their passenger and freight charges. Their proposals were endorsed by the Transport Tribunal. Nevertheless, the proposed increases were only partially allowed, as the Minister claimed to discern rapid improvements resulting from increased efficiency of operation, and that the Commission were in willing co-operation with this view. This one must take leave to doubt: the Commission could scarcely have been very willing about following a policy which, in their own considered view, and in the forcibly stated view of an independent Tribunal, was to force them even further into debt than they were already [3]. Such episodes are a remainder that, in the last analysis, the government must always carry the day. It is also a reminder of a point made earlier, that the political and the industrial time-scales are very different.

Mr Ernest Davies, writing in 1955 when he was chairman of the Transport Group of the Parliamentary Labour Party, probably gave a fair picture of the situation then obtaining when he wrote:

The consequence is that whereas behind the scenes they [Ministers] have exerted a greater influence on the boards, they have not accepted public accountability for their actions. They have exercised their responsibility in private and not answered for it in public. This tendency was noticeable during the previous administration but has been carried considerably further by present Ministries [4].

SOURCES OF INFORMATION ON NATIONALISED INDUSTRIES

The British public, and its Parliamentary representatives, dislike nothing more than to feel that their affairs are being settled in secrecy. There is, therefore, an avid demand for information, a demand often in direct conflict with the need—and certainly the convenience—of those concerned to conduct negotiations in confidence. The difficulties are self-evident of running a great public corporation on the basis that every confidential exchange between the board and the Minister, with private companies (perhaps basically foreign-owned); with trade-unions; and with other bodies, may ultimately be exposed in detail to the public gaze. On the other hand, it is equally clearly undesirable that so much secrecy should be permissible that inefficiency and abuse of power could be covered up. It is, therefore, pertinent to examine the means by which information about the running of the nationalised industries can be sought. In passing, it may be remarked that often the mere obtaining of information satisfies public curiosity; there may thereafter be a surprising indifference to consideration of its significance.

First and foremost, of course, there are the Annual Reports which are published and laid before Parliament. They can be very informative, and certainly those of the gas industry have been so for those prepared to study them carefully. In particular, they contain a great deal of statistical and graphical information; they are more forthcoming than the annual reports of many private industrial companies. At the same time, they are on the whole simply a factual statement of the year's events with a glimpse of future developments; those that have been a matter of controversy will be alluded to with caution. Those minded to probe into the intimate affairs of the industry concerned will find these Reports no more than a starting point, albeit a very useful one.

As far as our present interest is concerned, the gas industry's Annual Reports may be deficient in one important respect. The Gas Act 1948 explicitly states that:

Every such [annual] report of any Area Board or of the Gas Council . . . shall set out
any direction given to the Board or Council during that year. . . .

but immediately qualifies this by saying:

Unless the Minister has notified the Board or Council of his opinion that it is against
the interests of national security to do so.

The Gas Act 1972 includes the same reservation [5]. The choice of the
phrase 'national security' was no doubt designed to limit the Minister's
discretion. Elsewhere the Minister's power to give directions is defined in
terms of 'national interest', which can be less narrowly construed. Where
much of the 1948 Act is carried forward verbatim into the 1972 Act, it is
interesting to note a slight change of wording at this point. Under the
original Act, 'directions of a general character as to the exercise and performance . . . of their functions' could be given to the Gas Council or the Area
Boards, if they appear 'to be *requisite* in the national interest'. In the 1972
Act, however, the phrase used is 'matters which appear to him to *affect* the
public interest' [6]. The change is slight, but its effect is, if anything, to
increase the Minister's powers in this respect: almost anything can be taken
as 'affecting' the public interest.

   In any event, it is clear that the Minister has always had the power to give
the nationalised gas industry a direction without it ever becoming public
knowledge. This is not to say, of course, that such a direction has ever been
given. If it was, a grave dilemma would arise if there were any doubt about
its legality. On the one hand the industry is bound to give effect to the
Minister's direction; on the other, it is bound not to 'disregard . . . any
enactment or rule of law'.

   The Annual Reports come into the public domain when laid before
Parliament by the Minister, but they are not then normally debated as such.
The practice grew up for the Government to allocate some three days a year
for debate on the annual reports of nationalised industries; additionally, the
Opposition has occasionally used a Supply Day for this purpose. The intention has been to allow discussion not so much of a particular report, but of
the general state of the industry under review. It has been rare for a division
to follow the debate. Very often, it has been found convenient to debate
more than one industry at a time: gas has normally found itself as part of the
fuel and power industries or allied with electricity. The consensus of opinion
is that the level of debate was not high, Members tending to play to the
political gallery of their constituents [7, 8, 9]. *The Times* complained in 1948
that:

Too many Members of Parliament in all parties seem to believe that a shareholders'
meeting should be in permanent session, that extraordinary meetings should be held

throughout the year, and that individual members of public boards should be open to personal attack under parliamentary privilege. [7]

These infrequent debates provided opportunities for Members of Parliament to seek information, but there were many other opportunities open to them. One was the traditional device of the Parliamentary Question, though this too had its limits. Generally speaking the Minister, in accordance with custom established by the Postmaster-General as long ago as the foundation of the BBC in 1925, would answer only questions dealing with general principles and not those relating to the day-to-day running of the industries. Inevitably, argument arose about where general principles ended and day-to-day running began and Members exercised considerable ingenuity in formulating borderline questions in such a form that the Speaker would rule it to be admissible. The fact that a question was ruled admissible did not oblige the Minister to answer it.

In replying to questions Ministers are always reluctant, unless the answer is clearly to their credit, to accept responsibility. Evasion could easily be achieved by using a form of words which made it clear that the Minister was merely passing on to the questioner information imparted to him by the board of the nationalised industry in question. Equally, the Minister could undertake to make enquiries and inform his questioner of the result at a later date. That the Minister should protect himself was reasonable enough; and the required information was forthcoming. On the whole, sensible questions got sensible answers.

In many cases, however, the questions need never have been raised in the House, supposing that the Member's sole object was to obtain information that could properly be made public. The chairmen of all the nationalised industries have acknowledged the special position of Members of Parliament and those who write to them could expect prompt, full, and courteous replies. When Sir Hubert Houldsworth was Chairman of the National Coal Board (1951–56) he stated that he received 300 letters a year from MPs, to all of which he replied personally if this was at all possible. At the local level in the gas industry, and in other logically organised nationalised industries, the chairmen of Area Boards often took considerable trouble to establish contact with Members of Parliament having constituencies within their area. Apart from all this the gas industry, like industry generally, whether public or private, has a large public-relations department whose task it is to provide information about its activities.

For Members of Parliament the disadvantage of using this method of eliciting information was that it attracted no publicity. If a constituent, or a group of constituents, had appealed to him to save them from the oppressive action of a nationalised industry, he naturally wanted some visible evidence of his zeal on their behalf. In this respect, a letter from the Chairman, however courteous and forthcoming, was no substitute for a question in the

House under his own name. This would be reported in his local press, and perhaps even nationally. To say this is no cynical reflection on the generality of Members of Parliament. They are, after all, people in public life and to be demonstrably so is a measure of their success. To achieve public mention is as important for them as it is to others.

SELECT COMMITTEE ON NATIONALISED INDUSTRIES

The individual status of professional men is closely bound up with that of the group to which they belong, and there are many associations whose main task is to advance the status of a profession as a whole. For a Parliamentarian, it has always been very important to maintain the prestige and authority of Parliament. It is not surprising, therefore, that in the early days of post-war nationalisation Parliament sought to increase its influence on the running of the industries concerned, even though this was contrary to both the spirit and the letter of the Acts by which Parliament itself had brought them into being. To such natural aspirations we may ascribe the formation of the Select Committee on Nationalised Industries, a body formed not in response to any public demand but on an initiative within Parliament itself. This Committee has had a somewhat chequered history.

The rambling nature of many debates on nationalised industry has already been noted. In 1949 Mr Hugh Molson, then a back-bench Conservative Member of Parliament, suggested that Parliament could make a more effective contribution if instead of roaming over the whole field it concentrated on certain basic issues. He proposed the formation of a Select Committee to identify these issues and, as it were, present them in a predigested form as a preliminary to debate. The Labour government then in office would have none of this, but when the Conservatives were returned in October 1951 a move was made. Cautiously, a Select Committee was set up to investigate whether a Select Committee on the Nationalised Industries was desirable. It met with a mixed reception. Among those who welcomed it was Lord Hurcomb, then Chairman of the cumbersome British Transport Commission; he thought it would give him a much needed opportunity to state his own case and difficulties to Parliament, albeit indirectly. Opponents included Sir Geoffrey Heyworth, whose Report in 1945 had, in large measure, been a blue-print for the nationalisation of the gas industry. In their view, the very essence of nationalisation was that the industries concerned should not be subject to constant Parliamentary interference. Moreover, they doubted whether Parliament could contribute very much to the managerial problems of vast public corporations; the outcome was they thought, more likely to be detrimental than advantageous.

In the end, the Select Committee came down in favour of the proposal, with the pious hope that if a Standing Committee were set up expressly to deal with the affairs of the nationalised industries:

it would do so not as an enemy, or a critic, but as a confidant, and a protection against irresponsible pressure, as well as a guardian of the public interest.

This proposal was supported by the Government but only with substantial modifications that very considerably limited the Committee's terms of reference. The general effect of these was to restrict it to affairs that were not clearly already the responsibility of others. It could not trespass on the preserves of the Minister; it could not enquire into matters normally settled by collective bargaining; it was to leave consumers' complaints to the various consumers' councils; and so on. The Committee was to be limited to fourteen members, instead of the twenty-one originally recommended; and they were not to be permitted to form sub-committees nor have any special secretariat. In short, they were to have very limited facilities to do even the few things they were to be permitted to do.

Such a Committee was set up in 1955, but after a few meetings, and after seeking the Attorney-General's advice on the interpretation of their terms of reference, they concluded that there was little they could usefully do. A year later the government set up a new Committee 'to examine the reports and accounts of the nationalized industries'. This had much wider powers: at one end of the scale it still could not trespass on the responsible Minister's preserves nor could it at the other consider matters of day-to-day management. Herbert Morrison's policy of control 'at arm's length' was preserved. In between, however, there was much territory it could explore, although it was still denied a powerful permanent secretariat. The full extent of this territory was still not very clearly defined, however, and the Committee had to feel its way cautiously, the more so because its formation had been opposed by the Labour Opposition.

Although the Committee was given inquisitorial powers—being able to demand the attendance of witnesses, including the chairmen of nationalised industries, and to call for papers and records—they were careful from the outset to demonstrate their desire only to be helpful. While the industries themselves were wary of where this new development was to take them, they were by no means averse to it, for it provided a useful sounding-board for conveying their points of view to the public. Lord Hurcomb, Chairman of the British Transport Commission, for example, had supported the proposal from the outset; Mr Joseph Latham, as deputy Chairman of the National Coal Board, believed it to be 'desperately important that they should have a chance to express their point of view'. This chance they certainly had. For example, the 1960–61 Report of the Committee—the first to direct itself specifically to the gas industry—ran to 805 pages; it recorded answers to 3604 questions and there were 240 pages of appended memoranda. These dealt with such diverse topics as underground storage, tariff policy, the Lurgi process, mine-drainage gas, manpower, and the price and quality of coal. The enquiries were mostly in open sittings, but from time to time strangers—the Press and public—were asked to leave so that confidential matters could be raised. Thus in 1967–68 Sir Henry Jones, who had been Chairman of the Gas Council since 1960, was relieved of the necessity of discussing in public at that time the state of his negotiations with the oil industry:

> . . . I was asked a number of questions about the price of North Sea gas and the conditions under which we will supply it to major customers. As you will have noticed, I was not very precise in my replies . . . the people whom we will be fighting hardest are the oil people. Therefore, it would have been an embarrassment for us if you had pressed me too hard on the exact terms on which we expect to sell gas to heavy industry. [10]

By and large, the Reports of the Select Committee are sensible and informative documents, with not too much political prejudice in evidence. For the student, they are wearisomely exhaustive: exchanges of civilities and the most trifling comment being recorded verbatim as is normal Parliamentary practice. They involved a great deal of detailed work for all concerned, but the resources of the Committee did not allow them to keep all the nationalised industries, some fourteen in all, under constant review. There were, therefore, years of relative respite for any particular industry, though its senior staff might of course have to give evidence at inquiries into industries related to their own. Thus at the 1967/68 inquiry into North Sea gas, Dr H. M. Finniston, then Deputy Chairman of the British Steel Corporation, had to answer 31 questions dealing with the effect of North Sea gas on the operation of his Corporation. Similarly, Lord Robens (meticulously recorded as 'attending by leave of the House of Lords') was examined at length in respect of a long memorandum submitted by the National Coal Board. It was, of course, not merely desirable but essential that each industry should be considered not in isolation but in relation to others with which it was intimately related. In the case of gas these were most particularly, the other power industries, electricity and coal. Indeed, in 1965/6 the Select Committee chose to investigate all three of these industries collectively, though relatively briefly; the last year in which one of these (electricity) had been reviewed was 1962/63.

The Select Committee was sensible enough to realise that its resources did not allow it to investigate any nationalised industry in depth, and it therefore concentrated on major issues which it judged to be of particular current importance. As we have noted, this process of sifting had been advocated by Hugh Molson at the outset. In 1967–68 it was the exploitation of North Sea oil; in 1975–76 its target was gas and electricity prices. Although it had no executive authority the Committee had considerable influence; the information it elicited and the conclusions it reached were carefully studied in the quarters that mattered—the Ministries and the headquarters of the corporations. Appropriate action might then be taken or existing programmes modified or accelerated.

One inherent defect of the Select Committee system is its lack of continuity. The industries into which it had to inquire were very large and very complex, and a proper understanding of them could not quickly be acquired. Against this, Parliament is relatively short-lived; between nationalisation in 1948 and the Act authorising formation of the British Gas Corporation in 1972 there were no less than seven general elections. Even when there was no change in political complexion the composition of the new Parliament would differ substantially from its predecessor, and these changes were inevitably reflected in the composition of the Select Committee. The Committee that carried out the first investigation of the gas industry in 1960–61 consisted of thirteen members. Of these only four were members of the Committee that investigated it in 1965–66, and by 1967–68 there was only one survivor. By contrast, in the period 1948–72 there were only four chairmen of the Gas Council (of whom Sir Henry Jones served for eleven years 1960–71) and all their senior colleagues who gave evidence had long experience of the industry.

PRICES AND INCOMES BOARD

In 1965, the Select Committee was complemented by the Prices and Incomes Board. This, from its inception, made general enquiries into price increases made by the nationalised industries and from 1967 the government referred every major price increase to the Board as a matter of policy. This was prompted by the outcry that followed a concerted price increase by all the electricity boards in September 1967. In this very important and sensitive area there was thus a new measure of government control. The Board's decisions tended to be reached on political rather than commercial grounds, however, as did those of subsequent price control organisations; the Office of Prices and Consumer Protection later became responsible for the Price Commission. This political orientation was formally recognised in the Statutory Corporations (Financial Provisions) Act 1974 which provided for public corporations to be compensated for losses incurred as a result of their limiting prices in order to comply with national policy. We have already noted (p. 205) Sir Arthur Hetherington's objection to this, as Chairman of the British Gas Corporation; his wish was to run the corporation as a commercial enterprise [11].

The Prices and Incomes Board issued several Reports on the gas industry up to the time of establishment of the British Gas Corporation. Its first (1968) was concerned with proposals for increases in the price of gas [12], but its second, in the following year, explored the general efficiency of the industry and made a number of recommendations [13]. A further Report [14] in 1970 contained features not acceptable to the Gas Council [14, 15]. Briefly, the Board made proposals which, they suggested, could result in savings of £78 million over the four years 1970/71 to 1973/74. The Gas

Council considered that of this £29 million was subsumed in its own forward estimates, and that the balance was arguable because it was incurring costs other than those resulting from the pay settlements referred to the Board.

MONOPOLIES COMMISSION

Another government agency with which the gas industry had direct dealings was the Monopolies Commission. That it should have been called upon to submit evidence to this particular body, which had been set up under the Monopolies and Restrictive Practices (Inquiry and Control) Act 1948 may at first sight seem surprising, for the gas industry was not by its nature monopolistic. It had, it is true, an effective monopoly to manufacture and acquire gas, and to transmit and distribute it, but this right must be seen within the context of the fuel industries generally. It had long since lost its virtual monopoly in the lighting field, which had been assumed by the Electricity Council. There were virtually no applications of gas as a fuel (as distinct from a chemical feedstock) in which it was not in direct competition with coal, oil, or electricity.

In May 1971 the Secretary of State for Trade and Industry referred to the Monopolies Commission two specific questions relating to connection charges for gas and electricity:

(i) What are the principles which in all the relevant circumstances should govern the level and character of the charges made respectively for the connection of new domestic customers to a supply of electricity and to a supply of gas and the terms and conditions upon which such connection is made, including in particular any scales of rebates or discounts.

(ii) To what extent do the level and character of such charges and such terms and conditions as have been adopted or are proposed comply with such principles as are considered to be appropriate.

The Gas Council duly gave evidence and when the Commission's report was published in the summer of 1972 they saw no reason to recommend any change in the gas industry's practices relating to connection charges.

Mention of the Prices and Incomes Board and the Monopolies Commission has, as it were, bridged the gap between what one may call the qualitative political control of the nationalised industries and quantitative control exercised through the money supply.

FINANCIAL TARGETS

In its post-war nationalisation programme the government acquired both assets and liabilities. The assets had to be paid for immediately and the funding of the programme presented considerable difficulties: the fuel industries (electricity, gas, coal) demanded compensation of nearly £1200 million but this was slightly less than that for transport alone (£1217 million).

The full extent of the liabilities became apparent only later: all the industries were in a run-down state after the war—this was, indeed, a major argument for nationalisation—and needed massive injections of capital for development. This included development of some completely new and expensive technologies: for example, nuclear power and natural gas. To some extent the industries generated their own capital, but in the 1950s this sufficed for only about one-third of their needs; the balance had to be borrowed either directly from the Treasury, through the Ministry concerned, or by the issue of Treasury-guaranteed stock. Very substantial sums were involved as the situation of gas, one of the smaller nationalised concerns, in 1960 indicates. Up to the summer of 1956 capital finance had been provided by the issue of British Gas Stock, and provision had to be made to redeem this on a 90-year basis. At 31 March 1960 the outstanding liabilities of the gas industry in respect of loans for capital projects totalled £595 million, comprising £465 million stock, £104 million advanced by the Ministry of Power, and £26 million bank loan. The advance from the Ministry had to be repaid, in half-yearly instalments, over 25 years.

By 1960 the gross fixed investment of the public enterprise sector had risen to some £5870 million, representing nearly 17 per cent of total fixed investment in Britain. In 1952 the number of employees had reached a peak of just over two million and even at the end of the decade it was still over 1¾ million, representing nearly one-tenth of the nation's total employment force [16]. These figures speak for themselves: the nationalised industries collectively represented such a substantial share of the economy that their efficiency was a matter for national concern. In particular, there was concern about the evaluation of their capital investment programmes. This found practical expression in May 1961, when the Chancellor of the Exchequer presented to Parliament a White Paper on *The Financial and Economic Obligations of the Nationalized Industries* [17]. This set out the criteria that ought to be observed when allocating resources and represented a very considerable tightening up in the appraisal of capital investment before it was approved.

The introduction of this new policy demanded prior consideration of how performance was to be measured. Here there were two main alternatives: firstly, a simple measure of return on capital, as used in private industry, and, secondly, an assessment based on cost-benefit analysis. The second, which had, and still has, its advocates tried to take account of the fact that the nationalised industries had certain social obligations imposed on them and it was only fair that allowance should be made for these. For example, in planning the new Victoria Line for London's underground railway system it was argued, in justifying the expenditure, that there would be indirect public benefits, not reflected in revenue from fares, resulting from the relief of traffic congestion on the surface. Such 'social benefits' should be assigned some notional cash value and counted as part of the return [18]. This is a defensible argument, but in practice the benefits are too imponderable to be either predicted in advance or measured afterwards. In the event, therefore, the government came back to a simple measure of return on capital, but expecting of the nationalised industries a somewhat lower rate than that in the private sector.

A settlement on any other basis would have been quite unrealistic, for figures quoted in the White Paper [17] show that the nationalised industries were on average showing rates of return much lower than in the private sector. Thus in 1960/61 the gross return on investment in the main nationalised industries was 7.8 per cent, compared with 19.8 per cent for private industry. If the comparison is made on the basis of net return after allowance for depreciation (which is commonly done in the private sector) the disparity is even greater. Again taking 1960/61, the average for the main nationalised industries was 2.8 per cent, compared with 15.7 for private industry. To have expected the public corporations suddenly to bridge this gap would have been optimistic indeed.

As far as the gas industry was concerned the financial objective set by the Minister of Power was for a minimum return of 10.2 per cent of net assets. The somewhat ambiguous demand that expenditure and revenue should balance 'taking one year with another' was given up in favour of a quinquennial budgeting system. The Gas Council was required to keep on target for five years and to make an aggregate surplus of £48 million over the period of 1962/63 to 1966/67. In the event, this target was not quite achieved. Only in 1964/65 was 10.2 per cent exceeded (10.8 per cent), and the average for the quinquennium was 9.8 per cent: the total surplus earned was £44.7 million [19].

In assessing these results, and indeed the record of the nationalised industries generally in achieving their set targets, we must, however, note that a key factor in the calculation—the value of the assets—is not susceptible of exact computation. The figure arrived at depends to a considerable extent on the way in which the assets were acquired and the accountancy practice used in calculating depreciation. It is naturally easier to reach the percentage target if the assets are undervalued than if they are overvalued. The argument is complex, and controversial among economists [20, 21].

In December 1966 the Minister agreed, in view of the standstill on prices and incomes, that the Area Boards' annual target for 1967/68 should remain at 10.2 per cent. In the event, results fell well short of this (7.7 per cent), mainly because of the inability to adjust tariffs and the situation in the Middle East. A year later a further White Paper *Nationalised Industries: A Review of Economic and Financial Objectives* was published [22]. This left open the precise targets to be set for the future, but stipulated that no new investment should be countenanced unless the minimum return could be demonstrated to be not less than 8 per cent. Shortly afterwards, it was announced that the gas industry's target for 1968/69 was to remain at 10.2 per cent: this was marginally exceeded (10.9 per cent).

In October 1969 the Minister of Technology set new financial objectives for the next quinquennium (1969/70 to 1973/74); the gas industry would be expected to make a net return of 7 per cent on average net assets employed. This seemingly less ambitious target was the result of a different method of calculation. Previously the requirement had been in respect of average gross return (surplus, interest, and depreciation); now it was to be net return (surplus and interest, but excluding depreciation). Again, the industry fell marginally short of its target, averaging 6.5 per cent on this basis.

In carrying out investment appraisal the gas industry had to consider both tactics and strategy: that is to say it had to consider not only the costing of single projects—to be completed within, say, five years—but the overall profitability of the industry, looking ahead as much as 35 years. The methods used were indicated in a memorandum prepared at the request of the Select Committee in 1968 [23].

At the beginning of this chapter we stated that it would be difficult to present a coherent picture of the post-war relationship between the government of the day and the nationalised industries in general, and the gas industry in particular. In retrospect, it is clear that the whole business was ill-considered. Not necessarily ill-considered in principle—for after the war certain industries were natural candidates for nationalisation because of their run-down state and their need of capital on a scale that only government could supply—but certainly ill-considered in terms of their role in the national economy. They have been denied the freedom of action accorded to private industry (eroded though this has been) and yet they have been required to fulfil social obligations which are properly the responsibility of government and to attain quite exacting targets of profitability. That they should have found it difficult to adjust to national needs is not surprising, but it is disappointing that after thirty years their role is still a matter for argument. That progress has been slow in this sense is perhaps basically a consequence of two major disparities we have already noted, namely, that between the lengths of the industrial and the political cycle, and between the ultimate objectives of industry and politics. The significance of these disparities has been stressed in a recent report by the National Economic Development Office:

... with change in almost all its forms increasing in pace, amplitude and unpredictability, governments have tended to place a higher and higher value on flexibility for themselves, just at the time when, with the increasing size and complexity of their operations, the enterprises' time-scales have lengthened and given them a greater requirement for certainty. Here, then, is a fundamental dilemma [24].

If this is so, an uneasy relationship is likely to continue, for neither cycle is susceptible of significant change. As the Gas Council was at pains to point out to the Select Committee in 1968, the industry was already giving thought to its situation in the last decade of this century.

The evolution of the nationalised industry/government relationship has been succinctly summarised as follows:

The statutory control framework has not substantially changed since the original statutes of 1946–49. There has, however, been a gradual development in the formal structure and systems of control in response to the problems and priorities which have emerged subsequently. During the 1950s the issue of accountability to Parliament came to the fore. In the 1960s attention was focused on the dangers of resource misallocation; as a result guidelines on pricing policy, investment criteria and financial objectives were introduced. In the late 1960s and during the 1970s government has become more interventionist, reflecting not only the increasing use of the public corporations as a means of implementing macro-economic policy, but also the pressures of higher social expectations and of particular sectional interests.

Increasingly, the original expectation that there would be an identity of interest between government and corporations was not fulfilled. This was acknowledged in the White Papers of 1961 and 1967, in which the divergent interests were given explicit recognition by encouraging the corporations to act more commercially and the government to input the wider social considerations [25].

REFERENCES

[1] KELF-COHEN, R. *Twenty Years of Nationalisation: the British Experience*, pp. 67–9, Macmillan, London (1969).

[2] ROBSON, W. A. *Nationalized Industry and Public Ownership*, 2nd edn, p. 145, George Allen and Unwin Ltd, London (1962).

[3] Ibid., p. 153.

[4] DAVIES, Ernest. Government Policy and the Public Corporation, *Political Quarterly*, **26**, 115 (1955).

[5] Gas Act 1948 10(2): Gas Act 1972 6(3).

[6] Gas Act 1948 7(1): Gas Act 1973 7(1).

[7] THE TIMES. 'Parliament and Corporations', 3 March (1948).

[8] ACTON SOCIETY TRUST. *Accountability to Parliament*, p. 20, Nationalised Industry Series No. 1, Claygate (1950).

[9] ROBSON, W. A. op. cit., p. 181.

[10] SECOND REPORT FROM THE SELECT COMMITTEE ON NATIONALISED INDUSTRIES, Session 1967/8. *Exploitation of North Sea Gas*, p. 163, HMSO, London (1968).

[11] BRITISH GAS CORPORATION. *Annual Report and Accounts 1973–74*, p. 8.

[12] NATIONAL BOARD FOR PRICES AND INCOMES. *Report No. 57*, Cmnd. 3567 (1968).

[13] Idem. *Report No. 102*, Cmnd. 3924, HMSO, London (1969).

[14] Idem. *Report No. 155*, Cmnd. 4458, HMSO, London (1970).

[15] GAS COUNCIL. *Annual Report and Accounts 1969–70*, p. 7, HMSO, London (1970).

[16] PRYKE, Richard. *Public Enterprise in Practice*, p. 289, MacGibbon and Kee, London (1971).

[17] CMND. 1337 (1961).

[18] FOSTER, C. D. and BEESLEY, M. E. Estimating the Social Benefit of Constructing an Underground Railway in London, *Journal of the Royal Statistical Society* (A) 125, Pt I (1963).

[19] GAS COUNCIL. *Annual Report and Accounts 1966/67*, p. 18, HMSO, London (1967).

[20] PRYKE, Richard. op. cit., pp. 190–9.

[21] POLANYI, George. 'Comparative Returns from Investment in Nationalised Industries', Institute of Economic Affairs, London (1968).
[22] CMND. 3437 (1967).
[23] SECOND REPORT FROM THE SELECT COMMITTEE ON NATIONALISED INDUSTRIES. Session 1967–68, pp. 202–4, HMSO, London (1968).
[24] GARNER, M. R. *Relationship of Government and Public Enterprises in France, West Germany, and Sweden*, p. 3, National Economic Development Office, London (1976).
[25] NATIONAL ECONOMIC DEVELOPMENT OFFICE. *A Study of UK Nationalised Industries: their Role in the Economy and Control in the Future*, Appendix Vol., p. 84, HMSO, London (1976).

BIBLIOGRAPHY

ACTON SOCIETY TRUST. *Accountability to Parliament*, Nationalised Industry Series No. 1, Claygate (1950).

Idem. *The Powers of the Minister*, Nationalised Industry Series No. 2, Claygate (1951).

BARRY, E. Elson. *Nationalisation in British Politics*, Cape, London (1965).

CHESTER, Norman. *The Nationalisation of British Industry 1945–51*, HMSO, London (1975).

CLEGG, H. *Industrial Democracy and Nationalisation*, Blackwell, Oxford (1951).

Connection Charges for Gas and Electricity. Cmnd. 5036, HMSO, London (1972).

Control of Public Expenditure. Cmnd. 1432, HMSO, London (1961).

FLORENCE, P. S. *Industry and the State*, Hutchinson, London (1957).

FRIEDMANN, W. (ed.). *The Public Corporation*, Stevens, London (1954).

GOODMAN, Edward. *Forms of Public Control and Ownership*, Christophers, London (1951).

HANSON, A. H. *Parliament and Public Ownership*, Cassell, London (1961).

KELF-COHEN, R. *Nationalisation in Britain*, 2nd edn., Macmillan, London (1961).

KELF-COHEN, R. *Twenty Years of Nationalisation: The British Experience*, Macmillan, London (1969).

LITTLE, I. M. D. *A Critique of Welfare Economics*, Clarendon Press, Oxford (1957).

NATIONAL ECONOMIC DEVELOPMENT OFFICE. *A Study of UK Nationalised Industries*, London (1976).

The Nationalised Industries—Presented to Parliament March 1978 (Treasury) HMSO, London (1978).

POLANYI, George. *Comparative Returns from Investment in Nationalised Industries*, Institute of Economic Affairs, London (1968).

PRICES AND INCOMES BOARD. *Report on Electricity and Gas Tariffs*, Cmnd 2862, HMSO, London (1965).

Idem. *Report on Gas Prices* (First Report), Cmnd. 3567, HMSO, London (1968).

Idem. *Report on Gas Prices* (Second Report), Cmnd. 3924, HMSO, London (1969).

PRYKE, Richard. *Public Enterprise in Practice: the British Experience of Nationalisation over Two Decades*, MacGibbon and Kee, London (1971).

Public Investment in Great Britain, Cmnd. 1203, HMSO, London (1960).

ROBSON, W. A. (ed.). *Problems of Nationalised Industry*, Allen and Unwin, London (1952).

Idem. *Nationalised Industry and Public Ownership*, 2nd edn., Allen and Unwin, London (1962).

SELECT COMMITTEE ON NATIONALISED INDUSTRIES. *The Gas Industry 1961; Gas, Electricity and Coal Industries 1966; Exploitation of North Sea Gas 1968; Ministerial Control of the Nationalised Industries (3 vols) 1968, Gas and Electricity Prices 1976*, HMSO, London.

SIMON. *The Boards of Nationalised Industries*, Longman, London (1957).

THORNHILL, W. *The Nationalised Industries—an Introduction*, Nelson, Edinburgh (1968).

TIVEY, L. (ed.) *The Nationalised Industries Since 1960*. Open University Set Book. George Allen and Unwin, London.

21

Industrial Relations

ONE of the principal arguments advanced by the advocates of nationalisation was that, with elimination of the profit motive, the main source of industrial dispute would be removed. With employees serving not the interests of private owners and idle shareholders but their fellow citizens in the country at large, they would be content to receive such rewards as were amicably agreed around the conference table. As all were working for the same end, grounds for dispute would disappear. While this Utopian vision captured the imagination of many of those dedicated to social reform, realists were well aware that although industrial relations were entering a new phase, organised labour would be as ready to argue with the State as with private concerns. Events were to prove them right. Over the years nationalised industries have had their fair share of labour disputes, generally over traditional issues of wages and conditions of work or a determination to maintain hard-won differentials in respect of other groups of workers. Predictably, nationalisation was no panacea for ills—if such they can properly be called—that are inherent in working life the world over. The trade unions had come into being in the nineteenth century to secure a fairer deal for working people and from very modest beginnings they had developed in Britain into a powerful and well-organised political force. It was not to be expected that they would surrender their independence of action to a government which they had been largely instrumental in bringing into office. Besides, it would be sanguine to suppose that a Labour government would stay in office indefinitely, or even for very long. Other governments would be elected, with very different attitudes towards organised labour. The unions naturally desired not merely to consolidate their gains, but to strengthen their position.

EARLY HISTORY OF TRADE UNIONS

The history of the trade union movement is a complex one, and it would be inappropriate to attempt to recount it in a general work of this kind; those who wish to study it are referred to the bibliography at the end of this chapter. It would be equally inappropriate, however, to omit from this history of the British gas industry any account of the part played by organised labour in shaping it; any industry is, after all, the sum total of the contributions of those who work in it.

While it is arguable that the trade unions grew out of the medieval craft guilds, the movement is in practice little more than a century old and its real growth is very much a twentieth-century phenomenon. After the repeal of the repressive Combination Acts in 1824 a number of trade unions were formed, especially among miners and textile workers. They were mostly local, though there were a few grandiose schemes for a national organisation, such as John Doherty's National Association of United Trades for the Protection of Labour (1831), and Robert Owen's Grand National Consolidated Trade Union (1833). The Trades Union Congress was formed in Manchester in 1868, with initially a strong regional flavour, but its ambitions were modest until the turn of the century. In 1900 it set up the labour representation committee to promote political action by the working classes: this subsequently became the Labour Party.

Numerically the movement was small in the nineteenth century: the Board of Trade estimated that in 1889 its total membership was no more than 750 000, roughly five per cent of a working population of about 16 million. By 1948, when the gas industry was nationalised, the Trades Union Congress had an affiliated membership of 7 791 000, distributed among 188 unions. The greater part of the increase had occurred since the First World War. The middle years of that war were a period of considerable industrial unrest in Britain, much of it arising from the Munitions of War Act 1915 which prohibited strikes and lock-outs throughout a large section of industry. In October 1916 the government set up a Committee on Relations between Employers and Employees, under the chairmanship of Mr J. H. Whitley, then Speaker of the House of Commons. Among the recommendations of the Whitley Committee was the setting up of Joint Industrial Councils, meeting at regular intervals and representative of employers and work people. The National Gas Council of Great Britain and Ireland had been founded in 1916 to act as spokesman for the employers. In 1934 the British Gas Federation was formed as an amalgamation of existing bodies to represent all sections of the industry; from this the only major absentee was the South Metropolitan.

NATIONAL JOINT INDUSTRIAL COUNCIL

The National Joint Industrial Council for the Gas Industry was established in 1919. Its terms of reference included not only wages and conditions of employment—previously dealt with by the individual undertakings—but a wide range of topics of general importance to the industry: these included productivity, health, and research. Meeting regularly, and supported by Area Joint Industrial Councils, it made over the years valuable contributions to industrial relations by allowing responsible discussion of major issues before either side had taken up entrenched positions.

In the inter-war years the NJIC dealt with a variety of problems. These included the classification of undertakings to determine the rates of pay applicable to craftsmen such as stokers, boilermen, main-layers, fitters, etc.; this classification took note of such factors as the capacity of the works, its situation, and rates of pay in other local industries. Later agreement was reached on classification into two provincial categories (later one), and a metropolitan one. In the 1920s it considered many pay claims arising from the increasing cost of living; in the 1930s it made effective recommendations for compensation for redundancies arising from the rise of holding companies, amalgamations, and bulk purchases of coke-oven gas. The gas industry was, in fact, among the first to appreciate the need to deal fairly with the problem of redundancy. During the Second World War a Gas Labour Supply Committee was set up to ensure that essential services were maintained. After the war a new wages charter was established based on a six-shift week and a formal sick-pay scheme.

On nationalisation, the Gas Council agreed with the National Union of General and Municipal Workers, the Transport and General Workers Union, and the National Union of Enginemen, Firemen, Mechanics and Electrical Workers (subsequently merged with the Transport and General Workers) to establish a new National Joint Industrial Council and Area Joint Industrial Councils. The co-partnership schemes were phased out. Various modifications to the agreement were subsequently made and there was a further major revision in 1974/5, following the establishment of the British Gas Corporation. The general remit of the Council is:

To secure the largest measure of joint action between the British Gas Corporation and Manual Workers (excluding those craftsmen subject to Agreement established under other negotiating machinery) for the safeguarding and development of the Industry, for the general improvement of working conditions, and for the attainment of improved output with a view to promoting the best interests of the British Gas Corporation and workers engaged in the Industry [1].

Within these general limits the Council is free to take what action it feels fit, but the following are among the areas of interest specifically enumerated:

(1) Wages, hours, redundancy, and working conditions.

(2) Machinery to promote measures affecting safety, health, and welfare.

(3) Speedy settlement of disputes and organising formal arbitration if this proves necessary.

(4) Encouraging the inclusion of all manual workers in their respective Associations.

(5) Encouraging inventions and improvements in machinery, and safeguarding the rights of the authors and designers concerned.

(6) Training and education of young employees.

(7) Collection and publication of statistics and information.

(8) Publication of reports, arrangement of lectures, and organisation of conferences.

(9) Representing the needs and opinions of the industry to the Government and to Local and other authorities.

As constituted after the Gas Act 1972, the National Joint Industrial Council became a powerful body, consisting of 30 members. On the employers' side it consists of the Chairman and Deputy Chairman; the Member for Personnel; and the 12 Regional Chairmen. On the Union side are 16 full-time officers from the General and Municipal Workers Union and the Transport and General Workers Union. It meets regularly every quarter and on other occasions as necessary.

EARLY UNION ACTIVITY IN THE GAS INDUSTRY

While these provisions were the culmination of an evolutionary process going back to 1919, the Gas Acts of 1948 and 1972 imposed statutory obligations on the Gas Council/Corporation with regard to machinery for settling terms and conditions of employment. Like all the public corporations created immediately after the war, the gas industry was obliged to agree machinery for collective bargaining with the unions. All this represented a transformation of the situation pertaining at the beginning of the century. Then, in written evidence to the Royal Commission on Trade Disputes and Trade Combinations (1903) Sir George Livesey, Chairman of the South Metropolitan Gas Company, stated:

So far as the two gas companies of which the witness is Chairman—the South Metropolitan and the South Suburban—are concerned, a strike is, he thinks, unthinkable, impossible. No trade union has any power or any influence in either company. The company makes contracts of service . . . generally for twelve months, individual agreements expiring and renewed every week throughout the year, therefore no appreciable number of men can leave at the same time. But in addition and more important as a safeguard, very nearly all the company's regular employees, over 4,500 in number, of all ranks, are holders of the company's ordinary stock under the co-partnership system; in many cases their whole savings are so invested [2].

In fact, Sir George was wrong in saying that no trade union had any influence in his companies. We have already noted that as early as 1889, Will Thorne—who later had a distinguished career in Parliament and in the trade union movement, but was then a stoker at Beckton Works—established the National Union of Gasworkers and General Labourers, with the principal objective of achieving generally the eight-hour day, already adopted by many provincial gasworks. Success came quickly: within months the major London companies accepted a petition from their stokers for a working day of three 8-hour shifts instead of two 12-hour ones. This success had consequences extending far beyond the gas industry. In those days, gas companies commonly paid off many of their labourers in the summer months when demand was much reduced. Many of the men laid off found work in the nearby docks. Their success heartened the militant dockers and is generally supposed to have been a significant factor in the success of the London Dock Strike of August 1889, which earned for them the famous 'dockers' tanner', a day wage for direct labour of 6*d*. an hour. This was a famous victory in the history of trade unions, remembered not least because it prompted the writing in London of the Red Flag, traditional song of the Labour movement.

Originally, trade unions were founded to protect the interests of manual workers, but there were many other workers who felt a need to negotiate collectively rather than individually. Postal workers, for example, began to organise themselves in the early 1880s, beginning with the relatively new race of telegraphists in 1881. By the end of that decade the government, somewhat grudgingly, accepted that civil servants generally had a right to combine for mutual benefit. Workers in local government, too, were similarly placed. While their jobs were generally steady and secure—and, in the context of the day, had the important merit of 'respectability'—salaries were low. Contractually, the position of workers was often weak. Although they could, once established, normally look forward to a job for life many were in fact liable to dismissal at any time. Among some 2000 autonomous local authorities there were bound to be bad employers as well as good.

NALGO

To serve the interests of this very mixed group the National Association of Local Government Officers (NALGO) was founded in 1905, with pension rights for municipal officers as its principal objective. Over the years it was to develop into the biggest of the white-collar unions. Initially its growth was slow, being barely 40 000 by 1920 and remaining static for the next five years. This led, in 1923, to a proposal that the Association should enlarge its scope by recruiting members from public utilities—water, gas, electricity, etc.—that were not publicly owned. This opened up great possibilities for expansion, but the proposal was turned down. Ten years later, the formation of the London Passenger Transport Board (LPTB, 1933) led to the idea being put forward again, this time successfully. It was argued that many of the new Board's staff, taken over from municipal tramway services, were already NALGO members and ought not be disowned.

This particular innovation was not in fact a success, as the workers in the LPTB branch found themselves too isolated from their fellows, but the principle was established that NALGO might recruit staffs of 'any board or other authority to which the functions of a local authority . . . have been transferred.' Twenty-five years later this was to prove of great significance in the context of the Labour government's nationalisation programme. This concession led to renewed pressure to make eligible the staffs of 'quasi-public' undertakings such as the various boards and corporations created to run such services as transport, docks and harbours, fisheries, and broadcasting. The prospects for recruiting were glittering, but there was much opposition. Some felt that this would open the door to 'quasi-public' concerns that—seen through union eyes—were no better than examples of profit-making free enterprise, and there was internal dismay among the staff at the extra load of work entailed. The first objection was countered by a proposal to form a sister organisation—the Association of Public Utility Services—which would follow its own policies but use existing NALGO facilities. This proposal was in fact adopted, but in the end quietly withered away, stifled by the organising staff [4].

Another opportunity for expansion presented itself during the war. In 1943 NALGO was approached simultaneously by employers and employees in the gas industry. The Federation of Gas Employers invited them to represent the clerical and administrative staff of their constituent companies. The staff of all the London gas undertakings informed them that they proposed to form their own union but would prefer to join NALGO. Regrettably, this approach was rejected, on the ground that the extra burden of work was unacceptable under wartime conditions. As a result the British Gas Staff Association was founded, and for twenty years became NALGO's chief rival in the gas industry. The two finally merged in 1963.

Meanwhile, however, a new situation arose in the context of the nationalisation programme. As a result of this, some 20 000 local government officials would be transferred to nationalised industries, and would expect NALGO to continue to support them. Equally, many employees of utility companies would be transferred, and it was evident that a considerable proportion of these, too, would regard NALGO as the union best suited to look after their interests. In 1946, therefore, earlier policy was reversed and it was decided to admit both local government and public utility officers. This gave NALGO an important, but not overwhelming accretion of strength. By 1965 roughly one-third of its total membership of 350 000 was drawn from outside local government; 8 per cent of its total membership came from the gas industry [5].

The National Joint Council for Gas Staffs was set up in 1947. Following nationalisation, discussions took place with the Gas Council and in June 1950 general agreement was reached on salary scales and certain conditions of service [6]. This continued to be the recognised negotiating body, for all but the most senior staff. Constitutionally, it was similar to the National Joint Industrial Council. It has up to 32 members, half representing the employers—in precisely the same form as for the National Joint Industrial Council—and half the unions.

Of seats allocated to the latter, NALGO takes the lion's share; in 1975 it had twelve of the sixteen seats. Additionally, seats then went to the Managerial Administrative, Technical and Supervisory Association (two seats); the

Transport and General Workers Union (one seat); and the Association of Scientific, Technical and Managerial Staffs and the Amalgamated Union of Engineering Workers (one seat shared between them). The Council determines salary scales; working hours; sick pay; holidays; and so on. A similarly constituted Senior Officers' Joint Council was established in 1951, but in 1975 this was subsumed within the National Joint Council for Gas Staffs.

Finally, special provision was made for dealing with wages and conditions of maintenance craftsmen in the industry, of which there were about 2000 in 1975, though falling fairly rapidly. Their interests were looked after by the Craftsman's Committee. The employers' representation on this is the same as for the other Councils; trade union representation is from the Confederation of Shipbuilding and Engineering Unions.

WORKER PARTICIPATION

On the industrial relations front one of the major post-war issues is that known variously as industrial democracy or worker participation. This entails the participation of workers in major policy decisions at board level; its supporters often advocate some kind of two-tier directorate such as is found in Germany. The subject is controversial, and the outcome a matter not for history but for future decision, but it is perhaps appropriate to conclude this chapter by noting that the gas industry, in common with most large industrial and commercial concerns in Britain, has for some years past been moving informally in this direction. Without any enforcing legislation, many important areas of activity have long been the subject of joint discussion.

For example, a central Corporation Trade Union Advisory Committee was set up to provide a forum for informal exchanges of views on major Corporation and Union policy issues. It operates at the highest level, consisting of the Chairman and Members of the Corporation and the General Secretaries and National Officers of the trade unions—which we have already named—recognised in the industry. In many Regions there is provision for a regular exchange of views on similar lines. There is also a National Advisory Committee on Training and Education. This has a membership of twenty, including six trade union representatives.

REFERENCES

[1] National Joint Industrial Council for the Gas Industry. *Handbook of Conditions of Employment*, p. 83 (1976).
[2] Cmnd. 2826 (1906), p. 247 from FLANDERS, Allan and CLEGG, H. A. (eds). *The System of Industrial Relations in Great Britain: its History, Law, and Institutions*, Blackwell, Oxford (1963).

[3] CLEGG, H. A., FOX, Alan and THOMPSON, A. F. *A History of British Trade Unions since 1889*, Vol. I (1889–1910), p. 58, Clarendon Press, Oxford (1964).
[4] SPOOR, Alec. *White Collar Union: 60 Years of Nalgo*, pp. 307–9, Heinemann, London (1967).
[5] Ibid., p. 498.
[6] National Joint Council for Gas Staffs and Senior Officers, *Handbook of Salaries and Conditions of Service* (1975).

BIBLIOGRAPHY

BADGER, A. B. *Man in Employment*, 2nd edn., Macmillan, London (1966).

CLEGG, H. A., FOX, Alan and THOMPSON, A. F. *A History of British Trade Unions since 1889*, Vol. 1, 1889–1910 (only one published). Clarendon Press, Oxford (1964).

COLE, G. D. H. *British Trade Unionism Today* (1939).

COLE, G. D. H. *A Short History of the British Working-Class Movement* (revised ed.) (1948).

COLE, G. D. H. 'Trade Unions', *Chambers Encyclopaedia*, Vol. 13, Newnes, London (1950).

FLANDERS, Allan and CLEGG, H. A. (eds.) *The System of Industrial Relations in Britain: its History, Law, and Institutions*, Blackwell, Oxford (1963).

MOON, K. W. *Industrial Relations in the Gas Industry*, Lecture to Institution of Gas Engineers (London & Southern Section) 18 February 1975, I G E, London (1975).

RICHARDSON, J. H. 'Industrial Relations in Great Britain', International Labour Office (1948).

SPOOR, Alec. *White Collar Union: 60 Years of Nalgo*, Heinemann, London (1967).

WEBB, S. and WEBB, B. *The History of Trade Unionism* (revised ed.) (1920).

ZWEIG, F. *Productivity and Trade Unions*, Blackwell, Oxford (1951).

The Industry and its Customers

EVERY industry is dependent on its customers, in the sense that it remains viable only insofar as it can sell its products on mutually satisfactory terms. In some cases—as in shipbuilding and the manufacture of electricity generating equipment and railway locomotives—the number of potential customers is relatively so small that direct contact can be maintained with most of them. The big national multiple stores, with their customers numbered in millions, come into a different category, but at least they compete with one another to the extent that none has a major share of the market.

The public utilities are in a different world again. By 1912, for example, the gas industry had nearly 7 million customers, distributed over the length and breadth of the country. Today there are over 14 million. Clearly, no sort of personal link can be maintained with all of them and for the most part they must remain anonymous statistics: those who pay promptly and those who do not, those who use less than 200 therms yearly and those who use over 1000, and so on.

At the same time, provision must be made for dealing with individual customers when the need arises, as in dealing with complaints, giving advice on the choice of new appliances, and providing emergency services. Certain social obligations also must be recognised. As has been stressed earlier, gas is not strictly a monopoly, in the sense that for virtually every purpose alternative fuels—coal, electricity, oil—are available. Nevertheless, it is not possible to switch at short notice from one to another. If a customer has elected to use gas for cooking or central heating, then gas has become virtually an essential to him: if his gas supply fails or his appliance does not work satisfactorily, he suffers real hardship and must be relieved. Gas is a good servant but a dangerous master, and there is, therefore, also an obligation to ensure, as far as possible, that customers are not put at risk. How far these social obligations extend we must consider later: the difficult question arises, for example, of the disconnection of supply when bills remain unpaid.

For such reasons as these, the gas industry has from the very beginning had to pay close attention to the needs of its customers and to do so at two quite different levels. First, it was necessary to view them on a broad statistical basis in order to ensure, as far as possible, that enough gas was available, at all times, to meet their needs. Secondly, it was necessary to have the means of dealing directly and sympathetically with individual customers both to maintain standards, promote business, and deal with complaints. These continuing needs were recognised in the Gas Act 1948. The first was subsumed under the general duty 'to develop and maintain an efficient, co-ordinated, and economical system of gas supply': this would obviously not be possible without acquiring a clear understanding of customers' needs. Additionally, however, every Area Board was required to have an independent Gas Consultative Council which was to represent the interest of consumers. The 1972 Act spelt this out rather more explicitly by naming these bodies Regional Gas Consumers' Councils, to which was added, as an innovation, a National Gas Consumers' Council.

It is not to be supposed, of course, that over the years the industry/customer relationship was a paternalistic and one-sided arrangement: customers were always well aware that collectively they might win concessions that would be quite beyond the power of the individual. In the days of the private gas industry shareholders were often also customers: while there could be a conflict of interest between these two relationships there was at least a means of expressing the consumers' point of view.

In earlier chapters we have seen how the government served as a watchdog for the consumer by exercising close control over both prices and dividends. The system of controlling maximum price and maximum dividend was followed by the sliding scale, by which the dividend might be increased as the price fell, and *vice versa*. On the whole the consumer—especially the small consumer—got a favourable deal. We have seen, for example, that, unlike electricity, gas had to be supplied to any customer within a certain distance of a main, even if that customer used so little gas that costs were not covered. We have seen, too, how Dr E. L. Burgin, as Parliamentary Secretary to the Board of Trade in 1934, blandly turned down a request for a minimum charge 'not on any ground of logic or technicality [but] entirely on the political argument that the government are not prepared to face the opposition that would necessarily come from people . . . amounting to millions in total.' A cynic considering some of the price structuring imposed on the nationalised industries might reasonably remark *plus ça change plus c'est la même chose*!

EARLY HISTORY OF CUSTOMER RELATIONS

The importance of good customer relations became apparent in the earliest days of the industry, when a group of dissident shareholders engaged in a running fight with the Gas Light and Coke Company that went on for quarter of a century [1]. The complaints of mismanagement and overcharging were not well-founded and the dispute—which gradually withered away—was basically a clash of personalities; nevertheless, it was important as an early indication of the trouble that could arise from bad relations. The nineteenth century provides many other examples of brushes between organised consumer groups and the private supply companies, such as that between the Anti-gas League and the companies south of the Thames [2].

We have earlier noted ways in which consumers became embroiled also with many of the big municipal undertakings. In Manchester, for example, the corporation in 1843 took over the gas works that had been started by the Police Commissioners, and the profits were devoted to the relief of the rates. For the ratepayers this was no doubt an acceptable procedure, but many consumers were not ratepayers at all and saw no reason why they should subsidise their richer neighbours. All they were interested in was gas at the lowest possible price. There was, therefore, a strong and vociferous anti-profit group, the Manchester Gas Consumers' Association, but not until 1921 did it finally win the day [3].

Small consumers could exert pressure only by collective action but very large ones had sufficient power of their own to exact major concessions simply by threatening to build their own plants. Thus the railway companies—such as the Great Western, the Eastern Counties, and the London and North Western—demanded and got very big price reductions from the undertakings supplying their areas.

Such old disputes between the gas industry and its customers, large and small, are a reminder that the latter have never been disposed to be satisfied with the mere discharge of statutory obligations by their suppliers.

GAS-FITTING STANDARDS

Traditionally, the responsibility of a gas undertaking ended, as far as private property was concerned, when the supply was brought to the premises and connected to the meter. Indeed, under the 1812 Act the Gas Light and Coke Company was specifically forbidden 'to sell or furnish any store or pipe or apparatus . . . for carrying gas into buildings'. The subsequent distribution of the gas to the burners was the responsibility of the owner, who would normally turn to one of the multiplicity of private gas-fitting firms which had sprung into existence as the industry developed. Predictably, the results were very mixed. Some firms did excellent work, but others were totally incompetent: pipes were all too often of inadequate bore, with leaking joints. They were often badly sited and inadequately protected, liable to be punctured by screws or nails in the course of normal building work. Burners received gas at insufficient pressure and so performed inadequately: leaks not only caused unpleasant smells, but could be a cause of dangerous explosions. All this, tended to discredit gas itself, to the detriment of the undertakings. To minimise this, many companies, but not all, formulated and distributed rules specifying the size and quality of pipes appropriate for various circumstances. Gas-fitters agreeing to recognise these rates were accorded official recognition. Nevertheless, as late as 1882 it was remarked that: [4]

This was a step in the right direction, but its adoption was limited, and to this hour there are many gas authorities who continue, to their disadvantage, to neglect this duty . . . scamping work is far from being entirely eradicated.

The author went on to remark that the gas undertakings had it within their power—by adopting and enforcing certain regulations—to effect the necessary improvement without themselves being responsible for work within buildings. He formulated a comprehensive code of practice of which the last two are noteworthy in the context of the present time:

10. If the regulations were not conformed to in every respect, the company reserve the right to refuse a supply of gas until the necessary alterations are made.

11. Gas fitters complying with these regulations have their names registered on the company's list of approved fitters, and they are at liberty to designate themselves 'authorized gas fitters'. Repeated negligence will cause the licence to be withdrawn.

Nearly a century later the same concern for proper standards of installing and maintaining gas appliances in the interest of the consumer was embodied by the Gas Council in its CORGI scheme (Confederation for the Registration of Gas Installers), formally established in 1970. CORGI is a voluntary association comprising trade organisations, the British Gas Corporation and Area Boards. Its first task was to produce a national register of competent gas installers, whose work would comply with recognised standards. Within a year some 4500 businesses had been registered, and the register was available in gas showrooms throughout the country. By 1971/72 the number had risen to over 8000, and the co-operation of every local authority was sought to ensure that work involving the installation or servicing of gas-fired appliances throughout the country was given only to Area Boards or other members of CORGI.

CONSUMER-RELATIONS

While the robust days are long past in which dissatisfied customers could convincingly threaten to make their own gas if existing suppliers would not mend their ways, the consumer lobby, although quite differently organised, is still a powerful one. It must be recognised, however, that consumers' complaints are not necessarily well-founded, nor is it even in their own best interests that they should be acceded to. There might be much satisfaction to be gained from obliging the old private companies to cut their prices, but not necessarily any real advantage: the cuts might be made at the expense of proper provision of reserves for the replacement or extension of plant and mains, for a possible increase in the cost of coal or labour, and so on. Moreover, as the records of the Gas Light and Coke Company and other undertakings testify, even bills for cheap gas were by no means always met.

While the Victorian companies could put up a strong resistance to unreasonable demands by their customers—and this, with major labour disputes, was one of the few issues that could urge them to concerted action—they were by no means disinclined to lend a sympathetic ear in cases of real need. Those who sought special terms—except on the basis of very large consumption, when they could scarcely be resisted—were firmly told that no preferential terms would be offered. In the case of the Gas Light and Coke Company, this applied to such disparate inquirers as St James' Palace and the Licensed Victuallers. The latter, at least, need hardly have been surprised, for the industry had a traditionally strong antipathy towards drunkenness. However, records show that some exceptions were made and compassion shown in extenuating circumstances [5]. Hospitals and charitable institutions, for example, might be given reduced rates, and often certain lights in such places were provided free.

A sense of social obligation was from the very beginning inherent in the gas industry. It was, of course, not alone in this. Up to the First World War, when the old social order crumbled, a sense of duty pervaded life in Britain. In the Post Office and on the railways, for example, it was traditional that the services to the public were maintained if humanly possible and without much thought of extra reward. The problem now is to find a means by which the basic virtues of loyalty and service can be given expression within a totally new political, social, and economic framework.

To some extent the problem is one of size. While small companies served small areas consumers could effectively combine as a single body if they had a grievance, and with reasonable goodwill on both sides they could discuss it with the companies' representatives and achieve a settlement. But with the advent of much larger companies in the big urban areas, as a consequence of mergers, this was no longer possible. As long as the Gas Light and Coke Company's territory in central London amounted to no more than 10 miles from east to west it was feasible to arrange public meetings of interested parties, but by 1933 this had extended to 68 miles. Similar territorial expansions had taken place in many other parts of the country. With nationalisation, and the entire country divided into only twelve areas, any sort of collective action on an informal basis became impossible. In 1938 the average number of consumers per gas undertaking was about 16 000; at nationalisation, regarding each Board as an undertaking, it was about a million. The regional differences were enormous [6]. The area of the Scottish Board was thirty times greater than that of the North Thames, though it sold only half as much gas. The South Western Board's territory was 240 miles long—as long as four average Boards. In the Eastern Board 60 per cent of its gas was bought in 17 per cent of its area. Clearly, if any sort of continuing communication with consumers was to be maintained special arrangements would have to be made and they would have to be flexible to allow for the great differences between the Area Boards.

To some extent it was arguable whether special provision needed to be made at all. After all, the principal socialist argument in favour of nationalisation was that with elimination of the profit motive the industries would be able to devote themselves wholeheartedly to the interests of their customers, with whom there would be a warm community of interest. It was deemed unthinkable that consumers needed any sort of protection from those whom the Minister himself—as representative of the people's democratically elected government—had appointed to run the industry in their interest. Nevertheless, Mr Hugh Gaitskell, speaking at the Report Stage of the Bill to nationalise the coal industry, conceded that there was a 'remote' chance that consumers' interests might not be fully regarded. After much deliberation, it was decided to set up two advisory bodies for the coal industry—an Industrial Consumers Council and a Domestic Consumers Council. The general spheres of interest of the two bodies is implicit in their titles and it was clearly laid down that their roles were advisory: the Minister was not to consider himself in any way bound by their representations. On the other hand, if he did accept their representations he had the power to direct the Coal Board to give effect to them.

GAS CONSULTATIVE COMMITTEES

This decision for the coal industry set the pattern for the post-war nationalisation programme generally. In the case of the gas industry provision was made for each Area Board to have a Gas Consultative Committee. It is significant that this was not called a Consumer Council, indicative of the fact that its remit was rather wider. Specifically, the Gas Consultative Councils were charged with:

(a) Considering any matter affecting the supply of gas in the area, including the variation of tariffs and the provision of new or improved services and facilities within the area, being a matter which is the subject of a representation made to them by consumers or other persons requiring supplies of gas in that area, or which appears to them to be a matter to which consideration ought to be given apart from any such representation, and where action appears to them to be requisite, as to any such matter, of notifying their conclusions to the Area Board; and

(b) of considering and reporting to the Area Board on any such matter which may be referred to them by that Board.

The Area Boards were required to keep the Consultative Councils informed of 'their general plans and arrangements' and there was an elaborate procedure laid down by which the Minister might, by direction, remedy any defect in these plans and arrangements brought to his attention by the Councils.

Each Council was to consist of not less than 20, and not more than 30 members, all of whom, including the Chairman (an office from which Members of Parliament were specifically excluded) were to be appointed by the Minister. Not less than half, nor more than three-quarters, were to be nominees of local authorities; the remainder were to represent 'commerce, industry, labour and the general interests of consumers of gas and other persons, or organisations, interested in the development of gas in the area'. The Chairman was to be *ex officio* a member of the local Area Board, and was to be paid; other members received out-of-pocket expenses and compensation for lost earnings. The Area Board was responsible for providing the office accommodation and secretariat. Bearing in mind the territorial size of the Area Boards, provision was made for setting up local committees. A little surprisingly, in view of the importance of sales of coke to the commercial viability of the gas industry at that time, coke did not come within the remit of the Consultative Councils. In the government's view, this was properly the concern of the coal industry's Consumer Councils, presumably because it was a solid fuel.

A priori this appears altogether too cosy an arrangement for effectiveness, with the Councils too much under the shadow of the Boards. The latter provided the accommodation—often within the Board's own premises—and the office staff and paid the general running costs; the Chairman was a member of the Board and thus had a loyalty to them which might be prejudicial to his freedom to criticise. A consumer with a genuine grievance might well feel that the odds were loaded against him from the outset. A further difficulty lay in finding suitable members of the Council. It was not an appointment with much appeal to young and vigorous people intent on building up their own careers; almost inevitably appointments tended to go to older, retired people with time on their hands. This in itself was no bad thing, for age and experience are valuable assets; the disadvantage was that older members might be out of touch with the ideas of younger generations and could not be expected to serve usefully for very long. On the other hand, they would be likely to be more aware of the special problems of the old and infirm than younger people would be. Insofar as there was continuity, it was provided by the permanent staff, who were employees of the Boards and dependent on them for advancement. The Consultative Councils were regional in character. There was no central body to which they could all respond and discuss matters of general interest. A policy of divide and rule could be seen in this by those disposed to be critical.

These are all fair and obvious criticisms, but they are not wholly justifiable. For example, the key position of secretary to a Council was a job with no career prospects and therefore unlikely to attract keen and appropriate candidates if independently advertised. The Boards, however, could be expected to appoint able men—perhaps near retiring age—with long experience of the industry and its customers. Similarly, they could lay on better general facilities than could reasonably be provided in small offices operated independently by the Councils. For the Chairman of the Council to be a member of the Board ensured that he had early notice of developments of importance to consumers; similarly, he could advise the Board of the likely attitude of consumers to proposals they had in mind. Constructive discussion could take place before plans were too far advanced for modification.

The Consultative Councils took some time to set up and then to establish a consistent way of working. Not until 1968 was there a useful general survey of their role in the nationalised industries [7] and to this we will turn later. Meanwhile we will consider the activities of the Councils only briefly and divert our attention to other aspects of the nationalised gas industry's moves to identify itself more closely with consumers.

The Annual Reports and Accounts of the Gas Council from nationalisation in 1948 to the formation of the British Gas Corporation in 1973 are illuminating. In view of the fact that the Consultative Councils reported direct to their Area Boards, and there was no central body reporting to the Gas Council, we would naturally not expect the Consultative Councils to feature very largely in the Reports. Nevertheless, in the early years there was clearly an attempt to acknowledge their activities. Thus the very first Report (1948/50) remarks that the '[Consultative] Councils . . . have an important part in the interpretation of the Board's policy to the public'. In 1951 the Report says (again in the context of the Consultative Councils) that 'It is clear that . . . far more information about the gas industry is now regularly available to the public than was ever the case before vesting date.' As the Consumer Council study [7] of 1968 was to show, however, these were not much more than pious hopes. There are a few more specific allusions. In 1952 there was reported an unsuccessful bid by a Consultative Council to oblige an Area Board to provide gas to a colliery village. In the same year, however, a different Council had a success in obliging a local authority to rescind a decision to exclude gas from a proportion of houses under their control. This last topic was alluded to again in the Report for 1955. Thereafter reference to Consultative Councils degenerates into polite acknowledgement of their existence—'Both the Boards and the Consultative Councils pay tribute to the frankness of their relations and to the help which they have received from each other in the interests of the communities they serve' (1957/58). The Report for 1958/59, which reviewed the first ten years of nationalisation, did not mention them at all. However, this is understandable: nobody is disposed to give prominence to adverse criticism of themselves, and the Consultative Councils were, by their nature, essentially critical bodies.

It must be recognised, however, that although the Consultative Councils served, as it were, as courts of appeal for consumers who had failed to get satisfaction from their Area Board they also had a broader role to play. This was to provide, from the consumers' point of view, a sort of running commentary on the industry—to propose changes in existing practice and suggest innovations. In this respect they certainly provided a valuable—and no doubt less complacent—supplement to the feedback that the Area Boards themselves were getting from the public. Their weakness, of course, was in their facilities. Even if there was a strong case to be argued, they did not have resources, comparable with those of the industry, to establish the facts, marshall the evidence, present a convincing report, and argue it forcefully.

OTHER LINKS WITH CONSUMERS

Formal consultative Councils were not the only means by which useful links could be established with consumers, and during these years other possibilities were being developed. Particular attention was directed to women who, in view of the dominance of the domestic load at that time, represented the most important single group of consumers; not until 1976/77 was the industrial load to equal the domestic. There was, of course, nothing novel in this; in earlier chapters we have made passing reference to similar activities by the old private companies. One important existing organisation in this field was the Women's Gas Council, founded in 1935, which had active branches throughout the country. Its objects were to develop a wider understanding of the use of gas in the home and generally to represent with other organisations—such as the Women's Institutes—the interests of women in the betterment of domestic and social life. It was an independent body and was, therefore, not vested in the Gas Council in 1948; nevertheless, the latter continued to support it both financially and by appropriate collaboration. In 1953 the organisation changed its name to the Women's Gas Federation.

In 1951 the Gas Council appointed Dame Vera Laughton Mathews to be Adviser on Women's Affairs. The Area Boards all had Home Service Advisers who were regarded as an indispensable link between Boards and their domestic consumers, whom they helped with advice, demonstrations, and lectures. They also made many visits to schools and higher education establishments.

It is, of course, very difficult to draw a clear line between a disinterested concern for the consumer, to see that he is fairly treated within the general terms of reference of the business, and a commercial interest in him as a purchaser of gas and appliances. Obviously, the two interests to some extent overlap, for a satisfied consumer is potentially a reliable long-term customer. Consumerism, therefore, inevitably spills over into public-relations and publicity generally. In 1965, the Gas Council's Domestic Information section (part of Press and Publicity Services Department) was strengthened and re-organised. The section became responsible for all aspects of the domestic use of gas in the consumer and women's press and for maintaining liaison on these subjects with Area Boards, appliance manufacturers, and consumer organisations. Naturally, however, it was the Boards who continued the direct contact, for the Gas Council itself had no customers with which to liaise. The Boards continued their general policy of paying particular attention to the needs of the old and the infirm. The Gas Council's Report for 1964/65 records that during the year 150 000 visits had been made to consumers in this category, and that 2000 specially adapted cookers had been sold, many through Old People's Welfare Associations. We have already noted how, as a special case, close liaison with pensioners' and old people's organisations was an integral part of the conversion programme.

It would seem that in the 1950s and 1960s the industry did as much for consumers on its own initiative as it did through the Consultative Councils. As evidence of this we have the Consumer Council Report already mentioned [7], which considered the achievements, after some 20 years, of the consultative machinery set up for the electricity, gas, coal, and transport industries. The results were not impressive. The result of a field survey carried out by Social Surveys (Gallup Poll) Ltd indicated that very few people even knew of the existence of any consultative organisations, let alone what they did or how they should be approached. The level in electricity and gas (12 per cent each) was at least better than coal (8 per cent), and transport (4 per cent). There was much confusion in people's minds between Consultative Councils and local electricity or gas showrooms: half the people who thought they had brought their complaints to the former proved in fact to have gone to the latter. On the other hand, some people sought the aid of Consultative Councils for general information which was easily and immediately available from local showrooms.

As far as the gas industry in particular was concerned, a total of 17 per cent of the sample of 3303 gas users said that they had had cause for complaint during the previous year. Of these 44 per cent had in the event done nothing, usually because it 'was not important' or 'too much bother'. Another 4 per cent could not remember what their complaint had been about. Of the 56 per cent who had taken some action, 51 per cent had gone to gas showrooms, 2 per cent to manufacturers, and only 1 per cent to Consultative Councils.

The Report then sought to analyse the experiences of those who had actually used the consultative machinery, but ended up on statistically rather thin ice. Out of 15 000 households involved in the entire survey, only 68 had actually been in touch with any of the consultative bodies.

This the Report calls a 'disappointingly small sample'. Disappointing perhaps to those who had organised the survey, but presumably less so to the industry concerned, which on the evidence might reasonably congratulate itself on providing a generally acceptable product or service. Having remarked that the smallness of the sample means that any findings based on it must necessarily be accepted with considerable reservation, it was nevertheless claimed that two positive conclusions could be reached:

(1) From the first part of the survey, it becomes clear that only a marginal impact has as yet been made by the consultative organisations in the four industries;

and

(2) The verdict on the usefulness of these organisations by those consumers (68) who have had some recourse to the facilities provided is a decidedly favourable one.

However, the report places undue emphasis on the role of the Consultative Councils as a means of redressing complaints by individual dissatisfied consumers. As we have seen they had a broader role to play in safeguarding the interests of consumers generally.

NATIONAL GAS CONSUMERS' COUNCIL

With the first of the above conclusions it is difficult to quarrel. Nevertheless, the Gas Act 1972 largely perpetuated the old system. Twelve Regional Gas Consumers' Councils were set up on substantially the same lines as the old Consultative Councils. They were asked to maintain close liaison with the new Local Authority Consumer Advice Centres. However, they now re-ported to the new British Gas Corporation or to a new body, the National Gas Consumers' Council. The old defect of lack of some sort of central clearing house had been remedied. While these Councils were required to make the Secretary of State an annual report on 'the exercise and perfor-mance by them of their functions during the year', they were not empowered to make representations to the Minister. This power was transferred to the new National Council, with Lady Macleod of Borve as Chairman, which stood in relation to the Corporation much as the old Consultative Councils had stood in relation to their Area Boards. This re-organisation of the consumer councils was, of course, a natural consequence of the transfer of power from the old Area Boards to the new Corporation.

Of the work of these new Councils, the Corporation's Annual Reports tell us virtually nothing. The first of them (1972/73) briefly mentions their existence; its three successors merely lists them—with the officers of the Department of Energy, the trade unions, the Institution of Gas Engineers, the Society of British Gas Industries, CORGI, and the Women's Gas Federation—among organisations for whose 'assistance and cooperation' the Corporation was grateful. In the Report for 1976/77 it is stated that in October 1976 an undertaking had been given to the National Gas Consu-mers' Council that prices would be unchanged for twelve months 'subject only to the Government's management of the economy'. In the event the management of the economy was not all it might have been, and the undertaking had to be rescinded, in consequence of the Corporation being 'requested' to reduce its existing debt by £100 million to enable the Chancel-lor to secure the IMF loan he was urgently seeking at that time (p. 206). However, we again ought not to be greatly surprised at the industry's paucity of references to the watchdog set to report on it, especially as it was now an entirely separate organisation.

For a clearer picture of the activities of the National Council we must turn to its own Annual Reports [8]. The first of these is directed to the Secretary of State for Energy but, following an administrative reorganisation, subsequent ones went to the Secretary of State for Prices and Consumer Protection, which in 1975 assumed financial responsibility for its work. Before considering briefly the new National Council's activities, we should note the evidence for its impact on the public. A survey conducted in the late spring of 1975 indicated that about 25 per cent of gas users were at least aware of the existence of Gas Consumers' Councils, more than twice the 12 per cent recorded in 1968. We should not, therefore, take too seriously the simultaneous report of a substantial increase in the number of consumer complaints recorded; these reached a record of almost 50 000 in 1975/76, an increase of about 15 per cent on the previous year. It was only to be expected that the greater the number of people who knew about the existence of the Councils, the greater the potential number of complainants. The increase does not necessarily imply a falling off in the standards of the gas industry. Indeed, in a period in which the new Councils, by energetic public-relations activities, were making the public more aware of their existence it would be perfectly possible for the number of complaints to increase while standards of efficiency in the industry were actually improving. No more can be said than that the interpretation of the figures needs some care. The Councils certainly deserve credit for making their activities so much more widely known.

All the reports show that sales and service were the main cause of dissatisfaction, exceeding one-third of the total in all the Annual Reports of the National Council noted. Next in order was the conversion programme, though this fell sharply in 1975/76, not surprisingly as its end was in sight. Disputed gas accounts, and bills generally, also figure high on the list at around one-fifth of all complaints received. This figure, too, should be treated with a little reserve; to lodge a formal complaint is a good way of buying time when payment presents difficulties. Unfortunately, the Reports tell us the number of complaints received but not the number which were ultimately agreed to be justifiable. To keep the number in perspective it may be remarked that if all were justified they would represent roughly one dissatisfied consumer in every 300.

The first Reports of the National Gas Consumers' Council show that apart from specific complaints it brought to the attention of the Corporation—whom it formally met twice a year—a great variety of subjects of importance to consumers generally. Among its successes it claimed the introduction of a single credit tariff for domestic consumers and a fairer deal for pre-payment (meter) customers; reduction of a proposed increase in service charge (1975/76); and more publicity for gas safety. Its activities were by no means restricted to exchanges with the Corporation. It established a close liaison with appliance manufacturers, with special reference to the availability of spare parts; took part in discussions to harmonise UK and European gas appliance safety standards; issued a leaflet advising consumers of their legal rights and responsibilities; backed a campaign drawing attention to the inefficiency of certain 'log-effect' gas fires; took part in Government inquiries into hardship caused by cut-off for non-payment of bills; and mounted a campaign to avert the dangers of hypothermia in the old.

The last decade has seen great developments in consumerism generally and the establishment of an increasingly elaborate official machinery to safeguard the interests of consumers. That there was room for improvement is not in doubt, for many dubious commercial practices had gone unchecked for too long, but to some it seems that the reaction has been excessive and that much is done for consumers, at public expense, that they could reasonably be expected to do for themselves. Certainly there is some truth in this, and it is manifest also in the many protectionist measures that are a feature of modern government. The difficulty is to frame measures that are very necessary to protect the old and infirm, the handicapped, and the inadequate without extending their benefits—and thus increasing the overall costs—to those who have no real need for them. Apart from the purely technical difficulties, discriminatory legislation is not fashionable. So far as the gas industry is concerned, however, it would appear that the interests of consumers—both individually and collectively—have been adequately served. With upwards of 14 million customers, to be supplied not by occasional transactions but all the year round, a complaint rate of 0.3 per cent at most is not discreditable, especially as some proportion of this low figure must be unjustified or relate to trivialities.

REFERENCES

[1] EVERARD, Stirling. *History of the Gas, Light and Coke Company, 1812–1949*, pp. 111–14, Benn, London (1949).
[2] Ibid., pp. 248, 254.
[3] CITY OF MANCHESTER GAS DEPARTMENT. *One Hundred and Forty Three Years of Gas in Manchester*, Manchester (1949).
[4] NEWBIGGING, Thomas and FEWTRELL, W. T. (ed.). *King's Treatise on the Science and Practice of the Manufacture and Distribution of Coal Gas*, Vol. III, pp. 31–4, King, London (1882).
[5] HARRIS, Stanley, A. *The Development of Gas Supply on North Merseyside 1915–1949*, North Western Gas Board, Liverpool (1956).
[6] REPORT OF THE SELECT COMMITTEE ON NATIONALISED INDUSTRIES. *The Gas Industry*, Vol. 1: Report and Proceedings, p. 3. HMSO, London (1961).
[7] THE CONSUMER COUNCIL. *Consumer Consultative Machinery in the Nationalised Industries*, HMSO, London (1968).
[8] NATIONAL GAS CONSUMERS' COUNCIL. *Annual Reports 1973/74–1976/77.*

23

Gas and the Energy Pattern

ENERGY can, very roughly, be equated with the power to do work and, as such, has been of interest since the dawn of civilisation. For many millennia, however, man had to be content largely with his own efforts, augmented to only a limited extent by the use of draught animals and by harnessing the power of water and the wind. Although undue emphasis has been laid on the role of the steam-engine in the early years of the Industrial Revolution, the advent of new sources of power had far-reaching consequences. Indeed, the availability of new forms of mechanical power, and the more intensive exploitation of old ones, has been one of the major forces that has shaped modern society. It has not only largely eliminated the severe physical toil that was commonplace in former times but it has made possible many developments, such as flying and the large-scale generation of electricity, which manpower alone could not achieve, however prodigally and skilfully deployed. Energy thus plays a key role in modern technology, and western civilisation depends on its ready availability.

It is now all too clear that the assumption of ready availability was ill-judged, and since the OPEC crisis of 1973 the western world has had to reappraise its whole energy policy in respect of conservation of existing resources and the development of new ones. This is a matter of concern for technologists and politicians of the present and the future. Our interest here is in how Britain's energy pattern developed and the way in which, in successive stages of its history, the gas industry fitted into it. Despite its crucial importance at the present time there is widespread misunderstanding about the nature of energy and we may usefully begin by considering a few basic facts.

FORMS OF ENERGY

While energy is a universal commodity, it manifests itself in different forms. We may encounter it as heat, light, motion (mechanical energy), electricity, or as chemical energy stored in a battery or accumulator. Leaving aside the special circumstances of nuclear energy, we may regard it as indestructible. While the sum total of energy remains unchanged, one form may change to another, as for example when heat is transformed into mechanical energy in a steam-engine, or mechanical energy is transformed into heat when metal is cut with a hacksaw. The change of energy from one form to another is not haphazard, but follows strict and well-understood rules: for example, a given quantity of heat is equivalent to a fixed amount of mechanical energy. We may see an analogy in international banking, where—in stable conditions—the different currencies of the world can be exchanged at fixed rates.

The world's energy problems do not stem from overall shortages but from shortages of the particular kinds society is organised to utilise. Although we are literally surrounded by energy—solar energy from the sun, the ceaseless movement of the tides and winds, energy locked up in the crust of the earth and in the nucleus of the atom—we cannot readily use these simply through lack of the means to convert them economically and on a large scale to forms we can use. In the energy sense, mankind is in much the same position as the Ancient Mariner:

> Water, water, everywhere,
> Nor any drop to drink.

Large-scale utilisation of such alternative sources demands enormous investment and technological development, as well as creating great environmental problems, all of which their advocates tend to underestimate. However urgent the need, rapid change is impossible. That these alternative forms of energy will in future make an increasing contribution is beyond doubt, simply because the fossil fuels—coal, oil, gas—which have served us so well, are being so rapidly exhausted that within the foreseeable future there will be none left that it is economic to extract.

In the quite recent past, the present anxiety about essential activities having to be curtailed through an overall shortage of energy did not exist. There was an abundance of cheap coal and oil and the possibility of total depletion lay too far in the future to be worth thinking about. The factors that influenced fuel policy were basically ones of economics and convenience, with strong social and political undertones because of the key position of the fuel industries in the national economy.

We have reminded ourselves already that the various forms of energy are interconvertible at fixed rates of exchange, but in practice the efficiency of conversion is variable and may be quite low. For example, a traditional open coal-fire is very efficient in releasing the heat energy locked up in the fuel but the greater part of the heat escapes up the chimney and thus serves no useful purpose. Properly designed and maintained appliances can do much better: for example, in 1966 the boiler efficiency in the best of Britain's power stations was about 90 per cent. The efficiency of the generators was lower, however. Overall, only the best stations could convert as much as 30 per cent of the energy locked up in coal into electricity: many could achieve no more than 30 per cent. After this a further 10 per cent might be lost in transmitting energy to the point of use, whether it be home or factory. Thereafter, the efficiency of utilisation of electricity can vary greatly. For an electric fire it may be virtually 100 per cent, but for an ordinary electric lamp less than 10 per cent. For small electric motors, such as are used to drive domestic appliances or individual machines in industry, an intermediate value is to be expected: in most cases about 80 per cent of the electrical power put in will be converted into useful mechanical power. To take a different field, the efficiency of a petrol-engine is around 25 per cent; a diesel-engine does rather better at about 40 per cent [1].

Clearly, therefore, one factor determining choice of fuel must be efficiency of utilisation. Another is convenience. Up to the First World War, for example, most industrial machinery was driven by an elaborate system of overhead shafts and belts which was noisy and also inefficient because of mechanical losses in transmission. After the war, individual electric motors became increasingly used—despite being more expensive to run—because of their great convenience. Additionally, there were side benefits, such as the creation of pleasanter working conditions, making it easier to recruit labour.

Apart from the fact that the cheapest fuel may not be the most suitable—though it may nevertheless be chosen if fuel costs form a large part of total overheads—cost can be deceptive. Some fuels—such as petrol and oil—are not only heavily taxed but the tax may be arbitrarily changed at short notice. Apart from direct taxation, the price of fuel may be subject to statutory control.

For roughly half its history the principal use of gas was as an illuminant, but since the beginning of this century this role has been taken over by electricity. The turn of the tide was marked by the Gas Regulation Act of 1920, which required undertakings to state the calorific value of their gas: the growing importance of gas as a fuel was thus formally recognised. Gas resembles coal in being primarily a source of heat, but with the advantage of being more flexible and more easily controlled in its use: as the gas industry rightly judged, it is now a premium fuel that should as far as possible be reserved for purposes for which it is most suitable. It is comparable with fuel oil rather than petrol: although gas engines were widely used in the early days of the internal combustion engine, petrol and diesel engines are dominant today. Gas is less flexible than electricity, which can be easily converted not only into heat but into mechanical power and light. Whatever it may have been in the past, gas today is strictly a fuel in the conventional sense of being burnt to provide heat.

POLITICAL CONSIDERATIONS

Over and above questions of efficiency, convenience, and cost, fuel-policy involves important political considerations, many of which we have already considered either explicitly or implicitly. The fuel industries are very big employers of labour, both directly and indirectly, and a major switch from one to another may cause serious employment problems. Some fuels—

notably oil—have until recently had to be wholly imported, and thus presented various special problems, notably in regard to balance of payments and defence in the event of war. There are, therefore, very important national and international implications about the rate at which natural reserves are depleted. These we have already considered in the context of North Sea gas and oil.

The general importance of providing adequate and dependable sources of power at an economic price has long been a feature of national policy in Britain. For decades the achievement of a rational fuel policy has been a cherished aim of politicians and political economists. It would be very satisfactory to be able to conclude this history by reporting that this goal had at last been achieved, but in fact it seems as elusive as ever. For this, two main reasons can be adduced.

Firstly, nationalisation of the fuel industries—generally regarded as a prerequisite for formulating and enforcing a national policy—did not in fact create an appropriate milieu. The complex inter-relationships between the principal fuel industries—including the non-nationalised oil industry—and the long time-scale required to complete, say, a series of new power-stations are at odds with political requirements, which are essentially short-term. We have noted elsewhere other occasions when the great difference between the industrial and political time-scale has hindered rather than promoted progress. A year can be a long time in politics but a very short one in industry.

Secondly, the successful maturation of all long-term policies demands that the principal parameters either remain unchanged or change predictably. This condition has not been fulfilled for the fuel industry in Britain. We may note at least three major changes which, on the sort of time-scale we have been talking about, have appeared almost out of the blue.

(1) The advent of atomic power. Not until the beginning of 1942 was this acknowledged to be a technological possibility; in the summer of 1945 the first nuclear device—pointing the way to industrial power production—had been exploded. Three weeks later two atomic bombs brought the war against Japan to a sudden end. In barely three years atomic power had arrived in a world ill-prepared to deal with it.

(2) In the summer of 1959 the discovery of the vast natural-gas field at Slochteren, and the subsequent North Sea development, completely changed the energy picture in northern Europe, and especially in Britain.

(3) The action of the OPEC countries in sharply forcing up the price of oil in 1973 made necessary a major reconsideration of future needs for energy and the sources from which it was derived.

Any of these developments would have played havoc with the completion of an energy programme, however carefully planned.

As far as gas is concerned, the history of its role in the British energy pattern is further complicated by fundamental changes in its relationship with other fuels. We can, in fact, distinguish three distinct phases:

(1) The first, and by far the longest phase was that in which gas was made by the carbonisation of coal from British coalfields. During this period the fortunes of gas were directly related to those of coal for, in effect, those who burned gas were burning coal once removed. During this period coke was burnt in grates and furnaces just like coal. At the end of this phase, however, complete gasification processes were developing which produced no coke.

(2) Overlapping with the end of the first phase was a second, quite brief one, in the course of which increasing amounts of gas were made from imported oil. Some natural gas was also imported, and Britain was heading for a situation in which the availability of gas was dependent on imports.

(3) The second phase was just getting into its stride when a third one, based on natural gas from the North Sea, suddenly started. Once again Britain began to draw gas—but a new kind of gas—from an indigenous source.

With these fundamental changes in the source of gas superimposed upon an already complex relationship between the principal fuels, the task of describing the development of any one of them, and the factors that determined that development, is exceedingly difficult. In a general study such as this we must be content with recording the progress of events and trying to distinguish those which represented a response to external events and those which were the consequence of deliberate national planning.

GROWTH OF THE FUEL INDUSTRIES

Although this part of the work is concerned primarily with the period of nationalisation of the gas industry after 1948, it will be helpful to remind ourselves of the way in which the fuel industries had grown up to that time. As the oldest of the major fuel industries, we may appropriately start with coal. The following production figures show how the industry expanded from the late nineteenth century, when it was by far the most important source of energy, to reach a peak in the early 1930s, thereafter declining.

UK PRODUCTION OF COAL
1885–1946

Year	Production (thousands of tons)	Production relative to 1885
1885	161 455	100
1920	233 214	144
1930	247 795	153
1938	230 658	142
1946	191 647	119

These figures, taken from official returns, are unchallengeable insofar as they give a general picture of the development of the industry, but they do demand reservations. Firstly, they suggest that production was known to an accuracy of about 0.0005 per cent, which is manifestly absurd. Even if this precision were attained in the returns made by the producers it would have no validity in terms of energy production. Coal is a very variable fuel; even if pure, the best grades yield relatively much more heat than the poorest. In fact, however, all grades are contaminated with some incombustible stone and water as well as a variable amount of slack, much of which is wasted. It would be surprising if these figures are significant to more than 5 per cent.

The history of the electricity industry up to nationalisation in 1947 was very different, for its contribution to national requirements at the beginning of the century was negligible. Thereafter, it grew rapidly, roughly doubling every decade.

UK PRODUCTION OF ELECTRICITY
1907–1946

Year	Production (million units)	Production relative to 1907
1907	1432	100
1922	4572	320
1930	10 947	764
1939	26 814	1872
1946	41 253	2880

Quantitatively, the effect of this rapid increase was less than might be expected because it began from such a low level. Even in 1937, electricity generated was equivalent to no more than 15 million tons of coal. We must always remember, however, that in comparing such figures over a period we must allow for increases in efficiency of utilisation.

The position of oil was similar to that of electricity. At the beginning of the century consumption was very small: by mid-century it had multiplied many times over. The increase was due very largely to the development of a wholly new market in the road and air transport field, in which it had no effective rival. On Britain's railways, coal remained dominant until the introduction of diesel locomotives after the last war. Electric traction was then still largely limited to parts of the Southern Railway and the London underground. While electrically-propelled road vehicles of various kinds have been on the road since before the beginning of the century, and a few steam-driven lorries were in use until the 1930s, modern road transport is for all practical purposes wholly dependent on petroleum—the lighter fractions (petrol) for cars and heavier ones (diesel fuel) for many commercial vehicles. In the growing air-transport industry, too, petroleum fuels alone could be utilised. At sea, oil increasingly displaced coal for firing ships' boilers. However, all these uses, in fields in which the transport of passengers and goods was being literally revolutionised, represented a surprisingly small proportion of total energy consumption. The Secretary of Mines Report for 1937 gave the consumption of oil in Britain as 2747 million gallons, of which 1364 million were used in motor spirit. A further 849 million gallons were used as fuel and diesel oil. Thus, these two items alone accounted for around 80 per cent of the total. Total consumption of oil products then amounted, however, to no more than the equivalent of about 5 million tons of coal annually.

While consumption of coal was relatively static and electricity and oil had meteoric rises, gas occupied an intermediate position. During the first-half of the century production increased roughly five-fold, as the following table shows.

UK PRODUCTION OF GAS
1887–1947

Year	Production (million cubic ft)	Production relative to 1887
1887	56 241	100
1902	91 956	163
1912	126 002	224
1920	295 857	526
1930	313 046	557
1937	341 985	608
1946	446 124	793

On the above basis, the overall energy position in Britain before the war was roughly as follows:

CONTRIBUTIONS OF
PRINCIPAL FUELS TO UK
ENERGY PATTERN (1937)

	(%)
Coal	79
Gas	10
Electricity (including hydroelectricity)	8.3
Oil	2.7

While coal remained dominant, gas and electricity had gained roughly equal shares of the total market. The utilisation of coal was roughly static; gas was slowly strengthening its position; but electricity was forging ahead rapidly. We must emphasise again, however, that coal was, during this period, virtually the sole source of both gas and electricity.

In the immediate post-war period the general picture remained much the same. The urgent task was to make good the deficiencies arising from six years of operating under wartime difficulties: innovation had to wait. Much thought was given to future developments, both nationally and in the context of the individual industries, but sheer lack of material resources greatly restricted progress.

Production figures for coal published in the Annual Reports of the National Coal Board show a steady decline from a post-war peak reached in 1953. Although the production cost was held constant for the five years 1961/65—no mean achievement—the trend was steadily upwards. We have already marked this increase as being one of the principal reasons why the gas industry actively sought an alternative raw material.

UK COAL PRODUCTION 1947–67

Year	Output (millions of tons)	Production cost (shillings per ton)
1947	197	40
1950	216	48
1953	223	61
1956	222	77
1959	206	83
1961	191	91
1965	187	92
1967	172	99

By contrast, electricity was rapidly expanding its sales and keeping price increases low, as the following figures from the Ministry of Power Statistical Digests show.

UK PRODUCTION OF ELECTRICITY

Year	Total sales (thous. mill. units)	Average price per unit (pence)
1950	45.5	1.186
1955	67.4	1.384
1960	102.4	1.487
1965	151.1	1.706
1967	161.7	1.773

The post-war use of oil showed a dramatic increase. When the government surveyed the fuel situation in 1967 [2] it reported that oil then provided 37 per cent of Britain's total energy requirements, compared with 15 per cent in 1957, and less than 3 per cent in 1937. Average annual growth over the decade 1957/67 was $11\frac{1}{2}$ per cent, though in the last three years there was a slackening off to 9½ per cent. In the same decade the consumption of petrol, which had been rising steadily, roughly doubled. In 1955/60, however, the most striking development was in the use of fuel-oil, which rose from 25 per cent to 50 per cent of all petroleum products consumed. In this field, gains were made mostly at the expense of coal, and in the 1961 Budget a duty of 2d. per gallon was imposed on fuel-oil to protect the coal industry. Consumption of imported oil (excluding transport) rose from roughly 40 mtce (million tons coal equivalent) in 1961 to about 70 mtce in 1966, at which time North Sea oil and gas came into sight.

The government's 1967 review of Fuel Policy illustrates the problems of the long-term forecast of economic trends. In assessing the future costs of oil it stated:

It is difficult to predict the course of oil prices. There are a number of reasons for expecting them not to increase. . . . Competition is strong both between companies and between sources of supply, and the surplus of crude oil seems likely to persist for many years. . . . On the evidence available, it seems likely that oil will remain competitive with coal, and that pressure to force up crude oil prices will be held in check by the danger of loss of markets [3].

Yet the dramatic increase in oil prices by O P E C—which shook the Western world and changed the whole basis of North Sea economics—then lay only six years ahead!

Having thus surveyed the development of its principal rivals, we must now consider how the gas industry itself fared over the same post-war period. Initially, it failed to match the growth rate of electricity. Sales of electricity rose by 350 per cent between 1950 and 1967; by contrast, sales of gas rose by only 180 per cent in the same period. Thereafter, however, gas surged ahead, sales increasing by a further 230 per cent in the next decade. Moreover, in the latter years the price per therm was actually cut and a subsequent increase was partly accounted for, as we have previously noted, by what was, in effect, an undesired government direction. The following figures (from the Annual Reports of the Gas Council/British Gas Corporation) tell the story.

UK SALES OF GAS 1950/51–1976/77

Year	Sales (millions of therms)	Average selling price per therm (pence)*
1950/51	2402	12.98
1955/56	2584	17.2
1960/61	2612	21.51
1965/66	3484	22.52
1967/68	4199	22.47
1968/69	4664	23.69
1969/70	5235	22.75

UK SALES OF GAS 1950/51–1976/77 continued

Year	Sales (millions of therms)	Average selling price per therm (pence)*
1970/71	6133	20.95
1971/72	7992	18.86
1972/73	10 179	17.40
1973/74	11 487	16.92
1974/75	12 932	18.91
1975/76	13 454	23.69
1976/77	13 837	29.29

* old pence throughout, for ease of comparison.

The annual statistics from 1950/51 onwards show very clearly how far the manufacture of coal-gas was eclipsed by oil, and the latter in turn supplanted by natural gas. In the year that the British Gas Corporation came into being the gas industry's total annual demand for coal and oil together was less than 2 million tons; most of this was for stand-by plant kept in readiness to cope with any temporary interruption of natural gas.

RAW MATERIALS FOR
MANUFACTURED GAS
(MILLIONS OF TONS)

Year	Coal	Oil
1950/51	26.369	0.548
1955/56	27.738	0.502
1960/61	21.994	0.779
1965/66	17.490	2.722
1967/68	13.606	4.917
1968/69	9.261	5.941
1969/70	5.948	4.610
1970/71	3.411	4.727
1971/72	1.064	1.538
1972/73	.579	1.432
1973/74	.400	1.398
1974/75	.028	.759
1975/76	.008	.201
1976/77	.008	.092

GROWTH OF THE DOMESTIC, INDUSTRIAL, AND COMMERCIAL
MARKETS FOR GAS

Finally, we may instructively conclude this statistical survey by considering how sales of gas were apportioned over the years between domestic, industrial, and commercial/public administration consumers.

ANNUAL SALES OF GAS ACCORDING TO TYPE OF CONSUMER (MILLIONS OF THERMS)

Year	Domestic	Industrial	Commercial/ public admin.
1950/51	1391.7	589.7	366.8
1955/56	1350.3	751.2	439.9
1960/61	1291.2	851.8	446.6
1965/66	2005.5	928.2	550.6
1966/67	2267.2	908.4	579.0
1967/68	2652.1	914.5	632.5
1968/69	3010.8	976.4	676.5
1969/70	3362.1	1159.1	714.2
1970/71	3653.1	1704.2	775.5
1971/72	4045.1	3069.7	876.8
1972/73	4603.2	4530.2	1045.1
1973/74	5034.8	5299.1	1152.8
1974/75	5710.4	5920.6	1300.7
1975/76	5940.8	6072.2	1400.5
1976/77	6183.3	6106.6	1547.1

This table shows a steady rise in domestic sales throughout the period, but a sudden upward trend in industrial sales from 1969/70, indicative of the success of the Gas Council's marketing strategy. The year 1973/74 was the first in which industrial sales exceeded domestic, a turning-point in the history of the industry. Thereafter they remained roughly level-pegging to the end of the period of our review. In a quarter of a century domestic sales had increased by 344 per cent, but industrial sales had increased by no less than 935 per cent. This was, of course, a consequence of the successful implementation of the policy decision to concentrate on the premium industrial market to absorb the large quantities of natural gas becoming available. The commercial/public administration market closely resembled the domestic one, showing a satisfying increase of 314 per cent.

This pattern of growth was in marked contrast to that in the electricity industry. There, the immediate post-war sales to industry exceeded those to domestic consumers. Sales to both markets then rose fairly rapidly in the 1950s but less so in the 1960s.

UK ELECTRICITY SUPPLY 1950–1967 (THOUSANDS OF MILLIONS OF UNITS)

Year	Domestic sales	Industrial sales
1950	14.4	22.9
1955	20	34.6
1960	33.3	50
1965	56.5	65
1966	58.9	66.7
1967	61.3	67.4

This remarkable resurgence of the gas industry, for which no important future was foreseen in the years immediately after the last war, was the consequence of several factors which have been considered at length in earlier chapters. It would be invidious to single out any single one as being crucially important, because success was the reward for collective perseverance on several fronts. Technological success would have been insufficient without a carefully conceived marketing strategy; multiplying sales by a factor of six (1950/76) to some 13 million customers would have been impossible without adopting modern techniques of management; the use of natural gas demanded modification of a business structure designed for manufactured gas; and so on. Like any chain, the gas industry's strength is no more than that of its weakest link. This chapter may be appropriately ended by briefly reminding ourselves of the nature of the main links and how they were forged.

On the technological front the three main developments were successively the development of processes for the complete gasification of coal; the use of petroleum as a raw material; and the exploitation of natural gas. Historically and economically, complete gasification was of minor importance, not for lack of technical success but because it was overtaken by events and never made an important contribution in Britain. Its main significance perhaps was that it stimulated the acquisition of new technological skills and, in particular, familiarity with handling large volumes of gas at high pressures. With a steady upward trend in the price of coal, and a mistaken belief in a continuing low price for petroleum products, the gas industry then seemed launched on a lasting commitment to oil as a raw material. Technologically, the significance of this was that as no solid materials had to be handled, but only gases and liquids, the advanced technology of the chemical and petroleum refining industries could be used to supplement the existing skills of the gas industry. Persistence on this course would not have been the road to ruin, but the economics of a gas industry based wholly on imported oil would have been shaken at its foundations by the O P E C price increases of 1973 and subsequently. By that time, however, the technological basis had changed yet again, with the advent of North Sea gas and, as its precursor, imported natural gas. At the time of the O P E C crisis, the conversion programme was so well-advanced as to be within four years of completion. Dependence on imported oil was already much reduced and was soon to disappear altogether.

Technologically, there was in principle nothing novel about the utilisation of natural gas. It had already been practised in North America for a century or so, latterly on a vast scale. Off-shore drilling was a more recent development, largely confined to relatively calm and shallow waters. What was new and exciting about the North Sea was that never before had exploration and extraction been carried out in such cold and stormy waters. Here was technology at the very frontier of modern capability. In the future, no doubt, these early achievements will be looked on as commonplace, but in the 1960s and early 1970s the North Sea drilling rigs, and their associated gear, were centres not only of outstanding technical achievement but of great human courage and endurance.

But technology cannot flourish in isolation. The last forty years have seen two outstanding achievements in this field: the Manhattan project for the development of atomic energy and the Apollo Moon landings. These were a triumph as much for management as for technology. Each demanded that a most elaborate array of complex operations were all successfully brought to fruition within specified limits of time and budgetary provision. The North Sea operation was comparable. It was one thing to bring the gas ashore: it was another to ensure that when brought ashore it could be distributed to appliances capable of burning it. The ten-year conversion programme may have left a tiny residue of dissatisfied customers but overall it was a very remarkable achievement; as we have noted, it was conducted with far less disruption to the consumer than in any other country.

When the gas industry was nationalised more than 1000 separate undertakings were acquired by the Gas Council. Although the least efficient were soon closed, and others amalgamated, there were still 428 works operating in March 1960. But by the 1970s there were, for practical purposes, only five 'works' in operation: these were the North Sea shore terminals at Bacton, Theddlethorpe, Easington, and St Fergus, together with the original Canvey Island terminal for imported liquefied gas. The Area Boards no longer had manufacturing responsibilities and a radical reorganisation was necessary to take note of this: the old Gas Council, with its strength at the periphery, was transformed into the present British Gas Corporation, with its strength at the centre. A new technological basis required a new managerial organisation.

Inherent in the North Sea development was the imminent availability of very large quantities of gas for which there was no existing market. The industry had to show great flexibility and initiative in developing a new and aggressive marketing strategy based on gaining a substantial part of the premium market in the industrial field. This involved a calculated risk, for it might have happened that the gas was contracted for but an insufficient market developed, but in the event supply and demand were kept very nicely balanced.

For the industrial market, efficiency is more important than appearance, but this was not so in the post-war domestic market, which as late as 1976 was still marginally bigger than the newly expanded industrial one. There, a much more sophisticated public wanted not only efficiency and economy but fashion. In addition to designing burners to deal with gas having combustion properties very different from that of the old town gas made from coal, appliance manufacturers had to produce equipment that was much more attractive in appearance and operated with the minimum of trouble.

On the whole, the leaders of the new gas industry were very successful in weaving these different threads into an acceptable pattern. Even while they were doing so, however, they were having to make plans for the future and trying to ensure that the structure they were creating was flexible enough to deal, in the fullness of time, with quite a new situation. From the outset, before one therm of North Sea gas was burned in Britain, it was certain that the quantity available was limited. How long it would last depended on two main factors: firstly the total quantity ultimately available, and secondly, the rate at which it was extracted. Neither factor was then known with any precision, nor is it now: the only certainty was that there must be a time limit of some sort. Before that limit is reached—or, rather, when its timing becomes apparent—some new strategy must have been developed to ensure continuity of supply. If a second national conversion programme is to be avoided this must involve the provision of gas compatible with existing appliances. This may lead to a re-marriage of gas and coal, but on the basis of high-pressure total gasification processes rather than the crude carbonisation process that served the industry well for a century and a half.

REFERENCES

[1] BRAME, J. S. S. and KING, J. G. *Fuel: Solid, Liquid and Gaseous*, 6th edn, p. 504, St Martin's Press, New York (1967).
[2] MINISTRY OF POWER. *Fuel Policy*, Cmnd. 3438, HMSO, London (1967).
[3] Ibid., p. 26.

BIBLIOGRAPHY

An Energy Policy for EEC?, PEP, London (1963).

BRAME, J. S. S. and KING, J. G. *Fuel: Solid, Liquid and Gaseous*, 6th edn, St Martin's Press, New York (1967).

BYATT, I. C. R. *The British Electrical Industry 1875–1914: the Economic Returns of a New Technology*, Oxford University Press, Oxford (1979).

COOPER, Donald F. *Gas for Great Britain in the Coming Ten Years and Thereafter.* Energy Policy Foundation of Norway (1979).

CRABBE, David and MCBRIDE, Richard. *The World Energy Book: an A–Z Atlas and Statistical Source Book*, Kogan Page, London (1978).

Development of Oil and Gas Resources of the United Kingdom (Annually since 1972), HMSO, London.

Digest of United Kingdom Energy Statistics (Annually since 1974), HMSO, London.

Energy for Industry 1976. Cambridge Information and Research Services Ltd.

Europe's Growing Needs of Energy (Hartley Report), OEEC, Paris (1956).

Fuel for Twenty Years, PEP, London (1955).

Fuel Purchasing in Industry and Commerce. Cambridge Information and Research Services Ltd in Association with the School of Fuel Management. Cambridge (1976).

HEPPLE, P. (ed.), *Outlook for Natural Gas—A Quality Fuel.* Proceedings of the Institute of Petroleum's Summer Meeting, Bournemouth, 1972. Applied Science, Barking (1973).

HINTON, Lord. *Heavy Current Electricity in the United Kingdom: History and Development*, Pergamon Press, Oxford (1979).

Impact of Natural Gas on the Consumption of Energy in the OECD European Member Countries, OECD, Paris (1969).

JENSEN, W. G. *Energy in Europe 1945–1980*, Foulis, London (1967).

KELF-COHEN, P. *Twenty Years of Nationalisation: the British Experience*, Macmillan, London (1969).

LITTLE, I. M. D. *The Price of Fuel*, Clarendon Press, Oxford (1953).

Methods and Models for Assessing Energy Resources, First IIASA Conference on Energy Resources, May 1975. Pergamon Press, Oxford (1979).

LOVEJOY, W. F. and HOMAN, P. T. *Methods of Estimating Reserves of Crude Oil, Natural Gas and Natural Gas Liquids*, Johns Hopkins Press, Baltimore (1965).

MINCHIN, L. T. *The Gas Industry Today and Tomorrow*, Harrap, London (1966).

POSNER, Michael Y. *Fuel Policy: a study in Applied Economics*, Macmillian, London (1973).

Questions of Fuel Policy. PEP, London (1965).

Report of the Committee on National Policy for the Use of Fuel and Power Resources (Ridley Committee), Cmnd. 8647, HMSO, London (1952).

Index

Accum, F.   9
Administrative Staff College   234
Alaska oilfield   160, 228
Alexander, J. R. W.   66
Amerada Exploration Ltd   164
American Petroleum Institute   228
Ammonia   53, 65
Amoco UK Petroleum Ltd   164, 210
Amoseas   167
Andrew, L. W.   129
Anti-gas League   272
Appliances:
   Burners (lighting)   31, 32
   Cooking   35, 73, 140
   Canvey Island survey   184
   Conversion   196–8
   Heating   35, 36, 37
   Incandescent mantle   33, 44
   Safety   194
   Sales promotion   133
   Street lights   34, 192
Area Joint Industrial Councils   263, 264
Argand, F-P. A.   32
Armstrong, E. F.   45
Arpet Group   209
Association of Gas Corporations   117
Association of Scientific, Technical and
      Managerial Staffs   268
Aquifers   178

Banks, J.   19
Barnes, A.   111
Barnwell Offshore Co.   169
Beau de Rochas, A.   38
Beaver Committee on Pollution   128
Beckett, J. A.   161
Beckton gasworks   27, 60, 61, 70, 265
Benn, A. W.   206
Benzole   53, 65
Black, M.   129
Bone, W. A.   144
Boulton, M.   33
Boulton and Watt   6, 7
Bowditch, W. R.   15
Bray, G.   45
Brighton Pavilion   10

British Association of Gas Managers
   45
British Broadcasting Corporation   105,
   250
British Commercial Gas Association
   74, 133
British (later Central) Electricity Auth-
   ority   109, 110
British Gas Corporation   167, 230, 231,
   236–41
British Gas Council   95, 98, 117
British Gas Federation   74, 93, 95, 263
British Gas Staff Association   267
British Institute of Management   234
British Petroleum (BP)   143, 157, 161,
   167, 172, 174
British Steel Corporation   253
British Tar Association   65
British Transport Commission   110,
   114, 247
Brooklands Technical College   234
Buckley, J.   222
Bunsen, R. W.   33
Burgin, E. L.   271
Burmah Oil   170

Calder Hall power station   180
Calorific value   44, 57, 128, 182
Camp, W.   200
Canadian Pacific Railway   157, 176
Cannon Iron Foundries   135
Canvey Island   145, 177, 178, 182–9,
   195
Canvey–Leeds pipeline   147, 224, 228
Carburetted water-gas   60, 61, 62
Catalytic rich gas (CRG) process   128,
   140
Cavendish, H.   4
Central Electricity Board   70, 108
Central Electricity Generating Board
   218
Chantler, P.   71, 90, 131
City and Guilds Institute   46
Clayton, J.   3
Clegg, B. G. H.   205
Clegg, S.   7, 8, 15, 19, 45

Clow, A. 118
Coal supply 20, 21, 69, 84
Coal Commission 105
Coal gas:
  Bottled 28
  Distribution 16, 19, 64, 70, 119
  Early investigations 4
  Gasholders 19, 63
  Manufacture 15, 22, 31, 119
  Metering 19, 64, 188
  Pressure control 20, 135
  Purification 16
  Toxicity 62
  USA 140
Coal tar 18, 52, 65
Cobb, J. W. 124
Coke 18, 60, 62, 84, 87, 91, 129
Coke-oven gas 59, 60, 68, 71, 114
Commercial market, analysis of 218
Compagnie Algérienne du Méthane
    Liquide 146
Compagnie Française des Pétroles
    157, 167
Compensation (on nationalisation)
  Coal 107
  Electricity 109
  Gas 115
  Transport 111
Complete gasification 123, 296
Compressor stations 229–30
Confederation of Shipbuilding and En-
    gineering Unions 268
Constock Liquid Methane Corp. 144
Continental Oil Co. 144
Continental Shelf 150
Convention of the Seas (Geneva) 151,
    152
Conversion programme:
  Appliance manufacturers 196–8, 213
  Canvey Island 182–9, 202
  Completion 154, 190
  Executive 181
  Financing 214
  National 189–203
  Sub-contractors 198–200
  Timetable 191
Co-partnership 49, 52, 69
CORGI 273
Corporation Trade Union Advisory
    Committee 268
Country Landowners' Association 177
Crossley Bros 38

Dalton, H. 246
Dam, K. W. 160

Darby, A. 4
D'Arcy Exploration 143
Davies, E. A. J. 248
Davies, J. E. H. 237
Davy, H. 8, 9
Dent, F. J. 123
Districting 42, 89
Dividends, control of 41, 42
Dixon, G. 95
Doherty, J. 263
Drake, E. L. 168
Dresser Industries 144
Drilling techniques 167–71
Duckham, A. 62
Duncan, A. 84
Dunn, W. T. 66

East Ohio Gas Co. 143, 144
Edwards, R. 118
Egerton, A. C. G. 144
Electricity:
  Efficiency as fuel 68, 69, 284
  Grid 108
  Lighting 33
Electricity Commissioners 107
Elliot, W. 117
Ellis, W. D. 181
Engineering Research Station 123
Erroll, F. J. 156, 160
Evans, E. V. 90, 91, 92, 93, 95
Everard, S. 48
Exxon (Esso) 157

Faraday, M. 30
Federation of Gas Employers 74, 117,
    267
Financial targets 255–8
Finniston, H. M. 253
First World War:
  Production of high explosives 51
  Ministry of Munitions 51
  Silvertown explosion 52
  Charcoal for gasworks 53
Fisons Ltd 206
Flame speed factor 58, 128, 182
Flavel Ltd 135
Fletcher, T. 36
Foulis, W. 46
Fraser, E. 133
Fuel industries, growth of 287–92
Fuel policy (national) 97, 211

Gaitskell, H. T. N. 275
Gas Advisory Council 233
Gas Companies Protection Associ-
    ation 74

Gas Consultative Councils 275–8
Gas Council:
  Consultative Councils 277
  Contracts for gas purchase 174, 208
  Creation of 116
  Financial targets 257
  Imports liquid gas 145
  North Sea licences 164–5
  Reorganisation 230–3
Gas engines 37
Gas-fitting standards 272–3
Gas grid 70
Gas Institute 45
Gas Journal (originally Journal of Gas
  Lighting) 22, 47
Gas Legislation Committee 73
Gas Light and Coke Company (Char-
  tered Company) 8, 9, 15, 20, 21,
  26, 40, 45, 47, 48, 49, 60, 63, 70, 72,
  73, 83, 86, 88, 95, 133, 271, 273, 274
Gas recycle hydrogenerator (GRH)
  process 127, 128
Gas Research Board 74, 90, 123
Gas Stokers' Protection Society 48
Gas undertakings:
  Belfast 61
  Brentford 73
  Brentwood 73
  British Gas Light 73
  City of London 27
  Commercial 42
  Coventry 85
  Crystal Palace 36
  Debenham 70
  Devonport 36
  Early provincial 9, 10, 27
  Equitable 27
  Grays & Tilbury 73
  Great Central 27
  Ilford 73
  Imperial 21, 27
  Imperial Continental 28
  Ipswich 63
  Liverpool 48, 49, 83
  Manchester 10, 27, 28, 63, 84
  Phoenix 48
  Pinner 73
  Rhayader 70
  St Helens 63
  Sheffield 42, 44, 60
  Southend 73
  South Metropolitan 47, 49, 58, 70,
  132, 265
  Wedmore 70
  Western 27

  Victoria Docks 27
Gas warfare, charcoal for 53, 86
Gas Workers' Union 49
Gas World 22
George, G. Lloyd 96
George, D. Lloyd 51
Glomar IV 169
Glover, S. 63
Goodenough, F. W. 132
Grant, J. L. 8
Great Exhibition (1851) 46
Gulf Oil 157, 176
Gunter, R. J. 237

Haber-Bosch process 126
Hadley, T. A. 36
Harland and Wolff 145
Hartley, H. 72
Heard, E. 15
Heaton, H. 9
Hebden, D. H. 123
Hetherington, A. 113, 205, 233, 240,
  254
Heyworth, G. 96, 251
Heyworth Committee 96, 115, 116, 117
High-pressure gas grid 147, 177–8
Hills, F. C. 16
Hodsman, H. J. 124
Holding companies 73, 114
Holliday, G. C. 129
Holmes, W. C. & Co. 87
Hope Natural Gas Corporation 143
Houldsworth, H. 250
Hurcomb, C. W. 251
Hutchison, W. K. 118, 123, 212, 213,
  214
Hydrocarbons Great Britain Ltd 165

Imperial Chemical Industries 65, 126,
  157, 170, 206, 230
Incorporated Gas Institute 45
Incorporated Institution of Gas En-
  gineers 45
Industrial Market, analysis of 215–18
Institution of Civil Engineers 46
Institution of Gas Engineers 45, 46, 47,
  66, 74
Iron and Steel Corporation 114
Iron oxide, in purification 16, 18

Johnson, F. J. 205
Jones, H. F. H. 118, 136, 222, 233, 254
Jones, T. M. 118

Kelf-Cohen, R. 98

Kroeger, V. 181

Lacey, S. 64
Lampadius, W. A. 4
Lancet, The 36
Latham, J. 252
Lebon, P. 4, 6, 7
Lee, F. 163
Leeds University (Fuel Department)
    46
Lenoir, E. 37
Leoni and Co. 35
Lewes, V. B. 123
Lighthouses 32
Lime, in purification 15, 18
Liquefied natural gas 122, 130, 136,
    143–7
Liquid petroleum gas (LPG) 124
Litton Industries 167
Livesey, G. T. 46, 49, 265
Lodge, H. 7
London and Counties Coke Associ-
    ation 60
London Graduate School of Business
    Studies 234
London Hospital 36
London Passenger Transport Board 105
London Regional Gas Centre 83
London Research Centre 123
Lowther, J. 3
Lunge, G. 45
Lurgi process 124, 125, 128

Macintosh, C. 18
Mackay, D. I. & G. A. 161, 164, 221
Macleod, E. H. 280
R. & A. Main Ltd 135
Malam, J. 15
Management, restructuring of 233–6
Managerial Administrative, Technical
    and Supervisory Association 267
Manchester Business School 234
Manchester Gas Consumers' Associ-
    ation 272
Marshall, F. D. 46
Mason, R. 237
Mathews, V. L. 278
McGowan Committee 108
McKinsey and Co. 233
Maughan, B. W. 36
Methane Pioneer 145, 183
Meurs, A. P. H. van 158, 159, 160
Midlands Research Station 123
Milne-Watson, D. 95
Milne-Watson, M. 98, 118

Minckelers, J. 4
Ministry of Munitions 51, 81
Ministry of Transport 107
Mobil 157
Molson, A. H. E. 251, 253
Monopolies Commission 255
Monsanto 157
Montgolfier, J-M and J-E 4
Morrison, H. S. 246, 252
Morton, F. 194
Morton, R. 18
Morton Report 194
Mr Cap 169
Mr Therm 133
Municipal undertakings 27, 43
Murdock (Murdoch), W. 4, 6, 7, 9
Murphy Petroleum 170

NALGO 266–8
NAM Gas Export 148
National Advisory Committee on Train-
    ing and Education 268
National Coal Board 107, 112, 114,
    121, 127, 136, 165, 250, 253
National Economic Development Office
    258
National Farmers' Union 177
National Federation of Gas Coke Associ-
    ations 117
National fuel policy 97, 211, 286, 291
National Gas Consumers' Council
    239, 271, 280–2
National Gas Council of Great Britain
    and Ireland 74, 90, 263
National Joint Council for Gas Staffs 267,
    268
National Joint Council for Gas Staffs
    267, 268
National Union of Gas Stokers 49
National Union of General and Muni-
    cipal Workers 264
National Union of Mineworkers 114
Nationalisation programme:
    Coal 106
    Electricity 107, 109
    Gas 112
    Iron and Steel 114
    Transport 110
Natural gas:
    Early investigations 3, 4, 7, 139, 142
    In Europe 141
    In USA 121, 139, 140, 141, 143
    Origin 148–9
Natural gas fields:
    Brent 176

Cousland 143
Eakring 142
Frigg 163, 176
Hassi R'Mel 145
Hewett 175, 209
Indefatigable 175, 209
Lacq 142
Leman Bank 175, 209
Lockton 176, 209
Rough 176
St Marcet 141
Slochteren 147, 176
Viking 176
West Sole 147, 154, 172, 174
Needham, J. 3
Nederlandse Gasunie 148
Nobel, A. and L. 141
North Sea Gas:
  Distribution 225–30
  Interruptible supply 217
  Licensing 153, 154, 156–65, 167
  Major contracts 206, 208–10
  Market analysis 207–8, 292–3
  Marketing strategy 205–22
  Pipelines (underwater) 173–5
  Terminals:
    Bacton 175, 176, 177, 228
    Easington 174, 175, 176, 177, 228
    St Fergus 176
    Theddlethorpe 176
Northcliffe Developments 157
Norwegian Deep 152, 176

Ocean Prince 170
Odeco (UK) Ltd 170
Odorising 175
Office of Prices and Consumer Protection 254
Ohren, M. 35
Old People's Welfare Associations 186, 279
OPEC 164, 221, 283, 291
Orient Explorer 169
Otto and Langen 38
Owen, R. 263
Oxford Centre for Management Studies 234

Paris Opera House 33
Parliament, Acts of:
  Combinations (1824) 48, 263
  Gasworks Clauses (1847) 41, 95
  Metropolis Gas (1860) 42
  Trade Union (1871) 48
  Gasworks Clauses (1871) 44
  Borough Funds (1872) 43
  Public Health (1875) 43
  Electricity (1882) 104
  Trade Disputes (1906) 48
  Munitions of War (1915) 263
  Gas Act (Standard of Calorific Power) (1916) 44
  Statutory Undertakings (Temporary Increases of Charges (1918) 52
  Gas Regulations (1920) 44, 59, 285
  Railways (1921) 110
  Gas Undertakings (1932) 73, 131
  Gas (1934) 75
  Coal (1938) 105
  Electricity (1947) 107, 109, 113
  Transport (1947) 110
  Gas (1948) 113, 116, 117, 249, 265, 271
  Clean Air (1957) 129
  Gas (1960) 232
  Continental Shelf (1964) 137, 233
  Gas (1965) 232
  Gas (1972) 217, 231, 237, 239, 249, 265, 271
  Statutory Corporations (Financial Provisions) (1974) 254
Perkin, W. H. 18
Petrol, synthetic 65
Pipelines (high pressure) 147, 225, 226–7
Phillips, J. O. 21
Phillips, R. 15
Phillips and Lee 7
Phillips Group 209, 210
Pickel, J. G. 4
Pintsch Co. 30
Piper, J. 129
Pope and Son 30
Portable Gas Co. 29, 30
Prakla 167
Price, control of 41, 87, 205
Prices and Incomes Board 254, 255
Public relations 133, 200–3, 271–2, 273–5

Radiation Ltd 135, 198
Reader, W. J. 51, 52
Regional Gas Consumers' Councils 239, 271
Research 46, 72, 74, 122, 123
Retorts
  Cast iron 18
  Continuous vertical 62, 63
  Self-sealing 18
Ridley Report 122

Robens, A. 245, 253
Robinson, C. 160
Rooke, D. 154, 190, 206
Royal Dutch-Shell 157
(Royal) Institute of Chemistry 46

Scott, W. 8
Scottish Association of Gas Managers 45
Sea Gem 172
Second World War
  Balloon barrage 85
  Coal supply 85
  Heyworth Report 96
  Population shifts 87
  Rationalisation plans 90–4
  Structure of industry 94
  War damage 81–4
Select Committee on Nationalised Industries 237, 238, 251–4, 258, 259
Semet-Solvay Co. 123
Senior Officers' Joint Council 268
Shell 157, 167
Shinwell, E. 96, 106, 114, 118
Shirley, T. 3
Slagging gasifier 125
Sliding scale 42, 49
Smith, H. 118
Societé d'Exploitation des Hydrocarbures d'Hassi R'Mel 145
Society of British Gas Industries 22, 74, 197, 234
Soyer, A. 35
Spedding, C. 3
Steel pipe, supply 228
Stephenson, J. 118
Sugg, W. 32
Surveying techniques:
  Gravity 166
  Magnetic 166
  Seismic 166–7
Sylvester, A. E. 93, 95, 98, 118
Sylvester Report 94

Tardin, J. 3

Tawney, R. H. 241
Texaco 157
Texas Eastern (UK) Ltd 164
Texas Instruments 167
Thermostat control 135
Thorne, W. 49, 265
Trade Unions (see also individual unions) 48, 262–3
Transport and General Workers Union 264, 268
Tully, C. B. 123
Two-part tariff 74, 131

Union Stockyard and Transit Co. 144

Vickers Ltd 145
Vulcan Stove Co. 135

Water-gas 60, 61
Watkinson, H. A. 247
Watson, R. 4
Watson House 72, 123, 129, 130, 182, 197, 198, 213
Watt, G. 6
Watt, J. 6, 33
Weather, effect on demand 215
Webb, S. and B. 104
Weir Committee 75, 108
Welding, steel pipe 229
Welsbach, A. von 33
West, J. 63
West's Gas Improvement Co. 85
Westfield Centre 125
Whitehead, S. E. 93
Whitley, J. H. 263
Wilson, H. 163
Winsor (Winzer), F. 4, 7, 8, 9, 26
Wobbe Number 58, 124, 126, 128
Wollaston, W. H. 8
Women's Gas Council (Federation) 278
Woodall, C. 46
Woodall, H. W. 62
J. Wright and Co. 35

Yates, J. 135